Nov. 23, 1965

Frontispiece—Smokehole Caverns. (Photo by Richard G. Hunter.)

State of West Virginia

HULETT C. SMITH, *Governor*

Geological and Economic Survey

PAUL H. PRICE, *Director and State Geologist*

VOLUME XIX A.

Caverns of West Virginia

By

William E. Davies, *Speleologist*

July 1958

Reprinted, with
Supplement, 1965

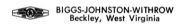

BIGGS-JOHNSTON-WITHROW
Beckley, West Virginia

i

LETTER OF TRANSMITTAL

HONORABLE HULETT C. SMITH
Governor of West Virginia and President,
Geological and Economic Survey Commission
Charleston, West Virginia

Dear Governor Smith:

In 1949 the West Virginia Geological and Economic Survey published the first edition of our Volume XIX, *Caverns of West Virginia,* by William E. Davies, Past President of the National Speleological Society and an authority on caverns. Over 500 caves were described, located, and, in many cases, mapped in considerable detail. That volume proved to be one of our most popular reports, and the edition was soon exhausted.

In response to hundreds of inquiries the original report was revised and updated by Mr. Davies, and was issued in 1958 as our Volume XIX(A). Public response was as great as before, and all supplies of the book were gone within six years.

Requests for the Volume and continued demand for information on the caverns of our State have necessitated the reprinting of Volume XIX(A). Only minor changes have been made in the text for this edition, but an important Supplement has been added that presents information on many new caves. The latter Supplement will be available in reprint form for those who have one of the earlier Volumes. Again we are indebted to Mr. Davies and his assistants, whose help is acknowledged by him, for his work on this reprinted edition and its Supplement.

Interest in the use of caves for shelter and protection for both people and industry continues to increase, and makes this report timely and more important than ever. We are pleased to be able to make this information available once again.

Respectfully submitted,

PAUL H. PRICE, *Director*
and State Geologist and
Professor of Geology

Morgantown, West Virginia
May 1, 1965

CONTENTS

ILLUSTRATIONS
Plates

iv

Figures

v

CAVERNS OF WEST VIRGINIA

By William E. Davies, Speleologist

INTRODUCTION

"Why study caves?" is a question that the speleologist is often called upon to answer. The answer can hardly be a reply concerning the financial rewards to be gained by an investor, for there are none. Nor can it be put in terms of the important effect caves have on man's existence, for most people go through life without seeing a cave, to say nothing of entering one. However, the mere fact that caves exist; that they are a part of the surface of the earth and an integral part of its history is reason enough to warrant study.

Systematic studies of caverns have been few in the United States. Speleologists in Europe have pursued detailed, scientific studies on caves for over 75 years and are ahead of their fellow workers in the United States. Dr. Ralph W. Stone of the Pennsylvania Geologic Survey studied the Caves of Pennsylvania and published a descriptive account of them in 1930. This report was revised and reissued by the National Speleological Society in 1954. William M. McGill prepared a report on the commercial caves of Virginia which was published by the Virginia Geological Survey in 1933. In 1950 a survey of the caves of Maryland was published by the Maryland Department of Geology, Mines and Water Resources. The Missouri Division of Geological Survey and Water Resources published a report on the caves of Missouri by J Harlen Bretz in 1956. At present cavern surveys are well under way or in process of publication in Tennessee, Alabama, Ohio, California, Virginia, Illinois, and New Jersey. The National Speleological Society, founded in 1939, has been a clearing house for information on caves and has steadily increased our knowledge of American caves. This organization has fostered many of the systematic cavern surveys now under way.

In West Virginia several publications have appeared concerning caves. The Bulletin of the National Speleological Society, replete with descriptions of individual caves and cave life, has brought together a great amount of information. Dr. A. M. Reese published in 1934 an account of a reconnaissance cave biological survey performed in 1931 and 1932. In addition to biological information the report contains a brief description of 43 caves visited by Dr. Reese. Dr. J. M. Valentine, of the University of North Carolina, collected and described beetles from a number of West Virginia caves in the early 1930's. Local historians, especially Hu Maxwell (Randolph County 1898; Tucker County 1884) and S. T. Wiley (Preston County 1882; Monongalia County 1883), who often show a flare for including geography and geology as a part of their writings, have published descriptions of many caves in their histories.

The information contained in this report is based on systematic field surveys performed in 1948. Additional field work since then plus a large quantity of information gathered by members of the National Speleological Society in recent years is the base for the material added in the present edition. An abridged revision to the original edition of this report was published in Bulletin 19 of the National Speleological Society in 1957. The study is still primarily exploratory and is a description of about 500 caves.

The author is well aware that additional caves will continue to be found; that new passages and chambers will be discovered by those who explore the many side passages and small crawlways leading off those already explored and described; and that pits now blocking further penetration will be conquered and exploration extended further into the unknown.

In naming caves the following system has been used. Where caves have well-recognized names, these have been used in preference to all others. In lieu of established names the following preferences have been followed: (1) Name of the owner, (2) Name of geographic feature to which the cave is related, (3) Arbitrary name derived from some physical characteristic of the cave. Naming of features within a cave has been avoided as far as possible.

A word of caution concerning cave exploration has its place in a report of this type. Caves should not be explored or visited by an individual alone. Always have a companion. The dangers of traverse and material to be transported make it necessary to have at least two persons in a party. In visiting a cave obtain permission from the owner first and respect his instructions. This will bring invitations to return again.

ACKNOWLEDGMENTS:

The writer wishes to express his indebtedness to many speleologists who have devoted much time to exploring West Virginia's caves. Without their work this report would not be possible. To Mr. Tom W. Richards of Cumberland, Maryland, the author owes much for his valuable aid as a capable assistant and companion during the field work in 1948. Many of the cave descriptions are based on his observations.

The National Speleological Society through its officers and members has contributed a vast amount of information as a result of their explorations. William B. White and the members of the Pittsburgh Chapter of the N. S. S. have supplied much of the data on the Swago Creek area in Pocahontas County. Mr. Earl Thierry, Portsmouth, Virginia, has furnished much additional information on Greenbrier and Monroe Counties. The District of Columbia Chapter is the source for much of the revision in Pendleton and other northern counties.

Ben Nelson and the members of the Explorers Club of Pittsburgh have also supplied data on the Swago Creek area. Their explorations along with that of the Pittsburgh Chapter of the N. S. S. are models of thoroughness and persistency.

Bert D. Ash, J. Lowry Bennett, Robert H. Flack, Emmons Graham, Robert H. Handley, and Haskell H. McGriff of the Charleston Chapter, National Speleological Society; Frank Silers, Martinsburg; and Andy Clark, Dayton, Ohio, contributed much data to the original edition. W. Howard Watkins, Annandale, Virginia, furnished several photographs. Maps of several caves are from the files of the National Speleological Society and credit should go to the members of the Society for their effort in surveying and producing the maps. These maps are: Duffys Cavern, Grapevine, Hellhole, John Browns, Molers, Mystic, Peacock, Piercys Mill, Propst, Sinks of Gandy Creek, Thorn Mountain, and Whitings Neck.

Thomas C. Barr, Jr., Department of Biology, Tennessee Polytechnic Institute investigated many West Virginia caves in 1958. He furnished information for revision and correction of the section on cave biology and descriptions of several caves.

In addition, Kennedy Nicholson furnished the map of Chambers Cave; William B. White and the Pittsburgh Chapter the maps of Swago Pit and Mott Hole; William J. Stephenson the notes for the map of New Trout; George W. Moore and Huntley Ingalls the map of Cass Cave; the Charleston Chapter the map of Greenville Cave. The author gratefully acknowledges the cooperation of Theodore Schad in the survey of Pattons Cave.

Many residents of the areas visited aided in the exploration of caves. During field work the fullest cooperation in locating caves was received from all who were approached for information. To those many West Virginians who gave such aid the author expresses his appreciation.

Dr. Paul H. Price's understanding of the problems involved in cavern survey and his excellent direction of the project made possible this report.

GEOLOGIC RELATIONS

West Virginia caves are most commonly developed in limestone and related carbonate rocks. A few are found in soft, lime-cemented sandstones and, in one rare instance, in a shale. These rocks outcrop in a variety of physiographic provinces which, taken collectively, are referred to as the Appalachian Mountains. Strictly speaking they are not mountains but a combination of valleys, mountains, and plateau.[1]

In the Eastern Panhandle a broad lowland is floored by complexly folded limestones and shales. Although commonly referred to as the Shenandoah Valley, it is, in reality, a series of valleys separated by low, rolling uplands. To the west is the Ridge and Valley Province. This area of folded and faulted rock, primarily middle and upper Paleozoic in age, is 10 to 60 miles wide, extending along the eastern counties from the Potomac River to the southeastern corner of the State at Bluefield. This area is characterized by long, parallel, even-crested ridges separated by relatively narrow valleys. Relief is low in the north, seldom exceeding 1000 feet but in the central portion it reaches a maximum of 2000 to 3000 feet.

The area lying west of the Ridge and Valley Province is the Allegheny Plateau. The rocks are relatively horizontal, disturbed in several areas by broad, gentle anticlines. Over much of the area the upland is concordant in height but dis-

---

[1] The various County Reports of the West Virginia Geological Survey contain detailed physiographic descriptions of each county. See also: West Virginia Geological Survey, Volume X, Geology and Natural Resources of West Virginia, Paul H. Price, R. C. Tucker, O. L. Haught, 1937.

sected by numerous narrow valleys. Broad, anticlinal valleys, occupied in part by the Tygart and Cheat Rivers, are developed along the major flexures of the plateau. The relief on the east side, along Allegheny Front, is the greatest in the State, exceeding 3000 feet. Westward it decreases to less than 1000 feet in the central part of the State and to a few hundred feet along the Ohio River.

Caves are found in all of the physiographic provinces of West Virginia. In the Shenandoah Valley, which forms most of the Eastern Panhandle, there are wide expanses of limestone but caves are not very numerous. The Ridge and Valley section contains extensive outcrops of all the major limestones and about half the caves in the State are in this province. The Allegheny Plateau contains extensive outcrops of the Greenbrier Limestone in its eastern part and accounts for over half of the caves in West Virginia. In Pocahontas, Greenbrier, and Monroe Counties the Greenbrier Limestone outcrops as broad plateau surfaces considerably below the level of the upland plateau. Elsewhere this limestone outcrops on the flanks of plateau fronts bordering anticlinal valleys and along Allegheny Front which forms the eastern border of the plateau. In the central and western part of the State thin limestones and lime-cemented sandstones outcrop in practically every county. Small caves in the form of shelters or short crawlways are found in them but have not been considered in this report as they are of little significance.

STRATIGRAPHY:

In West Virginia limestones and related rocks are distributed in the geologic column from the Cambrian through the Permian systems.[2] In addition marl deposits of Quaternary or Recent age are developed along many streams in the limestone area.

The Cambrian System[3] is divided into six formations, three of which contain limestones or dolomites of significant

---

[2] For complete descriptions see: West Virginia Geological Survey, Volume XII, Limestones of West Virginia, J. B. McCue, J. B. Lucke, H. P. Woodward, 1939.

---

[3] For complete description of Cambrian rocks see: West Virginia Geological Survey, Volume XX, Cambrian System of West Virginia, H. P. Woodward, 1949.

thickness. The limestones occupy the upper half of the Cambrian and the lowest, the Tomstown Dolomite, is 2600 feet above the base of the system. The Tomstown Dolomite outcrops in Jefferson County only, where it is a light blue gray to white, fine-grained dolomite. It is medium bedded and contains occasional zones of limestone or shaly material. Exposures are poor and are found in a relatively narrow belt lying along the Shenandoah River in the eastern part of the county. Only one (John Browns) cave is found in the Tomstown Dolomite.

Overlying the Tomstown Dolomite is the Waynesboro Formation which consists of three distinct members totaling 1250 feet thick in Jefferson County. The lower portion of the formation consists of gray, siliceous limestones and calcareous shales which are overlain by somewhat darker limestone beds. The upper portion is a red and purple siliceous shale. Although the limestone beds of the lower and middle portions of the Waynesboro Formation are pitted with shallow sinks, caves are rare, only four being known in the formation.

The uppermost formation assigned to the Cambrian in West Virginia is the Elbrook Limestone which lies above the Waynesboro. The Elbrook Limestone is a series of light-blue and gray shaly limestones and calcareous shales with intermingling beds of blue-gray, solid limestone which total more than 1250 feet in thickness. The formation outcrops in a broad band extending through the length of central Jefferson County and in a somewhat narrower band on the west side of Shenandoah Valley in Berkeley County. Although the outcrop covers considerable area only four caves have been reported in the Elbrook Limestone. These caves, however, are among the largest in Jefferson County, one of which (Molers) is over 1500 feet long.

Above the Elbrook is a thick series of limestones and dolomites that occur in the Shenandoah Valley, on the axis of the major anticlinal valleys in Hardy and Pendleton Counties, and along the east side of the St. Clair Fault in Mercer and Monroe Counties. The assignment of these rocks to definite geologic systems is still problematic as the line between the Cambrian and Ordovician is not exactly determined in the limestones. Apparently the upper portion is Ordovician and the lower portion Cambrian in age. Pending a clearer differentiation the limestones are grouped as "Cambro-Ordovician."

The lower portion, made up of the Chepultepec and Conococheague Limestones or their equivalents, form the Ozarkian group (probably Cambrian). In Jefferson and Berkeley Counties the Ozarkian Group is composed of the Conococheague Limestone, an impure, massive, dark-blue limestone with interbedded dark dolomitic limestones (1650 feet thick), overlain by the Chepultepec Limestone, a fairly pure, dove-colored or dark-gray limestone, 500 feet thick. Six caves are in the Conococheague Limestone and with two exceptions are small crawlways or shallow pits. One small cave is in the Chepultepec Limestone.

In Monroe and Mercer Counties the Ozarkian consists of the Copper Ridge Dolomite, a medium to massive bedded dolomite equivalent to the Conococheague Formation. The total thickness of the dolomite is not determinable as it is bounded by the St. Clair Fault on the west but 1500 feet is exposed along the east side of the fault. No caves have been recorded in this formation in Monroe and Mercer Counties.

The upper portion of the Cambro-Ordovician Limestones is made up of the Beekmantown Group which consists of the Nittany Dolomite in the lower part. The Nittany is a medium- to thick-bedded, fine-grained, light-blue to buff, magnesian limestone about 500 feet thick. Overlying the Nittany is the Bellefonte Dolomite, a thick-bedded dolomite, dark-blue to blue-gray in color, about 1500 feet thick. In Mercer and Monroe Counties the dolomites have numerous chert horizons in them. Fourteen caves, characterized by small, short passages with shallow pits, lie in the Beekmantown dolomites in West Virginia.

The Ordovician System[4] in West Virginia contains two groups of limestone in the lower portion. At the base, the Stones River Group is composed of three formations: the Murfreesboro, the Mosheim, and the Lenoir at the top. In Jefferson and Berkeley Counties and the Germany Valley section of Pendleton County, only the Lenoir and Mosheim are present. The Lenoir is an impure, fossiliferous, dark-gray limestone 20 to 40 feet thick in the north increasing to 275 feet in Pendleton County. The Mosheim, 100 to 200 feet thick

---

[4] For complete description of Ordovician rocks see: West Virginia Geological Survey, Volume XXI, Ordovician System of West Virginia, H. P. Woodward, 1951.

in the northern area, is a dove-gray to blue, pure, fine-grained limestone.

The Stones River Group attains a maximum thickness of 750 to 1000 feet in Monroe and Mercer Counties where it is made up of dove-colored to dark-gray or black limestones. In Jefferson and Berkeley Counties there are four small, shallow caves in the Stones River Group. In Pendleton County, however, the caves in these limestones reach spectacular development. The seven caves in Germany Valley are typified by deep pits extending vertically for over 100 feet. In Mercer and Monroe Counties the 16 caves in the Stones River are long, single passageways with streams flowing through them.

The Black River Group, overlying the Stones River, is composed of several facies that grade laterally one into another. In Jefferson County the Chambersburg Limestone is a fossiliferous, dark-blue limestone with argillaceous partings. In Pendleton County the Lowville Limestone, the sole representative of the Black River, is a thin-bedded, platy, highly argillaceous, lime rock, about 150 to 250 feet thick. In Mercer and Monroe Counties the Moccasin Formation is the only representative of the Black River. It is a red, highly argillaceous mud rock which contains some argillaceous limestones in the lower part. The Moccasin is 400 to 450 feet thick.

Eight caves, generally small with high and narrow passages, at times with complicated patterns, are in the Chambersburg Limestone. The Lowville Limestone contains four caves, all in Germany Valley, which are characterized by simple patterns with broad passages interrupted by shallow wells.

The upper part of the Ordovician System is increasingly arenaceous in nature and is represented by the Martinsburg Shale. The Silurian System overlying the Ordovician, is made up of clastic sediments in the lower and middle portions.[5] The upper portion, the Cayugan Series, is composed of sediments that are highly argillaceous and arenaceous in the lower part grading to marine limestones at the top. The lower part of the Cayugan Group is divided into two facies. The Bloomsburg is the non-marine facies of the Cayugan and progressively occupies more of the stratigraphic column northeastwardly. It consists of green, brown, or red sandstones and

---

[5] For a complete description of Silurian rocks see: West Virginia Geological Survey, Volume XIV, Silurian System of West Virginia, H. P. Woodward, 1941.

shales east of central Hampshire and Hardy Counties and has a maximum thickness of 125 feet in Hampshire County. West of this area, including Pendleton and Pocahontas Counties, a 20- to 30-foot greenish-brown sandstone, the Williamsport Sandstone, represents the non-marine facies.

The Wills Creek Limestone is the lowest marine member of the Cayugan and overlies the Bloomsburg or Williamsport. It is made up of calcareous shales and argillaceous limestones with thin lenses of platy, fine-grained limestone and has a maximum thickness of 400 feet in the area of the Potomac River reducing to less than 60 feet in the southern part of Pocahontas County. No caves are in this formation.

The Tonoloway Limestone lies at the top of the Silurian System. It consists of interbedded, laminated, argillaceous limestones, calcareous shales, and dark-gray to black, hard, platy limestones. In the middle part of the formation the beds tend to be more massive and irregularly bedded. The formation has a thickness of 600 feet in Mineral County, decreasing to the east and south to less than 100 feet in Monroe and Mercer Counties. The 28 caves in the Tonoloway Limestone generally have main passageways extending up to 1000 feet with few large wells or drops. Their patterns vary according to the local geologic structure.

The calcareous deposition of the Upper Silurian continues into the Lower Devonian with a change from thin-bedded laminated limestones of the Tonoloway to the knobby crystalline beds of the Keyser Limestone.[6] The significant limestones in the system are confined to the Lower Devonian Series which is composed of two groups of rocks. The lower subdivision, the Helderberg Group, is composed of five formations in West Virginia.

The basal formation, the Keyser Limestone, consists of nodular, blue-gray to black limestone with occasional zones of chert. Beds of crinoidal and crystalline limestones are scattered throughout. The formation is divided near the middle into two distinct parts by a shale horizon. The Keyser has a maximum thickness of 275 feet to 280 feet in Mineral, Grant, and Hampshire Counties. In the Eastern Panhandle it is 175 feet thick while to the southeast in Monroe County it reduces

---

[6] For a complete description of Devonian rocks see: West Virginia Geological Survey, Volume XV, Devonian System of West Virginia, H. P. Woodward, 1943.

steadily to less than 200 feet, over half of which is made up of the Clifton Forge Sandstone. The Keyser contains 18 caves, mainly in Hardy and Pendleton Counties, which are characterized by small short passages intersected by large pits or steeply sloping crevices up to 70 feet deep.

The Coeymans Formation is a coarsely crystalline, gray, crinoidal limestone which closely resembles the Keyser Limestone underlying it. The Coeymans ranges from 20 to 30 feet thick throughout much of its outcrop in the northeastern part of the State. To the south it thins to less than 5 feet in Monroe and Mercer Counties. Twelve caves are developed in the formation, most of them confined to a zone at the Coeymans and New Scotland boundary, and are all large with main passages over 1000 feet long.

The New Scotland Formation consists of 20 to 25 feet of crystalline limestone with prominent chert nodules weathering white overlain by calcareous shale 10 to 30 feet thick. To the south in Monroe County the shale disappears and the limestone is replaced by a brown crinoidal sandstone. Twenty caves are in the New Scotland and, except for six, are small passages less than 100 yards in length. The six large caves are near the base of the formation and should be considered a part of the cavernous zone at the Coeymans-New Scotland contact.

The upper part of the Helderberg Group is composed of the Port Ewen beds consisting of siliceous limestones and shales with abundant chert totaling 30 to 100 feet thick and the Port Jervis Limestone and Chert, which is similar in nature to the Port Ewen in the northern part of West Virginia but increases in purity to the south. The Port Jervis averages 60 feet thick throughout most of its outcrop. No caves are known to exist in the Port Ewen or Port Jervis beds.

The Helderberg Group is overlain by the Oriskany Group, which consists of one formation in West Virginia. The Ridgeley Sandstone is a coarse-grained, massive, calcareous sandstone that is dark gray in color, weathering to brown or graybrown on the surface. Conglomeratic beds are scattered throughout the formation but are of limited horizontal extent. In the northeastern part of the State the Ridgeley averages 150 feet thick with maximum thickness in Morgan and Hampshire Counties of 350 feet. To the south it thins to 50 feet in Pocahontas County and 5 feet in Monroe County. Five small shelter caves are developed in the calcareous sandstones of the Ridgeley.

The Middle and Upper Devonian formations are argillaceous or arenaceous in character with no true caves developed in them. The Marcellus Shale of the Middle Devonian is a black, fissile shale up to 500 feet thick with large concretions in zones 50 to 75 feet above the base of the formation. An interesting group of small shelter caves are developed in the zone of concretions near Forks of Cacapon. The shallow shelters, less than 6 feet long and wide, were enlarged by Indians for use as places of habitation.

The Mississippian System consists of arenaceous sediments grading into calcareous and argillaceous sediments in the middle and upper parts. The Greenbrier Series is a thick group of limestones extending throughout much of the plateau region of West Virginia. The Greenbrier is divided into eleven members [7] in the southeastern part of the State. These members in descending order are:

1. Alderson Limestone
2. Greenville Shale
3. Union Limestone
4. Pickaway Limestone
5. Upper Taggard Shale
6. Taggard Limestone
7. Lower Taggard Shale
8. Patton Limestone
9. Patton Shale
10. Sinks Grove Limestone
11. Hillsdale Limestone

The Greenbrier Series ranges from a total thickness of 1000 to 1200 feet in Mercer and Monroe Counties to 100 feet in Monongalia County. The Hillsdale and Sinks Grove Limestones are lithologically similar, consisting of massive, blue limestones with a large amount of black, nodular chert. These limestones have a maximum thickness of 230 feet in Monroe County and thin northward, disappearing in northern Randolph County.

The Patton member is a hard, blue, massive fossiliferous limestone which is quite arenaceous in the upper part. In Monroe County it is 147 feet thick and like the other basal members of the Greenbrier, it thins northward disappearing

[7] West Virginia Geological Survey, Mercer, Monroe, and Summers Counties, D. B. Reger, 1926.

in northern Randolph County. The Taggard member is a thin, gray, oolitic limestone mixed with red shale having a thickness of 35 feet in the southern part of the State. It, too, disappears in northern Randolph County.

The Pickaway is a dark, variegated, impure limestone that is 263 feet thick in Monroe County and can be traced through Pocahontas County where it disappears.

The Union Limestone is the most persistent member of the series. It is a pure, fossiliferous, dark- to blue-gray, crystalline limestone with a thickness of 235 feet in Monroe County thinning to 100 feet in Monongalia County.

The Alderson member is a thin-bedded limy shale or argillaceous, fossiliferous limestone. The Alderson is 155 feet thick in Monroe County but thins northward, disappearing in Monongalia County.

Two hundred and fifty caves of significant size occur in the Greenbrier Series. In Greenbrier, Monroe, and Mercer Counties, and part of Pocahontas County, they have been differentiated according to the members of the Greenbrier Series in which they occur. Elsewhere this has not been possible. The number of caves are as follows: Alderson Limestone, 35; Union Limestone, 40; Pickaway Limestone, 5; Taggard Limestone, none; Patton Limestone, 19; Hillsdale-Sinks Grove Limestones, 30; Greenbrier Series undifferentiated, 121. The larger caves are in the Union and Patton Limestones and have lengths ranging up to 15,000 feet. The other limestones have caves of lesser magnitude ranging up to 1000 feet in length.

Limestones occur frequently above the Greenbrier Series but are of little consequence in cavern development. Short crawlways or small shelters found in them are not included in this report because of their small size. Several limy sandstones in the lower part of the Pottsville Series (Pennsylvanian) have relatively large caves, the largest being McKinney Cave near Masontown, Preston County.

From a purely stratigraphic viewpoint few conclusions can be reached concerning cave development. However, it is clear that in flat-lying strata large caverns develop almost exclusively in thick-bedded, pure limestones while in areas of folding large caverns are developed regardless of the thickness or purity of the limestone. This observation will be pursued further in the section on patterns and origin.

AREAL DISTRIBUTION OF CAVES:

Although caves are found in all the counties of the State where limestones outcrop, there is a definite increase in the number and size of caves as the headwaters of the major drainage basins are approached. In Pendleton County, in the headwater areas of the Potomac, 60 significant caves are known. As one goes downstream the number decreases as the main branch of the Potomac is approached. This can not be ascribed to a change in stratigraphy or extent of outcrop as these factors are relatively constant. A similar condition prevails in the Shenandoah Valley. In the West Virginia section of the Valley there are relatively few caves and those found are small in size. However, in the headwater area of the Shenandoah River in Virginia the caves increase in size and abundance with some of America's most famous caverns located there. Similar distribution occurs in the Greenbrier drainage area but is not as conclusive since limestones are confined to the upper half of the river.

The reason for such a distribution of caves is not easily determined but is probably due to the upper parts of the drainage basin being less subject to geomorphic fluctuations than the lower reaches of the streams, thus permitting more uniform subterranean solution work.

PATTERNS:

Caves, like rivers, develop distinct patterns that can be related directly to the rock structure in which they lie. The controlling factor that determines the pattern is joints, for, with few exceptions, the passageways of West Virginia caves lie along joints. Bedding-planes are secondary as far as pattern control is concerned and mainly modify the cross-section of the passage and in only one type of cave do they control the direction. Faults also are secondary to joints in controlling the patterns. Several caves lying in part along fault zones show that, while some of the passageways are developed along the fault, the maximum development is along joints connecting with the faults.

Joints form consistent patterns according to their relation to rock structures and cave patterns reflect this consistency in their development. In simplest form the cave may consist of a single major passage, relatively straight and of uniform size. This condition or a variation in which two simple, parallel, straight passages exist is the most common pattern for caves in West Virginia.

The straight passage grades into one which has two or more consistent directions such that short stretches are in one direction turning abruptly for a short stretch in another direction and then reverting to the original direction. This change in direction is retained in relatively uniform segments throughout the cave. Where solution and corrasion have affected the passage to a considerable degree the angular conditions are modified and a sinuous pattern is developed. Hayes and Higginbotham Caves are excellent examples of such development.

A more complex type of development occurs where passageways are equally developed in two or more sets of directions. In such cases a maze of interlacing, uniform, straight passages occur that are similar in plan to city streets with each set of passages delimiting a block. Hamilton, Silers, and Cornwell Caves are of this type.

Caves generally exhibit a single type of pattern throughout their development. However, those caves that develop in zones where the structure varies exhibit different patterns according to the type of structure. Trout Cave is primarily a straight passageway where it lies on the flank of an anticline. However, in some portions that are near the axis of the anticline a maze of passages develops similar in form to Hamilton Cave that is on the axis of the same anticline. Similar conditions exist in Patton Cave.

The shape of cave passages, like the patterns, fall into several groups depending on structure. Most passageways that have not suffered breakdown exhibit a modified circular or elliptical cross-section. The curvature is relatively uniform on walls and ceiling and varies from a true circular cross-section to one with straight walls and ceiling with rounding confined to the area adjacent to the intersection of the walls and ceiling. The conformality of the rock floor with respect to the shape of the remainder of the cross-section is difficult to determine as in most caves it is covered by deposits of clay or rock. Where exposed, however, the rock floor generally conforms in shape to the rest of the passage. Long, narrow passages with circular shape are generally referred to as sewers if they carry streams, either intermittently or permanently.

In flat-lying structures circular cross-sections are often modified to wide, low sections with gently arched ceilings and floors. In this case the bedding exerts influence in confining the passage vertically and directing its development laterally. Laurel Creek, Poorfarm, and Tub Caves have passages of this type.

Where vertical or nearly vertical joints are the controlling influence in cave development the passages develop as relatively narrow fissures extending across the bedding-planes. In size these fissures range from a foot across up to 20 feet in width. The narrower fissures have depths of 10 to 30 feet on the average while the large fissures range up to 100 feet or more in vertical extent. Some passages are compound in nature consisting of a broad or circular passageway with narrow fissures developed in the floor. In this case the fissures are referred to as crevices. When the dimensions of the crevice and the circular part of the passage are proportional the passage is termed a "keyhole" because of its characteristic cross-section.

In some caves, especially those with maze patterns, the passages are rectangular in cross-section with straight walls and flat ceilings intersecting at right angles. These passages generally average 5 to 10 feet high and 2 to 4 feet wide.

In profile, caves range through a variety of conditions. In simplest form the passages are on one level. The majority of West Virginia caves are of this type. Gentle slopes are characteristic although the direction of slope may vary with relation to the entrance according to the method of development of the cave. Most cave entrances develop where surface erosion intersects the cave passage with the result that few are directly related to the upper or lower end of the passage slope.

In both flat-lying and folded limestones it is common to find caves with more than one level of passages. Where structural control is along a set of vertical joints the various levels will coincide in pattern. However, in cases where the control is more than one set of joints the levels quite often develop similar patterns but their plans do not coincide. Haynes Cave, Monroe County, is a two-level cave that shows a similar sinuous pattern on each level but while the general trend is coincidental the individual curves in the passages on each level are in opposite directions at most points. In folded or tilted structures where multiple levels occur the passages are offset level to level along the dip. Sinnit and Trout Caves exhibit this condition.

Connections between levels generally are by vertical shafts, crevices, or, in the case of broad passages, by way of cliffs. The original vertical slopes are often modified by rock falls and clay fills to the point where passages connect by gentle, continuous slopes.

As indicated at the beginning of this section patterns are primarily controlled by joints with the individual pattern of each cave depending on its relation to local rock structures. From a structural standpoint the simplest conditions are found in the horizontal or gently dipping beds of the Allegheny Plateau in Greenbrier, Monroe, and Pocahontas Counties. Where thick limestones cap the surface of the upland, caves develop simple patterns consisting of single, or, in some cases, several parallel passages with few side passages. Multiple-level caves are met with more often in this type of structure than in any other but even here are not very common. Vertical shafts and dome pits are quite abundant especially in areas where the limestones flank higher ridges. Mott Hole, Grapevine Cave, Snedegars Cave, and Lewis Hole are examples of such shafts.

Caves show no consistent relations to the dip of formations. Where distinct slopes of cave floors over considerable distance can be determined the results are contradictory. Organ, General Davis, McClung, and Snedegars Caves tend to slope with the dip but this slope is not absolute as it is diverted in the direction of regional surface slope which is generally at right angles to the dip. Steeles Cave exhibits a trend along the dip slope but if the entire subterranean courses of Burnside and Taggart Branches, of which Steeles Cave is a part, are considered it is found that they cross distinct anticlines and synclines. Coffman and Higginbotham Caves are part of a system of subterranean watercourses that wander sinuously along a course parallel to the strike with segments in accord with the dip slope and others opposite the dip slope. Piercys Mill, Piercys, and Poorfarm (Pocahontas County) Caves trend parallel to the strike with little or no relation to the dip slope. The subterranean course of Milligan

Creek, from Central School to its apparent resurgence at the large spring, three-fourths of a mile northwest of Fort Spring, follows a similar channel parallel to the strike.

The Laurel Creek-Greenville Cave system cuts directly across an anticline exhibiting sections that are in accord with the dip and others that are in opposition. The subterranean drainage of Culverson Creek from Unus to its apparent resurgence just west of Spring Creek Station exhibits a similar condition in passing across a syncline. The large subterranean drainage net of Hills Creek-Bruffeys Creek and Locust Creek in Pocahontas County slopes directly opposite the dip. The caves in the Swago Creek area near Marlinton (Cave Creek, Overholts Blowing, and Tub Caves) all trend directly opposite to the dip. After an examination of cave slopes it is evident that they are not directly related to the dip but rather to a combination of dip and regional surface slope with greatest emphasis on the latter.

In gently dipping structures that occur in the Greenbrier Limestone on the flanks of anticlinal valleys in Randolph, Tucker, and Preston Counties, the caves develop simple passages trending parallel to the axis of the valleys. The caves are generally less than 1000 feet long with small, irregular passageways. Multiple passageways are the exception as are multiple levels. Caves found in the Greenbrier Limestone along Allegheny Front exhibit similar conditions.

The maximum development of cave patterns occurs in folded structures. The patterns can be grouped into three general types according to the position on the structure. Caves that lie on the flanks of folds are simple in pattern, consisting of one or more parallel, straight passages trending along the strike. Caves with multiple levels are common with the levels offset in the direction of the dip. The passages vary in size from crawlways to large fissures up to 50 feet high.

Caves that lie on or near the axis of broad anticlines or subordinate flexures exhibit maze patterns consisting of intersecting, regularly spaced passages of uniform dimensions. Although rare, caves on the axis of broad synclines exhibit similar patterns.

A distinct type of cave is developed in strata that are vertical. The passages are straight with vertical walls following the bedding-planes. It is fissure-like with ceiling heights of 60 to 100 feet and widths up to 20 feet. The ceiling exhibits dome-like excavations while the floor has numerous shallow wells connected by occasional small passages at the base. Smokehole Caverns (commercial) and Rexrode Cave are excellent examples of this type.

Faults apparently exert little influence on the caves encountered in West Virginia. Several caves developed along the St. Clair Fault indicate that the fault is secondary to joints in controlling the pattern. Passages follow faults for short distances reverting to joints for the greater portion of the cave. Coburn and McClung-Zenith Caves are developed in such a manner.

CAVERN FEATURES:

Subordinate features that modify walls and floors of caverns exhibit a range of variations. Cave floors seldom show bedrock except in a few caves where streams have removed fills of clay and gravel. When bedrock is exposed in the floor of large passages, as in Laurel Creek Cave, it generally has an irregular, pitted surface. Small, shallow pockets occur occasionally but large, deep ones were not observed in West Virginia caves. Small, sewer passages commonly have bare rock exposed on the floor. Where the sewers are active watercourses, the floors are pitted and polished. In dry sewers they are smooth but unpolished with many minute, pore-like pits.

Practically all cave passages are floored with fills of clay, silt, or gravel. In thickness the fills vary from a few inches to many feet. Laurel Creek, Poorfarm (Pocahontas) and Tub Caves contain fills that are over 60 feet deep in places. In Poorfarm Cave over 75 feet of fill is exposed in a vertical section where an old stream cut a canyon-like channel through it. The fills contain a variety of materials. In Laurel Creek and Poorfarm Caves it is composed of soft, buff, dry, sandy silt. In Tub Cave the fill is predominantly a wet, brown clay. Patton Cave has extensive areas in which the fill is made of well-rounded and sorted gravel averaging two inches in size. In other caves fills are found that are similar to those described above or are mixtures of two or more types. Where the fills are of wet clay or silt they are commonly referred to as mud.

Clay fills are not confined to the floors alone as remnants are commonly found in alcoves or niches in the walls of passages many feet above the present floor. In such cases they are remnants of more extensive deposits.

The fills vary in structure as widely as they do in materials. Some show no bedding whatsoever. Others, as in Laurel Creek Cave, are distinctly bedded and in some cases exhibit cross-bedding. The section below was observed in a slump pit at the rear of the upper level of Laurel Creek Cave:

Feet

1. Floor of cave ....
2. Stalagmitic layers mixed with clay 6
3. Fine sandy silt 4
4. Sandy silt with pebbles up the 1½ inch diameter scattered throughout. Crumbly snail shells abundant 2
5. Cross-bedded, sandy silt. Thin bands of pebbles up to 4 inches thick 1½
6. Fine sandy silt at top with sandy silt mixed with small pebbles (½ inch diameter) at base............... 2
7. Rock floor 2

Total 15½

The bedding in this deposit is irregular and varies in thickness from point to point. All the silts are olive drab color and the pebbles are of black limestone and white, sugary sandstone. It is evident that alternate phases of deposition from running water and still water are represented in this section. Similar conditions were observed in deep clay fills in other caves.

The upper passage of Schoolhouse Cave contains an interesting phase of clay deposition. The clay fill formerly extended to the ceiling but saltpeter miners have cut a narrow trench the entire length of the passage. The fill, 6 to 8 feet deep, shows distinct laminations throughout. The laminae are paper thin with pronounced partings in zones 1½ inches apart. In appearance it resembles varved clays of glacial origin.

Streams flowing through caves are engaged in removing the clay fills that now floor passages. In some caves, such as Higginbotham, the streams are uniformly removing the clay in a manner that the floor remains relatively flat. In other caves, General Davis Cave as example, where the gradient is steep the stream has cut deeply into the clay forming a deep, narrow channel.

Where streams enter caves from the surface they bring considerable debris and silt into the passages. Most of this material is deposited near the entrance and seldom affects the inner portion of the cave. At times the deposits accumu'ate to such an extent that they block the passage as in the case of Hills Creek and Herbert Hills Caves. These blockades are not permanent and are periodically removed and the passages flushed clear of debris.

Wells and crevices are developed in many cave floors. Wells are circular pits ranging in depth from a few feet to over 100 feet. Crevices are narrow fissures of similar depth extending along the passage. Some wells and crevices connect with lower passages while others are plugged by clay or rock debris at the base.

Walls and ceilings display a number of features comparable to those found in floors. Large, circular, vertical openings in the ceiling are known as domepits or chimneys. The domepits range from a few feet to over 100 feet in height and at times contain water that falls from higher levels. Snedegars, Hinkles Unus, and Martens Caves and caves in the Swago Creek area display large domepits and, in the case of Snedegars, a massive flowstone and rimstone terrace is developed at the base from the large amount of falling water.

Cave walls generally are formed of rock. In some cases the solid unaltered limestone lies at the wall face while in other cases, especially where shallow, smooth pockets are developed in the wall or ceiling, the surface is of loose, soft clay, apparently a residual product after the soluble lime material has been removed.

A number of other subordinate features are found on cave walls and the reader is referred to Bretz's [8] paper on cave origin for their description.

Rock falls, resulting from the collapse of passage ceilings, cover the floor of many sections of caves. The rock falls, known as breakdown, are in three forms. Slab breakdown consists of huge flat slabs of rock and extends for considerable distance along a passage. It is confined, however, to single beds of rock. This type of breakdown results from solution along bedding-planes. Poorfarm and Trout Caves have extensive areas of slab breakdown.

Plate breakdown is similar to slab breakdown except that small plates of rock, rather than large slabs, collapse along

[8] Bretz, J H. Vadose and phreatic features of limestone caverns: Journal of Geology, Vol. 50, No. 6, Pt. II, pp. 675-811, Aug.-Sept. 1942.

bedding-planes and, at times, cover the floor to considerable depth.

Block breakdown is limited to short sections of passages. It consists of large blocks of rock that form huge piles on the floor. The breakdown is not confined to a single bed but extends far into the ceiling. It results from solution work along bedding-planes and joints. Rock falls in Laurel Creek and Greenville Saltpeter are of this type.

Cave passages are modified after excavation by deposits of calcitic material collectively referred to as speleothems. Flowstone is the term applied to those speleothems in the form of crystalline sheets or mounds of calcite and related materials deposited by films of water. Dripstone results from dropping water and takes the form of stalactites and stalagmites. It is common to find combinations of dripstone and flowstone in the speleothem and often speleothems show characteristics that are transitional between flowstone and dripstone. Rimstone is formed on the floor of caves and consists of narrow, interconnected ridges bounding pools of water.

Some cave passages are lined with rough, sharp, minute knobs that are called cave coral. They resemble small corals in shape and at times make it painful and difficult to traverse passages.

Speleothems are developed from the precipitation of material carried in solution by ground water. The exact method of precipitation, however, is open to various interpretations. The material enters the cave and is precipitated primarily along joints or, in the case of vertical strata, along bedding-planes.

Popular ideas concerning caves picture the passages as being filled with speleothems. As far as West Virginia is concerned, this is a fallacy. Speleothems are the exception as most passages show bare rock or clay and silt on the walls. Speleothems are abundant and large in sections of Smokehole Caverns, Seneca Caverns, Grapevine, Piercys Mill, Elkhorn Mountain, and Brants Caves.

MINERALOGY:

The number of minerals found in caves is relatively limited. Calcite is the most common mineral and occurs in a number of forms. Typical rhombohedral crystals of calcite make up the bulk of formations and are readily seen where stalactites or flowstone are broken. The crystals vary from those that are opaque and milky to relatively clear, transparent ones. Some formations composed of calcite are colored red, blue, or gray, according to the impurities contained in the calcite. Aragonite is occasionally found but in comparison to calcite it is extremely rare.

Gypsum occurs in rather large quantities in several West Virginia caves. Haynes, Trout, Sinnit, and Thorn Mountain Caves have conspicuous deposits. The gypsum crystals are found scattered in clay fills or as gypsum flowers (oulophodites) on the walls and ceilings. In Haynes Cave veins of fibrous gypsum, up to four inches thick, are encountered. The gypsum is associated with clay deposits from which saltpeter was extracted but little is known concerning the relation between the two. The origin of cavern gypsum deposits is not clear. The deposits have been ascribed to the reaction of pyrite in the limestone to form a gypsum which is deposited from solution in the silt or clay fills of the cave. The application of this theory, however, is difficult for published analyses of limestones in the vicinity of the caves indicate no appreciable amount of pyrite.

Saltpeter deposits in caves at one time were of considerable economic value. The saltpeter, in the form of niter (potassium nitrate) and nitrocalcite, is scattered throughout the clay or silt fills. Distinct large crystals are seldom met with. The origin of these deposits has been discussed to a considerable degree but no satisfactory theory advanced. Many investigators have ascribed the origin to bat guano deposits but this does not appear to be supported by the small amount of niter-forming material in the guano. Furthermore, in some caves, as Higginbothams No. 3, there is a thick impervious layer of stalagmitic material that covers the saltpeter deposit which would block the circulation of niter solutions resulting from guano. The deposits in this cave practically reach the ceiling, a condition that is not favorable to the hibernation of large numbers of bats necessary to produce the guano. Analyses of limestones indicate practically no nitrates that could be removed from the rock and redeposited in saltpeter beds. Investigators now are turning to nitrogen fixation by bacterial processes an an explanation of the deposits.

Interesting deposits of manganese dioxide are found in several West Virginia caves. In Trout and Sinnit Caves a thin soot-like deposit which covers the walls, floors, and ceilings was formerly thought to be soot resulting from saltpeter mining but spectroscopic examination indicates that part of it is manganese dioxide. The deposit is very thin and only in occasional pockets does it reach a thickness of one millimeter. It is underlain by soft, crumbly travertine one-half to one inch thick. The origin of the deposit is problematic. It is relatively recent in age for it covers travertine deposits formed in the later stages of the cavern cycle. Since it is uniformly distributed over the entire cave, including fallen rock, it requires that a uniform condition of precipitation exist at the time of its origin. The original source of the manganese is also a problem for analyses of limestones do not indicate manganese in the bed-rock.

Chert is found in many caverns but is residual from the bedrock. Unique forms, or possibly new species of minerals, are found in many caves. In Poorfarm (Pocahontas) Cave an interesting form is developing in and adjacent to small pockets in the ceiling. It is a layer of brown, opaque, fine-grained, non-crystalline material that has a high polish on the surface. This has been identified as francolite. It was observed also in other caves throughout the State. Intensive search of cave walls and ceilings may reveal many additional unique specimens similar to that described.

In concluding the discussion on minerals, mention should be made of the interesting vugs found in the ceilings of Haynes and Poorfarm (Pocahontas) Caves. They are small egg-shaped hollows averaging one to two inches in size bordered by a brown casing and lined with well-developed crystals of clear, dog-tooth spar (calcite). The vugs are abundant in local areas in the caves and can be removed intact from the limestone.

In Laurel Creek Cave, 200 feet from the end of the upper level, an interesting form of "boxwork" replacement occurs. In the ceiling are clusters of apparent prismatic calcite crystals up to two inches long and a quarter of an inch square. Examination, however, reveals that these are formed of a thin shell of brittle calcite and are hollow inside.

ORIGIN OF CAVES:

In America theories concerning the origin of caves did not appear until recently in geologic literature. Previous to 1930 no detailed theories were formulated and the ideas expressed were incidental to publications on related subjects. In 1930 W. M. Davis [9] published a paper that dealt in detail with the subject and aroused considerable interest. Following Davis' publication several major papers as well as a number of short articles appeared expressing ideas that deviated in many ways from Davis' theory.

The more important theories will be discussed in this report as they apply to West Virginia caves. However, a discussion of the theories of cave origin should be prefaced by information on the movements of water within the ground. This water can be divided into two distinct zones. The upper zone (zone of aeration) is characterized by rocks that are porous or fissured and filled with air most of the time. Water in this zone is transitional, travelling from the surface to deeper zones of saturation. The zone of saturation is characterized by fissures and pores in the rock but, unlike the zone of aeration, water completely fills all openings. The water in the zone of saturation is commonly referred to as ground water and its upper surface is called the water-table. The water-table is not a level horizon but is irregular, conforming to the topography and at times it fluctuates according to seasonal conditions. Within the zone of saturation ground water (phreatic) may circulate by means of gravity or hydrostatic pressure. Much of the circulation is slow seepage along pores or fissures but sizeable streams flowing under hydrostatic head may be encountered.

The basic problem in cave origin is that faced in the creation of any natural object—the making of something from nothing (or more correctly nothing from something). As far as is known all limestones are relatively compact when formed and therefore the first important step in cave creation is the development of minute openings in the rock that will permit passage of water. Apparently this initial step is performed by phreatic waters deep in the zone of saturation with openings developed along zones of solutional weakness, mainly joints or bedding-planes. This initial phase is of extreme importance in cave development for it is apparently the stage at which the basic pattern is determined. Most of the theories on cave origin agree on this initial phase. The method of

---

[9] Davis, W. M. Origin of Limestone Caverns: Geological Society of America, Bulletin, Vol. 41, pp. 475-628, 1930.

enlargement and integration of the minute openings into large passages, however, is the point on which the theories show the greatest diversity.

Davis' theory postulated a two-cycle development of limestone caverns. The first cycle is wholly phreatic in nature with the development of passages, rooms, and similar openings below the water-table. Davis believed this cycle to be related to regional peneplanation. The second cycle takes place upon uplift of the cavern openings and the consequent removal of ground water from them. This change results from normal regional uplift and downcutting of surface streams. In this cycle vadose conditions prevail with the development of formations and the invasion of surface and vadose streams. The streams, however, modify the existing passages but do not produce new patterns or passages. Davis' theory, because of the two distinct stages postulated for cavern development, is referred to as the "two-cycle theory."

In 1942 Bretz published an extensive paper [10] on cave origin which modifies Davis' idea somewhat. Bretz, like Davis, believes that the main development of passages takes place in the phreatic zone, and that uplift which brings the openings above the water-table results in a second phase of deposition of formations and modifications of the passages. Bretz, however, emphasized a third phase, occurring between the two outlined by Davis. In this phase, between the phreatic and vadose periods, clay deposition occurs in large subterranean reservoirs of still water that occupy all of the space in the passages. The clay is residual from surface weathering and is transported to the phreatic lakes by descending water.

Swinnerton in 1932 published a paper [11] which opposed the views of Davis. A single cycle of development is postulated by Swinnerton in which both excavation and replenishment (development of formations, etc.) occur. This cycle is carried out by vadose water close to the water-table in its normal, lateral flow. Interruptions due to fluctuations of the water-table are recognized and the growth of formations is partly accomplished during this period. Swinnerton, however, recognized

[10] Bretz, J Harlen. Vadose and phreatic features of limestone caverns: Journal of Geology, Vol. 50, No. 6, Part II, pp. 675-811, Aug.-Sept. 1942.

[11] Swinnerton, A. C. Origin of limestone caverns: Geological Society of America, Bulletin, Vol. 43, pp. 663-694, 1932.

that even in a one-cycle development the initial openings in the limestone are developed under phreatic conditions.

Malott [12] proposed a theory of cave origin in 1932 which has been called the "invasion theory." It is similar in nature to Swinnerton's except that it gives more emphasis to the development of patterns below the water-table with a stage of enlargement of small openings to form cave passages above the ground water by active vadose and diverted surface streams.

The theory proposed by Gardner [13] is similar to those of Swinnerton and Malott except in the initial stages. Gardner postulated that the development of initial openings takes place in porous zones of limestones under hydrostatic pressure (aquifers) and that as valley erosion taps these zones it releases the ground water leaving small but integrated openings sloping with the dip. Following the removal of ground water, subterranean piracy of surface drainage occurs which aids in the enlargement of the small openings to passage size. During this phase formations are also developed. Gardner confined his theory to thick limestone terranes with relatively low and uniform dips.

It is interesting to note that all the theories cited deal at great length with conditions met in strata of low dip. Even in the case of Bretz, who went to considerable length in describing individual caves pertinent to his theory, the greatest emphasis was on caves in strata of low dip.

In West Virginia caves are distributed in strata that range in dip from horizontal to vertical with distribution roughly equal between relatively flat-lying rocks and those at steep angles. Features that support each of the theories of origin can be found in the caves of the State. This distribution is well suited for the purpose of evaluating existing theories and modifying or promulgating new ones. In the folded limestones a condition exists that is not adequately accounted for in Bretz's and Davis' approach wherein solution is a random affair. In the folded limestones the cavern passages have two important features: (1) the passages trending across the

---

[12] Malott, Clyde A. Lost river at Wesley Chapel Gulf, Orange County: Indiana Academy of Science, Proceedings, Vol. 41, pp. 285-316, 1932.

[13] Gardner, James H. Origin and development of limestone caverns: Geological Society of America, Bulletin, Vol. 46, pp. 1255-1274, August 1935.

strike or along the strike are nearly horizontal and show very little modification by bedding, (2) most caves have two or more distinct levels of passage and these levels are separated by generally uniform vertical spacing. The idea of random solution beneath a peneplane fails to account for these features.

Since 1947 the author has been investigating the relation of solution levels to relatively recent geomorphic forms, especially the river terraces of the Potomac Basin. From these studies four distinct phases in cavern development are recognized.

(1) Development of primitive tubes and pockets at random within the limestone. This is the initial stage of solution and takes place in the phreatic zone well below the water-table. Small, nonintegrated tubes and pockets are developed. Initially, in tight limestone, the solution is probably intermolecular; later as spaces are opened it follows joints, fractures, or bedding-planes. In some cases this solution may be at great depths; in many cases it may honeycomb the rock without producing true caves or it may produce only a few openings along joints leaving most of the limestone intact.

(2) Integration and development of primitive tubes and pockets into mature cavern passages. In the area of folded rock the development of cavern passages in more than one level with uniform spacing between levels has been cited. This feature along with the horizontal development of passages across folded strata or horizontally along the strike of beds can not be accounted for by a theory of random solution. In such a theory the cavern passages would follow the most soluble beds and would develop along the dip rather than across or horizontally parallel to it. The close relation of passage levels to river terrace levels as displayed in Trout, Schoolhouse, Hamilton, Hellhole, Hoffman School, and other Pendleton County caves is a solution to the problem. In this part of the Potomac Basin river terraces are 60 feet, 170 feet, and 230 feet above the present river. The passages of the caves are developed also at about the same elevations. In addition Hamilton Cave gives similar evidence. This cave is at the top of an anticline and the passages extend far into both limbs. While the beds of limestone are arched across the cave area the passages are horizontal and are independent of the bedding. These features would indicate some control was

exercised in solution development by the river level. It is postulated that during the time of lateral planation that is reflected in the river terraces, the water-table was uniform in slope and fluctuated very little for long periods of time. During this period the flow of ground water in the water-table was toward the river and the solution took place directly below the water-table. This interpretation is further supported by the facts that all large caves open on major stream valleys, cavern passages are largest near stream valleys and become progressively smaller inward in the cave away from the valleys, and most caves consist of one or two simple passages near their entrances (toward the valleys) but divide and become more complex inwards away from the valley. The possibility that the passages are a result of vadose waters can be ruled out as the equal development of passages, as in the labyrinth of Hamilton Cave, makes it necessary that phreatic conditions exist at the time of development. The lack of caves in many limestone areas or the large zones barren of caves in an otherwise cavernous area is also accounted for by these observations. If the water-table fluctuated too greatly during the time when the limestone area was near the surface of the water-table the development and integration of primitive tubes into caves would not be possible.

(3) Initiation of vadose conditions with uplift of the land, incision of the river, or other effects of rejuvenation the cave is brought above the water-table. At this stage there is generally an epoch of filling. Gravel, sand, silt, and clay are introduced; the coarser materials come via streams while some of the finer material is derived from the surface soils by migration along open joints and fractures. The unctuous clays cited by Bretz as developed in phreatic reservoirs, are absent in West Virginia caves. The typical sequence in West Virginia caves is gravel, sand, or silt overlain by silty clays. This sequence is typically vadose and reflects the uplift of the cave from the phreatic zone and the invasion and occasional flooding by surface streams. The clay deposit overlying coarser material reflects a flooding or pooling in the cave caused by plugging of the passages by fill but is not a true phreatic condition. In some caves, where clay is interbedded with coarser material, alternating vadose and phreatic conditions are indicated. These conditions would be expected as withdrawal of phreatic waters was accomplished.

(4) Vadose conditions. When the cave is in the vadose zone the streams in the cave remove the fill, as exemplified in the canyon sections of McClung and General Davis Caves. Flowstone, stalactites, stalagmites, and other decorations are formed from water seeping through the overlying limestone.

The features cited above substantiate, in part, Swinnerton's statement of development of caverns by lateral flow directly beneath the water-table but they do not support in full the other implications of a vadose nature inherent in his theory.

AGE OF CAVES:

If little is known concerning the origin of caves, even less is known concerning their age. A large number of calculations, based on the rate of growth of formations, have been put forth as indicating the age but these have been contradictory as no definite rate of growth can be rigidly established for formations. Similar calculations based on the time necessary to dissolve the limestone to form passages are of no value as they give no information on the lapse of time since such excavation was completed. The relation of river terraces and cave levels, however, offers a possible clue to the age of caverns. If the maximum enlargement of passages is related to the water-table at the time terraces or erosion levels develop, the age of the cave is that of the terrace.

At this stage of investigation the conclusions are still in the realm of speculation but indications are that caves occurring near the top of high ridges are related to the Schooley Peneplain and probably Cretaceous in age. Another large group of caves, especially those lying at the summit of subordinate ridges and in the pediment limestone plateau in Greenbrier, Monroe, and Pocahontas Counties, are probably related to the Harrisburg Level which is early Tertiary. The largest group of caves, however, are those lying in the zone of river terraces which are Pleistocene in age. If, with continuing study, the indications cited are substantiated the age of some caves will be far greater than that usually assigned—some originating over 30,000,000 years ago.

HYDROLOGY:

The mysteries surrounding streams that flow underground fascinates all who have a chance to observe such phenomena. Where do the streams sink into the ground? What courses do they follow? Where do they emerge? are questions that both scientists and laymen have tried to answer. The layman, generally an inhabitant in the area where the subterranean stream flows, has approached the problem by introducing sawdust, chaff, and similar material and observing at which stream or spring the material resurges. The scientist uses methods that are much the same except the chaff and sawdust are replaced by powerful non-toxic dyes. Even with the most elaborate materials, the work of determining subterranean watercourses requires considerable patience for it often takes days for the dye to reappear after it has been introduced into a stream.

Space permits the discussion of only major subterranean drainage systems in this report. In Greenbrier, Monroe, and Pocahontas Counties practically all drainage is subterranean in limestone areas and a detailed report on this condition would fill a volume in itself.

In Monroe County two distinct types of subterranean drainage are developed. In the area of Ordovician limestones along the east side of the county the streams rise as large springs or from large cavern streams which flow to the northwest off the flank of Peters Mountain. In general the subterranean courses are not integrated, each being parallel to and separate from the other. The flow in these subterranean streams is large, some reaching a volume of a million gallons a day. Similar conditions prevail along the Ordovician outcrop in Mercer County.

Laurel Creek flows along a subterranean course near Greenville. The stream disappears in a sink at the entrance to Laurel Creek Cave and flows along a sinuous course through Cross Road Cave, resurging near the northeast entrance to Greenville Saltpeter Cave. It then flows through a lower level of the latter cave emerging north of the mill pond at Greenville.

The headwaters of Indian Creek, which drains a vast area south of Pickaway, are subterranean watercourses throughout much of their length. Taggart Branch is entirely subterranean being visible in Steeles Cave only. Burnside Branch, which sinks and rises several times, passes through Cold Spring Cave. No permanent surface streams exist in the limestone area north of Pickaway but surface indications are that a large underground system drains towards Second Creek.

In Greenbrier County the subterranean drainage net is not as conspicuous as in Monroe County. Sinking Creek disappears south of Hughart and resurges three miles to the south in Piercys Mill Cave to form Muddy Creek. The stream in Piercys Cave apparently is a branch of this drainage. The flow through Piercys Mill Cave is relatively uniform, being regulated by a small hole at the end of the cave. Piercys Cave apparently lacks such control and is subject to wide fluctuations in volume. Organ and Hedrick Caves are a part of a large underground drainage net that empties into Second Creek.

Milligan Creek flows intermittently on the surface and in subterranean channels, draining an area from Richlands south along the east front of Muddy Creek Mountain. Milligan Creek apparently also drains much of the plateau southwest of Lewisburg, resurging in the large spring three-quarters of a mile northwest of Fort Spring.

Culverson, Roaring, and Buckeye Creeks form an integrated subterranean drainage system which covers much of the northern end of the limestone plateau in the Frankford-Renick area. The streams in Coffman and Higginbotham Caves apparently are a part of this drainage net. The probable resurgence of this subterranean system is a large spring on Spring Creek a mile above Spring Creek P. O. The underground drainage net around Maxwelton and south to Lewisburg is fed by a number of streams but little is known concerning it.

In Pocahontas County the subterranean drainage nets are somewhat more localized as broad expanses of limestones are lacking. Rush Run and its tributaries drain to Snedegars Cave and then underground along Friars Hole to Spring Creek. Hills and Bruffey Creeks, however, unite underground near Lobelia and apparently flow northeast to Blue Hole on Millstone Creek, which also drains much of Little Levels west of Hillsboro. The drainage from Blue Hole flows south to resurge at the head of Locust Creek. North of Hillsboro, where the limestone outcrops on the flank of the plateau front, underground drainage is confined to many obsequent valleys that

drain east to the Greenbrier River. Such drainage is not
integrated and numerous parallel, subterranean courses are
developed.

Elsewhere underground drainage is present but is not of
large magnitude. In Randolph, Tucker, and Preston Counties
underground streams flow in many caves but do not form
systems as each stream flows along an independent course.
Similar conditions prevail in the area of folded rocks. In
Germany Valley, however, a possible integrated system may
exist which drains the area and emerges at Judy Spring. The
most spectacular and well-known case of underground drainage of West Virginia is along Lost River near Wardensville
where the river sinks and flows along a subterranean course
for more th. n two miles.

In the Cambrian-Ordovician Limestones of the Shenandoah
Valley little is known of underground streams. While much
of the area has good surface drainage, the numerous large
springs indicate some type of integrated subterranean
drainage.

The observations cited above can not be considered final
as they are based on incomplete studies incidental to the investigation of caves. Much additional study is necessary to
decipher the complexities of underground drainage.

KARST:

The peculiar geomorphic aspect of limestone terranes,
characterized by sinkholes, lack of integrated surface valleys
and streams, and bare limestone outcrops alternating with
normal soils, is designated karst. In West Virginia three distinct types of karst are recognized. In Greenbrier, Monroe,
and Pocahontas Counties extensive areas of karst are developed in the pediment limestone plateau area extending intermittently from Greenville in Monroe County through Lewisburg to Renick. In the Little Levels area near Hillsboro,
Pocahontas County, another broad karst area is developed.
The surface of the karst is rolling with thousands of sinkholes, which grade one into another, developed in it. The sinkholes are so numerous that one feels the Greenbrier Valley
may well be termed "The Valley of Ten Thousand Sinks."
The sinks range from small, shallow, gently sloping ones, 10
to 20 feet wide and 10 feet deep, up to those over a mile in

Plate I—Lapiez resulting from solution along joints in karren blocks, Whitmer, Randolph County.

length with depths up to 200 feet. Vertical-sided sinks are relatively rare. In some cases, as along Millstone Run, in Little Levels, the sinks are narrow and elongated, and have been called valley sinks. Uvala, the large composite sinks formed by the uniting of several smaller sinks, are common, with large ones developed north of Pickaway and near Sunlight.

Karren, bands of bare limestone forming the surface, are not common nor well developed in the area. Locally, as along Rush Run near Lobelia and in the vicinity of Union, low out-crops of limestone are scattered across many of the fields on flanks of hills but are not continuous over wide areas. Lime-stone cliffs, with accompanying talus, are also rare.

Compared to karst in the Dalmatian area of Yugoslavia, the development of karst in West Virginia is quite limited. Rugged, bare rock terranes are rare and soils in general are relatively deep and rich. Climate as well as topography accounts for the difference in the degrees of development. For the restrained development, typified by karst in the Green-brier Valley, the term subdued is proposed.

Plate II—Sinkhole near Maxwelton, Greenbrier County. Typical karst landscape in Greenbrier and Monroe Counties.

In the region of folded rocks, karst is developed along valleys floored by limestone. The Shenandoah Valley contains the most extensive development of this type. Sinkholes pit the surface but are not as numerous or large as those in the Greenbrier Valley. The limestone upland, with surface drainage, remains relatively intact. Cliffs and talus are occasionally encountered along major streams, especially the Potomac. Karren cover considerable area varying from thin parallel bands of limestone alternating with large soil areas to fields that are practically all bare limestone. The most extensive development of karren is along U. S. Highway 11 near the Virginia-West Virginia State line. The karren in this area are long thin bands of parallel, low limestone outcrops which follow the strike. Since it gives the appearance of large, white, or gray ribbons stretched across the surface, the term ribbon karst is proposed for such features.

Karst is developed along the tops or flanks of limestone ridges in quite different form than that found in valleys. Cliffs and talus are the rule rather than the exception. Karren, however, are not common. Sinks develop in varying degrees ranging from small vertical pits up to large, broad, shallow depressions measuring a mile across. The latter type, termed dolines, are an integral part of Knobly Mountain, in Grant and Mineral Counties. The summit of this ridge is relatively rolling, being cut at intervals by deep gaps. At a distance the gaps appear to be typical Appalachian wind-gaps. However, a different picture is obtained when the top of the ridge is visited. The inner or mountain side of each gap is a large doline sloping towards the gap. A steep wall in the gap closes the outer side of the depression and drainage is by subterranean streams that issue as springs along the lower flanks of the ridge. The relation of gaps and dolines indicates that the wind-gaps of this ridge result from solution work rather than normal surface erosion processes. Similar conditions were observed along parts of Mill Creek and Patterson Creek Mountains in Hampshire, Hardy, and Grant Counties.

TEMPERATURE AND HUMIDITY

Caves can be divided into three distinct zones of temperature and humidity. The entrance is characterized by variable temperatures that generally parallel those of the earth's surface. A second zone extending from just inside the entrance to variable depths in the cave has temperatures that fluctuate slightly depending upon air currents in the cave. The third zone, which occupies most of the cave, has constant temperature and humidity.

The temperatures in caves approximate that which is the mathematical mean for the area in which the cave lies. In West Virginia the temperatures encountered lie in the range of 50° to 54° F. Noticeable extremes occur in Schoolhouse Cave where a temperature of 41° was recorded at the rear of the entrance room. The table below shows sample temperatures recorded in specific caves. The outside temperature ranged from 62° to 95° at the time the readings were made.

Monroe County

Haynes Cave	56°
Laurel Creek Cave	52°
Steeles Cave	53°

Greenbrier County

Coffmans Cave	53°
General Davis Cave	52°
McClung Cave	54°
Peck Cave	53°
Pollock Cave	53°

Pocahontas County

Cave Creek Cave .... 52°
Clyde Cochrane Sinks .... 56°
Marthas Cave .... 49°
Martens Cave .... 54°
Overholt Blowing Cave .... 49°
Saltpeter (Lobelia) Cave .... 48°
Snedegars Cave .... 48°
Tub Cave .... 47°

Pendleton County

Cove Knob Cave .... 51°
Hoffman School Cave .... 51°
Kenny Simmons Cave .... 51°
Minor Rexrode Cave .... 46°
Schoolhouse Cave .... 41°
Seneca Caverns .... 55°
Trout Cave .... 53°

Mineral County

High Rock Fissure Cave .... 50°
Kites Cave .... 50°

Grant County

Klines Gap Cave .... 50°

Preston County

Cornwell Cave .... 49°

Berkeley County

Jones Quarry Cave .... 56°

The humidity in practically all caves is 100%, the only exception noted being in Haynes Cave where it is 82%.

Some caves have strong currents of air moving through them. In summer this effect is detected by the cold stream of air that flows from such caves. Overholt Blowing, Martens, Minor Rexrode, Hoffman School, Saltpeter (Mineral County), and Wind Caves show this phenomenon well.

The streams flowing in caves have temperatures that are close to that of the cave air and surface streams that enter caves are quickly cooled. The following observations made at Martens Cave indicate the rate at which cooling occurs. The stream flowing in the cave is 2 to 4 feet wide and 2 to 4 inches deep with a flow of approximately 40 cubic feet per minute.

External temperature—Air 85°; water 72°.
Temperature 100 feet inside south entrance—Air 75°; water 68°.
Temperature 300 feet from south entrance—Air 54°; water 54°.

A strong current of air flows from south to north through the cave.

ECONOMIC VALUE OF CAVES

Until military and political events recently focused attention on caves as possible shelters for industry in case of war, little thought had been given to their economic use. From the military standpoint caves would be of value only as a last resort. The greatest drawback to use, outside of the lack of enough large caves, is the lack of good transportation near the large caves now known. Most large caves, like Laurel Creek and Tub, are situated many miles from railroads or heavy-duty highways. Hydrologic conditions also prevent the use of many caves. Laurel Creek Cave is anything but tenable under conditions of flood that lodged the highway bridge in a passage over 500 feet from the entrance. The cost of controlling such conditions along with modifying the cave and providing adequate transportation to the cave would be astronomic, even in this day when budgets of billions of dollars are considered commonplace. The caves large enough to warrant any consideration from a military viewpoint are Greenville, Saltpeter, Laurel Creek, Organ, Tub, Poorfarm (Pocahontas), and Sinnit. These caves have over 150 feet of cover above them which is sufficient for all purposes.

Storage of bulk petroleum and natural gas in caves has been proposed but rejected on economic and engineering grounds. The costs of renovating the cave is far greater than the cost of storing petroleum or natural gas by reinjecting them into exhausted oil and gas fields.

Water supplies are often obtained from springs or streams that issue from caverns. In days gone by these supplies were apparently more dependable than at present. Removal of timber and pumping of deep wells has altered the water-table to the point where many springs now flow but part of the year, if at all. Pollution, especially near cities, has increased and in many cases rendered water from springs unfit for human use. Dumping of sewage and industrial wastes into caverns has spread pollution over far greater areas than in the case of that put into surface waters. The caves lying along Peters Mountain, some of which are used for the water supply of Bluefield, generally have copious streams of relatively pure water flowing in them and are potential sources for additional city water supplies.

Several cavern streams are used to run grist-mills in Monroe and Pendleton Counties. At Zenith, Monroe County, a large mill is operated by water power from McClung-Zenith Cave. The mill, with its large overshot wheel, is a picture worthy of any artist. Similar mills utilize Blue Spring as a source of water at Mill Point, Pocahontas County, and Rich Creek Cave, Monroe County. On Roaring Spring Run a large mill with a long flume, part of which has collapsed, used water from Roaring Spring Cave. Piercys Mills obtained water from Piercys Mill Cave. The first mill west of Allegheny Mountain in southern West Virginia was built inside Higginbotham Cave in 1769. Argobrites Cave has been used to power both a grist-mill and sawmill although all evidence is now gone.

Three commercial caves are open to the public in West Virginia. They are Organ Cave in Greenbrier County, Smokehole Caverns, and Seneca Caverns in Pendleton County. Formerly two other caves, Stratosphere Balloon near Seneca Caverns and George Washington near Charles Town, were commercialized but expense of upkeep did not justify their operation. Commercial caves, to be a success, must have something of interest to the layman. Beautiful formations and historic relics are typical attractions. However, location is as important, if not more important, than other factors and to be a success commercial caves must be within easy access of main travelled highways. Few caves in West Virginia possess any potential commercial value. Grapevine Cave, with its magnificent formations, is within reasonable access of U. S. 219 and U. S. 60, but engineering costs to fit the cave for public use would probably prevent any profitable operation.

The greatest economic boom for caves occurred during the War Between the States. The Confederacy, hard pressed for saltpeter to make gunpowder, turned to caves as a source. Twenty-two caves in West Virginia were mined for saltpeter from 1862 to 1865. In addition, four caves, namely, Lost, Mill Run, Saltpeter (Pendleton County), and Saltpeter (Mineral County), were mined by local inhabitants for saltpeter as far back as the War of 1812.

Methods of extraction were rather crude. The saltpeter earth, dug from the clay and silt fills, was placed in wedge-shaped hoppers and water poured over it to leach the saltpeter. Saltpeter liquor was evaporated outside the cave to obtain raw saltpeter which, after further processing, was used as an ingredient in gunpowder. Considering the amount of saltpeter earth that was easily accessible in some caves it is amazing how little was actually used. In addition it is quite puzzling why tortuous, small passages, as in Snedegars Cave, were exploited when more accessible deposits were left untouched.

Relics from saltpeter operations remain in many caves but dampness has caused most of them to decay to the point where they crumble on touch. Hoppers seldom remain recognizable except in Organ Cave where 37 are in excellent state of preservation. Troughs, hewn from logs, however, remain in better condition and are seen in practically all caves used for saltpeter. In Snedegars Cave a trough 12 feet long and 3 feet wide lies at the end of a small, low, tortuous passage. This is the largest trough in a West Virginia cave. Bridges, ladders, and windlass are found along with other relics, the best preserved being in Haynes Cave. Paddles, puddlers, and pick handles are occasionally found but are rare. In many caves the marks made by mattocks wielded by saltpeter workers remain as fresh as the day they were made. In Greenville Saltpeter Cave the prints of the feet of the men and mules as well as cart tracks are still preserved. The saltpeter caves and their relics are outlined below:

Monroe County:

Bradley Saltpeter Pit: Reported used 1862-1865. No positive evidence.

Greenville Saltpeter Cave: Tracks of mules, men, and carts. Rotted remains of hoppers.

Haynes Cave: Troughs, bridges, windlass.

Doan Ballard Cave: Reported used 1862-1865.

Greenbrier County:

Bob Gee Cave: 4 broken hoppers, 3 troughs, 10 piles of saltpeter earth, mattock marks.

Hanna Cave: Piles of saltpeter earth.

Higginbotham No. 3 Cave: Mattock marks.

Lost Cave: Used in 1812 and Mexican Wars. Scant remains of hoppers.

McFerrin Cave: Several troughs and broken hoppers. This is the only saltpeter cave in West Virginia with an active stream.

Organ Cave: 37 hoppers in good condition. Several troughs.

Pollock Saltpeter Cave: 2 troughs. Broken hoppers. Piles of saltpeter earth.

Pocahontas County:

Overholt Saltpeter Cave: Trough, mattock handle.

Saltpeter (Lobelia) Cave: 1 hopper and trough, stone steps, mattock marks.

Snedegars Cave: 3 troughs, numerous piles of saltpeter earth.

Pendleton County:

Cave Mountain Cave: Diggings.

Cove Knob Cave: Mattock marks.

Hoffman School Cave: Diggings.

Mill Run Cave: Reported in use before 1862. No positive evidence.

Saltpeter Cave: Reported in use before 1862. No positive evidence.

Schoolhouse Cave: Excavation of passage, remains of tramway.

Sinnit Cave: Plank bridges, mattock marks.

Trout Cave: Water trough, plank bridges, ladders, diggings. A large gunpowder mill was operated along the river below Trout Cave.

Hampshire County:

Fairview Mountain Pit: Reported to have been used 1862-1865.

Mineral County:

Saltpeter Cave: In use previous to 1862. Piles of saltpeter earth near entrance.

Randolph County:

Fortlick Cave: Reported in use before 1862. No positive evidence.

Grant County:

Peacock Cave: Old ladder, platform, mattock marks. Probably used for ochre although reported in use for saltpeter.

RESUME OF THE BIOLOGY OF WEST VIRGINIA CAVES

A report on the Caves of West Virginia can hardly be considered complete unless some mention is made of the animals and plants that inhabit this realm of darkness. Observations presented here are broad and general as a detailed scientific study of cavern biology would fill a number of volumes. Lack of sight and pigment are generally accepted for all subterranean dwellers but this is far from correct for the majority of cave animals in West Virginia have color and are seldom without eyes.

A myriad of small animals live in caves but are seldom noticed unless they are specifically looked for. Several species of spiders, mice, dace, lacewing, gnats, beetles (some of which give off offensive odors) and millipeds are found living in areas of abundant decaying organic material. The most conspicuous forms of insects found in caves are the cave crickets, which in company with the harvestman (daddy-long-legs), are found in varying numbers in all caves. In some caves, as Laurel Creek and Hoyt, the walls and ceiling have thousands of crickets while elsewhere only a few may be seen in the entire cave. Several forms of mosquito and flies are abundant in some caves, especially Hoyt Cave where they are so numerous they fill the air while flying and are quite annoying to the visitor. Moths have been observed in several caves. Crayfish are found in practically all caves with streams or ponds and are especially abundant and large in Coffman and Steeles Caves.

The following is a brief summary of some specific occurrences of invertebrates in West Virginia caves:

Eyeless, white flatworms of the family Kendiidae are in Mystic, Hinkles Unus, and Organ Cave, and probably elsewhere; these are rare forms and the majority are undescribed.

Eyeless pseudoscorpions are in caves in Monroe and Greenbrier Counties.

Isopods: true cave forms of two familes. Asellidae (aquatic) and Trichoniscidae (terrestrial) are in caves. Common surface forms are near entrances and in affluent stream caves.

Several species of true cave amphipods (fam. Gammaridae) occur in West Virginia caves.

Millipeds: cave forms are principally of genera *Zygonopus, Pseudotremia,* and *Dearolfia.* First two genera are fairly widespread in West Virginia; latter is restricted to Pocahontas and Pendleton counties.

Springtails (Ord. Collembola, cl. Insecta) are numerous and include several true cave species; many are undescribed forms.

Bristletails (Ord. Diplura) occur in West Virginia caves; all belong to the genus *Plusiocampa.*

Cave crickets are mostly *Hadenoecus putaneus* (unbanded); others (banded) are of genus *Ceuthophilus.*

Beetles: several species of ground beetles (Carabidae) and rove beetles (Staphylinidae) are in caves. Among the former are eyeless, reddish, true cave species, all in genus *Pseudanophthalmus.* There are many different species and subspecies, the majority undescribed, though under investigation, that are known from Monroe, Pocahontas, Mercer, Greenbrier, Randolph, Tucker, and Pendleton counties.

Flies: many species of flies, gnats, mosquitoes occur. Most conspicuous are narrow flies (fam. Heleomzidae) which are in large numbers on walls and ceilings. Larvae of fungus gnats (Fungivoridae) occur beneath stones, rotten wood, and in crevices.

The invertebrate fauna is rounded out by two interesting forms; earthworms are found in almost all caves with streams. Gastropods (snails) are in McClung Cave [14] and Laurel Creek Cave.

Vertebrate animals are the most conspicuous forms of life in caves. Several species of salamanders are abundant. The Spring Salamander *Gyrinophilus p. porphyriticus* and Dusky Salamander *Desmognathus fuscus* are common near cave entrances. Species of *Eurycea l. longicauda* and *E. lucifuga* are abundant in caves of Pocahontas, Greenbrier and Monroe counties. *Eurycea bislineata* is common near some cave entrances. Other species of salamanders are relatively rare in West Virginia caves.

The Allegheny Cave Rat dwells in many caves, though it is seldom seen. Its nest, consisting of leaves, paper, or anything the owner can beg, borrow or steal, however, is a conspicuous object in many passageways. The rats are especially abundant in Ridgeville, Smokehole, and Cornwell Caves.

A host of terrestrial animals seek caves as shelters but are not permanent inhabitants. They include skunks, fox, raccoons, deer, mice, frogs, and bears. In Muddy Creek Cave beavers have been known to invade the cave to build dams. Snakes do not inhabit caves but often are found where they have fallen into entrance pits.

Bats are the animals associated most often with caves. These maligned animals have long suffered from false legends and superstitions that have caused many persons to go out of their way to do harm to them. In reality the bat is a useful, harmless animal that aids greatly in the control of insects. No bat in West Virginia inflicts injury on man nor do they become entangled in women's hair as is so commonly supposed. In self defense, especially on capture, they will bite and fight back at their captor. Only in rare cases do bats collide with people in a cave. The author has noted bats flying

---

[14] Reese, A. M. The fauna of West Virginia caves: **West Virginia** Academy of Science, Proceedings, Vol. 7, p. 50, 1934.

erratically when disturbed from hibernation and has had several collisions with them from this cause.

In the last few years rabies have been found in bats. Although no cave bats in West Virginia have been reported rabid, precautions should be taken when peculiarly behaving bats are encountered, and if bitten by a bat normal precautions against infection by rabies, including capture of the bat for examination, should be undertaken.

Bats use caves primarily for hibernation during cold weather. Although this period of hibernation extends from late fall through spring, bats, especially the long-eared bat, have been observed entering caves in great numbers during a cold spell in mid-summer of 1948. Six species of bat are known in West Virginia and are distributed throughout most caves. The little brown bat is confined to caves in the northern part of the State while the long-eared bat is common in caves that lie above an altitude of 2000 feet.

A word of caution is necessary concerning the capture of cave animals. Most species are relatively rare and subject to extinction if too many specimens are taken. Collecting should therefore be kept to a minimum and no attempt made to collect everything that is seen in a cave. During winter, traverses of caves should be avoided or if necessary should be done without disturbing hibernating bats. A continual parade through a cavern will disturb the bats and cause death to many if their metabolism is maintained beyond the minimum of hibernation for any period of time.

Cavern flora is confined to fungi and moulds. The largest plants are the polypores (shelf fungi) that grow profusely on wood and similar vegetable matter. In Stratosphere Balloon Cave sheets of white slime mould over 2 feet long hang from the wood in the stairs and walks. The wood has been reduced to a soft, wet, mass that crumbles on touch. Little work has been done on cave flora but, with increasing use of fungi and moulds in medicine and industry, an economic return might result from such investigations.

The recovery of fossil remains in West Virginia has been few compared to those found in Pennsylvania and Maryland. Thomas Jefferson [15] reported extensively on the remains of a

---

[15] Jefferson, Thomas A memoir on the discovery of certain bones of a quadruped of the clawed kind in the western part of Virginia: American Philosophical Society, Transactions, Vol. IV, pp. 246-260, 1799.

fossil sloth from an undesignated cave which is now believed to be Organ Cave. Remains of a fossil peccary were described by Gidley [16] from the cave at Renick Quarry. In 1951 members of the Charleston Chapter of the National Speleological Society discovered the skelton of a peccary in Organ-Hedricks Cave. A fossil bear tooth was found in the new section of Laurel Creek Cave in 1952 and a bear skeleton was obtained from the water passage in Sinnit Cave in 1953. These finds were made by members of the National Speleological Society. These species are the only ones reported thus far from West Virginia.

BIBLIOGRAPHY

The publications cited contain detailed information on the caves of West Virginia. Papers which refer briefly to such caves are not included.

Culverwell, Tom   Mountaineering under West Virginia: Potomac Appalachian Trail Club, Bulletin, January 1941.

Culverwell, Tom   Subterranean rock climbing: Appalachian, June 1943.

Culverwell, Tom   On underground trails: Potomac Appalachian Trail Club, Bulletin, October 1943.

Culverwell, Tom   About as far as we can go: Potomac Appalachian Trail Club, Bulletin, October 1944.
        The four articles by Culverwell contain descriptions of Schoolhouse Cave, Pendleton County.

Gidley, J. W.   A Pleistocene cave deposit of western Maryland: Smithsonian Institution, Annual Report 1918, pp. 286-288, (1920).
        Describes fossil remains found in Renick Quarry Cave.

Green, N. Bayard   Representatives of the family Gyrinophilus in West Virginia: West Virginia Academy of Science, Proceedings, Vol. 15, pp. 179-183, 1942.
        Mentions the collection of specimens from two caves.

Haymond, Henry   History of Harrison County : Acme Publishing Company, Morgantown, 1910.
        Description of Indian Cave, Two Lick Creek, on pp. 396-398.

Holmes, William H.   A West Virginia rock shelter: American Anthropologist, Vol. 3, No. 3, July 1890, pp. 217-223 (Indian Cave, Harrison County).

Hovey, Horace C.   The Jewell Cavern: Scientific American, Vol. 60, No. 22, June 1, 1889, pp. 339-340; also in Exchangers Monthly, Vol. 5, 1890, No. 9, July, p. 71, No. 10, Aug., p. 79, No. 11, Sept., p. 87, No. 12, Oct., pp. 90-91.

---

[16] Gidley, J. W. A Pleistocene cave deposit of western Maryland: Smithsonian Institution, Annual Report 1918, pp. 286-288 (1920).

Jefferson, Thomas A memoir on the discovery of certain bones of a quadruped of the clawed kind in the western part of Virginia: American Philosophical Society, Transactions, Vol. IV, pp. 246-260, 1799.
Description of discovery of Megalonyx in cave (Organ) in Greenbrier County.

Jordan, George. The great cave of Cheat River: Hanzsche and Company, Baltimore, 1855.
48-page pamphlet devoted to an exaggerated description of a cave in Tucker County, probably Cave Hollow Cave.

Kercheval, Samuel. History of the Valley of Virginia: Shenandoah Publishing House, Strasburg, Va., 1925 (4th ed.).
Caves described on pp. 311, 316, 317, 365-368.

Loomis, H. F. The millipeds collected in Appalachian caves by Mr. Kenneth Dearolf: Harvard, Museum of Comparative Zoology, Bulletin, Vol. LXXXVI, No. 4, pp. 165-193, 1939.
Describes specimens from eight caves in West Virginia collected by Mr. Kenneth Dearolf, West Lawn, Pennsylvania, in 1935-1938.

Loomis H. F. New cave and epigean millipeds of the United States with notes on some established species: Harvard, Museum of Comparative Zoology, Bulletin, Vol. XCII, No. 7, pp. 373-410, June 1943.
Describes collection of Mr. Leslie Hubricht, Missouri Botanical Garden, St. Louis, made in 1939-1941. Four caves in West Virginia cited.

Maxwell, Hu History of Tucker County: Preston Publishing Company, Kingwood, 1884.
Contains a brief description of caves on pp. 136-138.

Maxwell, Hu History of Randolph County: Acme Publishing Company, Morgantown, 1898.
Detailed description of caves, pp. 281-285.

Maxwell, Hu and **Swisher, H. L.** History of Hampshire County, West Virginia: A. Brown Boughner, Morgantown, 1897.
Brief description of caves on p. 418.

Mease, James A geological account of the United States: Birch & Small, Philadelphia, 1897, pp. 468-469.
Description of sinks of Sinking Creek.

Morton, O. F. History of Preston County: Journal Publishing Company, Kingwood, 1914.
Brief description of caves, Pt. I, p. 21.

Nelson, Ben Swago Creek-Marlinton Caves: The Explorer (Explorers Club of Pittsburgh), pt. 1, Feb. 1956, 9 pp.; pt. 2, June 1956, 9 pp.; pt. 3, Aug.-Sept. 1956, 7 pp.; pt. 4, June 1957, 6 pp.

Perry, Clay The bottom fell out of a well: Nature, Vol. 50, No. 8, Oct. 1957, pp. 426-428.

Reese, A. M. Fauna of West Virginia caves: West Virginia Academy of Science, Proceedings, Vol. 7, pp. 39-53, 1934.
Contains brief description of 43 caves and a list of fauna found in each.

Stimson, H. F. and Culverwell, Tom. The survey of Schoolhouse Cave: Potomac Appalachian Trail Club, Bulletin, January 1945.
Contains a detailed description and map of Schoolhouse Cave.

Strother, David H. (Porte Crayon) The mountains: Harpers New Monthly Magazine, Vol. 45-51, 1872-1875.

Writing under the name Porte Crayon, Strother published a fictitious travelogue based on actual experiences in the mountains of West Virginia. A trip through Gandy Sinks is briefly described in Vol. 45, pp. 359-360 (Part IV), August 1872.

Valentine, J. Manson New cavernicole Carabidae of the subfamily Trechinae Jeannel: Elisha Mitchell Scientific Society, Journal, Vol. 46, pp. 247-257, 1931.

Valentine, J. Manson A classification of the genus Pseudanophthalmus Jeannel (Fam. Carabidae) with descriptions of new species and notes on distribution: Elish Mitchell Scientific Society, Journal, Vol. 47, pp. 261-280, 1932.

Dr. Valentine's papers describe beetles found in several West Virginia caves.

Wiley, S. T. History of Preston County: Journal Printing House, Kingwood, 1882.

Brief description of caves on pp. 360 and 447.

Wiley, S. T. History of Monogalia County: Preston Publishing Company, Kingwood, 1883.

Brief description of caves on pp. 623 and 669.

Wister, Caspar A description of the bones deposited, by the President, in the museum of the society: American Philosophical Society, Transactions, Vol. IV, pp. 526-531, 1799.

Description of the remains of Megalonyx recovered by Thomas Jefferson from Organ Cave.

Popular articles, generally well illustrated, on West Virginia caves have appeared in the following publications:

Life Magazine, November 4, 1947, pp. 142-145. Life goes spelunking.

Describes Grapevine Cave.

Saturday Evening Post, July 12, 1941, pp. 14-15, 36, 38. Come let's go spelunking by Clay Perry.

Describes Sinks of Gandy Creek.

Science Illustrated, November 1948, pp. 40-45. How to explore a cave by Marie Hanson and David W. Nussbaum.

Describes Sinnit Cave.

Spot Magazine, February 1942, pp. 11-12. Cave debunking.

Describes Whitings Neck Cave.

Washington Sunday Star, Gravure Section, November 26, 1939, p. 3. Cave explorers find near-by wonderland.

Picture story of Schoolhouse Cave.

Washington Sunday Star, Gravure Section, September 8, 1946, pp. 1, 8, 9. Adventures inside the earth by John W. Stepp.

Describes Mongold Cave.

Washington Sunday Star Magazine, June 15, 1952, pp. 4-5. Going underground for the weekend by J. Norwood Hamilton.

Describes Kenny Simmons Cave.

DESCRIPTIONS OF THE CAVERNS
OF WEST VIRGINIA

Over 400 caves in West Virginia are large enough or important enough to warrant description. The descriptions are grouped according to counties. The map references are to the standard 15-minute quadrangles published by the United States Geological Survey except in the area east of 78° where 7½-minute quadrangles (published by Army Map Service and issued by the U. S. Geological Survey) are standard.

The names in parenthesis are alternate names commonly associated with the caves. The accuracy of measurement varies according to the units used to express the size. In general, cave distances measured in yards are based on estimates.

Limestone horizons in which the caves are developed are identified as closely as possible. Those designations suffixed with a question mark indicate that the identification is not positive. The limestone horizon and elevation for each cave, unless otherwise indicated, refer to the entrance of the cave.

BERKELEY COUNTY

The Cambrian and Ordovician limestones outcrop over broad areas in eastern Berkeley County and are highly folded with distinct cleavages developed. Dips are steep and vary considerably, even in short distances. Nineteen caves are reported from these limestones. Two caves are known from the Tonoloway Limestone which lies in a syncline along Wilson and Ferrel Ridges, west of Tomahawk.

ANDERSON CAVE 39°31'45" N.; 77°54'55" W. Hedgesville (Williamsport) Quadrangle.

Anderson Cave is on the south side of a shallow ravine ¼ mile north of Hainesville, 100 yards east of U. S. 11 (elevation, 415 feet). The entrance is blocked now by trash but reports indicate the cave trends south for 100 feet as a crawlway with a large drop near the entrance. The cave is in the Chambersburg Limestone.

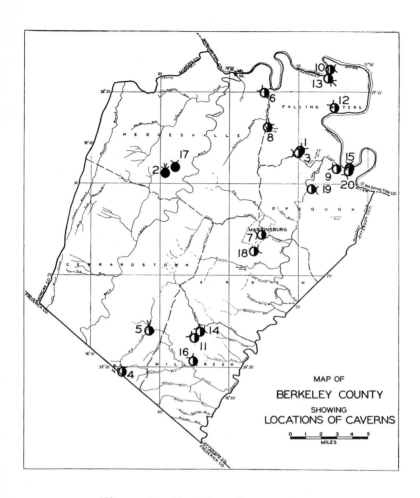

Figure 1.—Berkeley County Caves

1. Anderson.
2. Applejack.
3. Benders.
4. Boyles.
5. Carter Orchard Pit.
6. Donaldson (Georgetown).
7. Frog Pond.
8. Hiett.
9. Hundred Holes.
10. Indian Church.

11. Inwood.
12. Jones Quarry.
13. Nestle Quarry.
14. Pig (Darkesviile).
15. River (Indian).
16. Rocky Bottom.
17. Silers (Meyers).
18. Standard Quarry Caves.
19. Thousand Caves.
20. Whitings Neck.

LEGEND FOR ALL COUNTY MAPS

⍺ CAVE

⦶ CAVE IN PLEISTOCENE

⍺⊢ CAVE WITH STREAM

◎ CAVE IN MONONGAHELA SERIES

⍺ CAVE WITH STREAM FLOWING IN

○ CAVES IN GREENBRIER LIMESTONE

⍺ CAVE WITH STREAM FLOWING OUT

● CAVES IN DEVONIAN - SILURIAN LIMESTONES

⍭ VERTICAL PIT

◖ CAVES IN ORDOVICIAN - CAMBRIAN LIMESTONES

⍭ VERTICAL PIT WITH CAVE AT BASE

LEGEND FOR ALL CAVE MAPS

⌒ SURVEYED PASSAGE

 SAND

⌒ UNSURVEYED OR CONJECTURAL PASSAGE

 CLAY OR MUD

⌒ LOWER LEVEL

 LARGE ROCKS OR BREAKDOWN

③ CEILING HEIGHT

 COLUMN

$\overline{50}$ DEPTH OF FLOOR BELOW CAVE ENTRANCE

▲ STALAGMITE

$\underline{50}$ ELEVATION OF FLOOR ABOVE CAVE ENTRANCE

▼ STALACTITE

 DROP OR LEDGE

 FLOWSTONE

 WELL OR SINK

 STREAM

 STAIRS OR LADDER

 POOL

APPLEJACK CAVE 39°30'45" N.; 78°04'30" W. Hancock
Quadrangle.

This cave is on the Tomahawk-Jones Spring road, 2.0 miles
southwest of Tomahawk. The entrance, in an orchard 100
feet north of the road (elevation, 740 feet), is a shaft 65 feet
deep with a passage 70 feet long at the base. The cave receives
its name from the use made of the shaft as a refuse dump for
spoiled apples. Applejack Cave is in the Tonoloway Limestone.

BENDERS CAVE 39°31'35" N.; 77°55'04" W. Hedgesville
(Williamsport) Quadrangle.

Benders Cave, at Hainesville, is 100 yards east of U. S. 11
and 100 yards north of the Hainesville-Bedington road. The
entrance (elevation, 400 feet), in a shallow sink, is a small

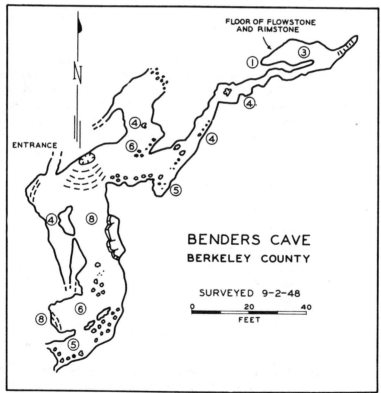

Figure 3.—Benders Cave.

opening with a vertical drop of 15 feet to a room, 40 feet long, 10 feet wide, 6 to 8 feet high, extending northeast-southwest. A passage leads southeast for 60 feet and is 6 to 8 feet high and 10 feet wide. Formations, so dense they practically block the passage, consist of delicate soda straw stalactites, thin, long columns, and bacon rind. The passage, extending northeast from the entrance, is 60 feet long with a ceiling height of 6 feet at the beginning reducing gradually to a crawlway near the end where it is blocked by a clay bank. Two small rooms lie along the north side of the passage. Formations in the form of columns, stalactites, and serrated bacon rinds are found along the front part of the passage.

Benders Cave is in the Chambersburg Limestone (strike N. 30°E.; dip, 80°S.E.) and is developed along joints at N. 60°E., N. 10°W. and the bedding-planes.

BOYLES CAVE 39°19'39" N.; 78°07'45" W. Gerrardstown Quadrangle.

Boyles Cave lies just north of the West Virginia-Virginia State Line, 0.6 mile southeast of Mt. Pleasant Church (elevation, 760 feet). The entrance is 10 feet square in cross-section but after 10 feet is reduced to a crevice 2 feet wide that slopes steeply downwards for 10 feet. The cave extends south for 500 feet as a crevice passage up to 10 feet high. A few sections require crawling. The floor is wet clay. At the end the cave opens to the surface in a narrow hole. Boyles Cave is in the base of the Conococheague Limestone.

CARTER ORCHARD PIT 39°22'02" N.; 78°05'45" W. Gerrardstown Quadrangle.

On the south side of Mill Creek at Gerrardstown (elevation, 650 feet) is a vertical shaft 20 feet deep that opens into a short water passage at the base. The pit is in the Conococheague Limestone.

DONALDSON (GEORGETOWN) CAVE 39°35'00" N.; 77°57'28" W. Hedgesville (Williamsport) Quadrangle.

This cave is 0.4 mile southwest of Little Georgetown, at the north edge of an orchard 200 feet west of the Georgetown-North Mountain road (elevation, 440 feet). The entrance, a small opening 2 feet wide, 4 feet high, on the west side of a shallow sink, opens into a wide passage 50 feet long, 20 feet wide, 5 feet high sloping down 15 feet to a room heading north, triangular in plan, 100 feet long, 30 feet wide at the south end, and 10 feet high. The floor is covered by breakdown. At the southwest corner of the room a small passage drops steeply over breakdown covered by wet clay to a shallow pool in a small passage trending southwest for 25 feet to a clay fill.

The cave, in the Conococheague Limestone (strike, N.10°E.; dip, 20°W.) follows the bedding-planes. Joints at N.30°W., N.60°E., and due east shape the room and determine the direction of the lower passages.

FROG POND CAVE 39°27'18″ N.; 77°57'40″ W. Martinsburg Quadrangle.

Frog Pond Cave is in a low limestone ledge at the east end of South Street in the city of Martinsburg (elevation, 400 feet). The cave is a sloping passage, 4 or 5 feet high, that drops steeply for 20 feet to a passage 50 feet long. It is in the Mosheim (Stones River) Limestone.

HIETT CAVE 39°33'03″ N.; 77°57'13″ W. Hedgesville (Williamsport) Quadrangle.

Two hundred yards northeast of Harland Spring is a shallow vertical shaft (elevation, 440 feet), 6 feet deep, that opens at the base to a crawlway 100 feet long. The entrance is now blocked by trash. The cave is in the Conococheague Limestone.

HUNDRED HOLES 39°30'55″ N.; 77°51'55″ W. Williamsport Quadrangle.

On the south side of Opequon Creek, 400 feet from its mouth, are a series of sinkholes (elevation, 380 feet), many of them with small rooms and short passages at their base. The passages, small crawlways up to 300 feet long, are in the top of the Beekmantown Limestone.

INDIAN CHURCH CAVE 39°36'08″ N.; 77°52'51″ W. Hedgesville (Williamsport) Quadrangle.

Indian Church Cave is in a bluff of limestone 100 yards north of the north end of Nestles Quarry (elevation, 500 feet).

The entrance is on the face of the bluff, 60 feet above Potomac River, and measures 10 feet square. The cave extends east for 120 feet and is gradually reduced to a crawlway. Indian Church Cave is in the Mosheim (Stones River) Limestone.

INWOOD CAVE 39°21′32″ N.; 78°02′30″ W. Gerrardstown Quadrangle.

In a meadow, 100 yards east of the packing-house at Inwood (elevation, 580 feet), is a small opening that connects with a crawlway extending east for 100 feet. The cave is in the Beekmantown Limestone.

JONES QUARRY CAVE 39°34′02″ N.; 77°55′31″ W. Hedgesville (Williamsport) Quadrangle.

This cave is on the northeast side of Jones Quarry, on the north side of the Potomac River, 1 mile northeast of Falling Waters (elevation, 400 feet). The entrance is a small crawlway 30 feet above the quarry floor and opens into a twisting passage, 4 to 10 feet wide, averaging 10 to 15 feet high. It extends northeast for 150 feet, crossing several wells and intersected by several small side passages, where it connects with a north-south passage, 4 to 20 feet high and 8 to 15 feet wide. Sixty feet south along this passage is a room 10 feet high, 40 feet long, 20 feet wide, which slopes southeast to a clay-filled pit 20 feet deep. On the west side of this room is another room of similar dimensions. The latter room connects with the entrance passage and also opens into the quarry face in a narrow cleft. On the north side of the passage, at the end of the sinuous entrance passage, is a maze of small, dry passages. Throughout most of the cave the floors are of wet clay, although river gravel is found scattered in many parts. Flowstone decorates the walls of the passages. Columns and stalactites are found in the back rooms of the cave. The east side of the cave is close to the surface and slabs of breakdown cover the floor. Human bone fragments, probably of a young male Indian, were found in a small side passage, off the main north-south passage, in 1947. Since 1955, the Pittsburgh Chapter of the National Speleological Society, in conjunction with the Carnegie Museum, has investigated the human remains in the cave and has recovered a large quantity of bones and artifacts. Jones Quarry Cave is in the Chambersburg

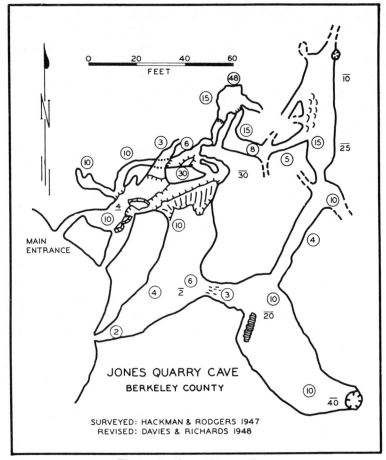

Figure 4.—Jones Quarry Cave.

Limestone which dips 18° E. and strikes N.20°E. It is developed along vertical joints at N. 20°E., N. 50°W., N. 70°E. and a joint trending due north with a slope of 40° W.

NESTLE QUARRY CAVE   39°35′44″ N.; 77°52′53″ W. Hedgesville (Williamsport) Quadrangle.

This cave is 500 feet west of the junction of the county road and the road leading to Nestles Quarry (elevation, 460 feet). The entrance, a small cleft in the base of a shallow sink 25 feet south of the quarry road, opens into a narrow sinuous fissure dipping steeply to the east for 90 feet to a low room, 40 feet wide and 20 feet long. Twenty feet beyond the room, the passage intersects a north-south passage, 150 feet long, 4 to 15 feet wide, with a ceiling made up of dome pits 15 to 25 feet high. The cave ends by lowering of the ceiling and accumulation of clay. A stream flows between banks of clay along the north-south passage. The cave is in the Chambersburg Limestone.

PIG (DARKESVILLE) CAVE 39°21′56″ N.; 78°02′03″ W. Gerrardstown Quadrangle.

Pig Cave is 25 feet west of U. S. 11, ½ mile southwest of Darkesville (elevation, 570 feet). The entrance, a low, steeply sloping crawlway, is in a lawn close to a private residence. The entrance slope opens into a passage trending south for 150 feet, 8 to 18 feet high, and 3 to 8 feet wide. A small, short, lower passage parallels the main passage to the east. The cave formerly trended east for 1000 feet but a rock fall now blocks it after 150 feet. A pig, for whom the cave is named, is reported to have entered the cave and come out in a cellar over 300 yards to the east. Pig Cave is in the Beekmantown Limestone.

RIVER (INDIAN) CAVE 39°31′03″ N.; 77°51′15″ W. Williamsport Quadrangle.

This cave is at river level, at the base of an escarpment on the south side of the Potomac, 1000 yards east of the mouth of Opequon Creek (elevation, 330 feet). The entrance is triangular in cross-section, 10 feet high and wide. A passage, which is progressively reduced in size, extends south for 100 feet to a close down. A number of columns and stalactites decorate the passage. Pottery and similar evidence of Indian use have been obtained from the cave. River (Indian) Cave is in the Beekmantown Limestone.

ROCKY BOTTOM CAVE 39°20′20″ N.; 78°02′34″ W. Gerrardstown Quadrangle.

A series of sinks, ½ mile northeast of Bunker Hill (elevation, 550 feet), have small cave passages at the base, the longest of which extends 100 feet. The passages, in the Beekmantown Limestone, may have been a part of a larger cave system now collapsed.

SILERS (MEYERS) CAVE 39°30'54" N.; 78°03'56" W. Hancock Quadrangle.

Silers Cave is 1¼ miles southwest of Tomahawk, 200 yards east of the Tomahawk-Jones Springs road (elevation, 720 feet). The entrance is a vertical shaft 20 feet deep that opens into a maze of passages to the north and west. The passages vary from crawlways to fissures 20 feet high, all averaging 2 to 6 feet wide. The passages along the west and south part of the cave are in a zone of breakdown and are dangerous because of loose rock. The floors are of wet or damp clay throughout. Formations are not plentiful but flowstone and a few columns are found in dome pits which occasionally interrupt the passages. The cave is essentially on one level although rises and drops occur because of clay fill in the passages. The cave is in the base of the Keyser Limestone and the top of the Tonoloway Limestone, near the axis of an anticline. The dip is gentle to the east. The passages are along joints at N. 60°E., N. 20°E., and N. 30°W.

STANDARD QUARRY CAVES 39°26'45" N.; 77°58'04" W. Martinsburg Quadrangle.

The Standard Lime and Stone Company owns six quarries south of Martinsburg. Small fissure-like passages are reported in Quarry Number 2, on the north side of West Virginia Highway 9 at the south end of Martinsburg; in Quarry Number 3, 100 feet to the south; and in Quarry Number 5, 1000 feet south of the highway. The passages open near the top of the east faces of the quarries (elevation, 400 feet) and, with the exception of Quarry Number 5, are short and of no consequence. The cave in the Fifth Quarry is a narrow passage, 3 to 6 feet high, 200 feet long, parallel to the axis of the quarry. Two side passages open into the quarry face. A similar but smaller set of passages open in the Third Quarry. The caves are in the top of the Mosheim (Stones River) Limestone.

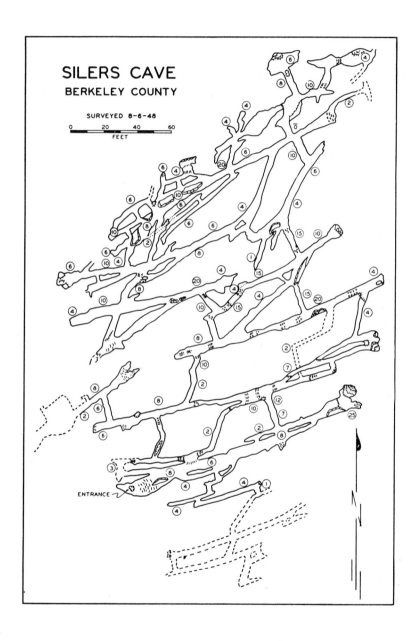

Figure 5.—Silers Cave.

THOUSAND CAVES 39°29'40" N.; 77°54'00" W. Martinsburg Quadrangle.

One mile northwest of Greenburg is a broad upland studded by many small sinkholes. A cave consisting of several rooms and passages over 200 feet long is reported to open from one of the sinks.[17] The sinks are in the Stones River-Chambersburg Limestones at the north end of an outcrop brought up by an anticline along the east side of Opequon Creek.

WHITINGS NECK CAVE 39°31'00" N.; 77°51'15" W. Williamsport Quadrangle.

Whitings Neck Cave is in a rolling meadow, ¼ mile south of the Potomac River, 1000 feet east of the mouth of Opequon Creek (elevation, 400 feet). The south entrance, on the east side of the meadow 600 feet north of the county road, is in a shallow sink. The opening, 5 feet high and wide, heads east 15 feet to a shallow pit, 15 feet in diameter. Beyond this pit the cave is a crawlway for 50 feet to the north after which it enlarges to 10 feet high and 6 to 20 feet wide for 130 feet to a pit 45 feet deep. Beyond the pit the passage is a narrow crevice, 2 to 3 feet wide and over 20 feet high, which is lined on the east side for 40 feet with a large deposit of white flowstone. The passage continues for 160 feet beyond the flowstone as a narrow opening, 3 to 4 feet wide and 5 to 6 feet high, with a floor of clay and silt. The floor slopes steeply upwards towards the rear for 35 feet.

Fifty feet south of the pit a small passage opens to the west. The entrance to this passage is across a large rock 8 feet high and opens into a narrow "keyhole" type of passage, 20 feet high and 10 feet wide which connects with the surface after 100 feet. This second entrance is a small hole in the base of a vertical-sided sink 220 feet northwest of the south entrance.

At the junction of the passages a small pit connects with a tortuous opening that can be followed for 20 feet vertically and 70 feet laterally. A small room, connecting by a narrow, low slit, opens on the west side of the passage at the base of the 45-foot pit. It is beautifully decorated with terraced flowstone and rimstone.

---

[17] National Speleological Society, Bulletin 9, p. 61, 1947.

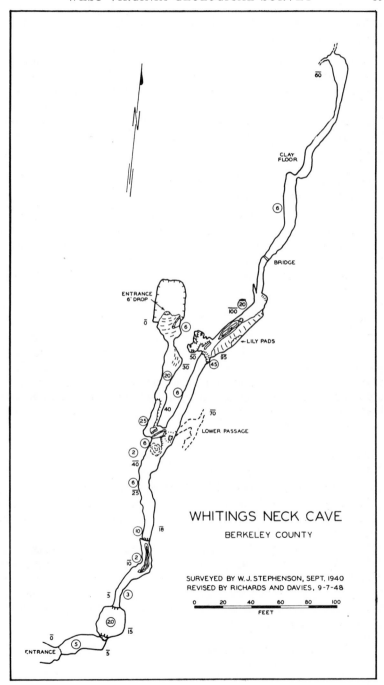

Figure 6.—Whitings Neck Cave.

Whitings Neck Cave, in the Beekmantown Limestone which strikes N. 20°E. and dips 65°N., is developed along joints at N. 20°E. (slopes 60°E.), due north, and N. 50°E.

GRANT COUNTY

Limestones of the Silurian and Devonian Systems outcrop along four anticlines in Grant County. On the eastern edge of the county the Elkhorn Mountain Anticline brings the limestones to the surface along the summit and flanks of Elkhorn Mountain. Similar outcrops occur on Patterson Creek, Cave, and New Creek Mountains.

Eighteen caves have been reported in these limestones and one cave is known in the Ridgeley Sandstone which is closely associated with them.

The Greenbrier Limestone is found along the east side of Allegheny Front and two caves are reported in it in Grant County. A marl bed at Williamsport, probably Pleistocene in age, contains several small shelter caves.

CEDAR HILL CAVE 38°59'43″ N.; 79°13'12″ W. Petersburg Quadrangle.

Cedar Hill Cave is in a small hollow, 200 yards north of West Virginia Highway 28, ¾ mile southwest of Corners (elevation, 1250 feet). The entrance passage is 4 to 8 feet wide, 5 to 20 feet high, heading N. 30°E. for 20 feet and then east for 60 feet to a room 30 feet wide, 40 feet long, and 20 feet high. The cave continues east as a passage 5 feet wide and 10 feet high with a narrow crevice base, connecting three small rooms, 20 to 30 feet wide and long, 15 feet high. The passage is blocked by clay fill 300 feet from the entrance. The slope of the cave floor is gentle, interrupted by two vertical drops of ten feet, one at the entrance to the first room, the second at the entrance to the second room. The end of the cave is about 80 feet below the entrance. Cedar Hill Cave is in the Tonoloway Limestone and developed along joints at N. 30°E. and due east with modification from joints running due north and S. 70° E.

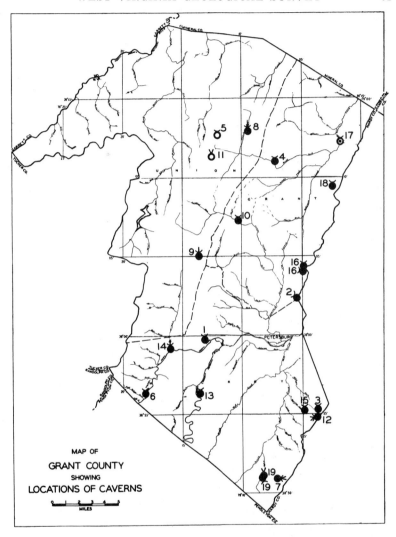

Figure 7.—Grant County Caves

1. Cedar Hill.	11. Munsing.
2. Charles Knob.	12. Mongold (Elkhorn Mountain).
3. Deaheart.	13. Peacock.
4. Greenland Gap.	14. Smokehole Caverns.
5. Hanline.	15. Spring Run.
6. Jim.	16. Veach.
7. Kesner.	17. Williamsport Marl Caves.
8. Kessel.	18. Wolf Den Rocks.
9. Klines Gap.	19. Wolfpen Caves.
10. Mays Gap.	

CHARLES KNOB CAVE 39°02'20" N.; 79°05'17" W. Greenland Gap Quadrangle.

On the north side of Charles Knob, two cave openings lie on opposite sides of Patterson Creek Mountain, near the summit (elevation, 2500 feet). The opening on the east side heads southwest for 500 feet. A branch leads to several rooms 20 to 30 feet in diameter while a second branch leads to a pit 100 feet deep. The west opening enlarges to a single room 50 feet in diameter and height. The caves are in the New Scotland Limestone.

DEAHEART CAVE 38°55'18" N.; 79°03'45" W. Petersburg Quadrangle.

Deaheart Cave is at the base of an escarpment, on the north side of the gap, 0.65 mile east of Cedar Knob (elevation, 1950 feet). The cave is a crawlway heading north and sloping downwards 20° for 600 feet. The floor and walls are of wet clay. It is in the Tonoloway Limestone.

GREENLAND GAP CAVE 39°10'52" N.; 79°07'15" W. Greenland Gap Quadrangle.

This cave is at the east end of Greenland Gap, ½ mile northwest of Falls. It is on the north side of the gap at an elevation of 1300 feet. The entrance, a recess in a cliff, opens into a low crawl for 100 feet that follows a joint at N. 30°E. Nests of the Allegheny pack-rat are in great number at the entrance. The cave is in the Coeymans Limestone.

HANLINE CAVE 39°12'34" N:; 79°11'58" W. Greenland Gap Quadrangle.

Hanline Cave is ½ mile due north of West Virginia Highway 42, on the east side of Allegheny Front (elevation, 2450 feet). The cave is a crawlway 600 feet long which heads north. The passage is very broad and in some places is 30 to 40 feet wide but only 3 feet high. The floor is wet clay with numerous pools of water. Hanline Cave is in the Greenbrier Limestone which dips 20° to the northwest.

INDIAN HOUSE CAVE 38°57′ N.; 79°13′ W. Petersburg Quadrangle. (Not shown on County Map.)

A large cave is reported to lie along the South Branch in the northern part of the Smokehole. The entrance is at river level and opens into a large passage that contains considerable amounts of wet clay. The cave was not located during field work.

JIM CAVE 38°56′19″ N.; 79°18′06″ W. Onego Quadrangle.

Jim Cave is in a bluff on the west side of North Fork, one mile northeast of the Grant-Pendleton county line (elevation, 1350 feet). The cave, a small shelter extending 50 feet into the bluff, is in the Ridgeley Sandstone.

KESNER CAVE 38°51′26″ N.; 79°07′12″ W. Petersburg Quadrangle.

The entrance to this cave is a 75-foot pit, one mile north of Deep Spring (elevation, 2325 feet). The pit is ½ mile northeast of a triangular-shaped sinkhole. At the base of the pit is a small room and 200 feet of passage, mainly crawlways connecting small dome pits. The cave is in the Tonoloway Limestone.

KESSEL CAVE 39°12′46″ N.; 79°09′30″ W. Greenland Gap Quadrangle.

A large doline is developed in the flat between Elklick Run and New Creek Mountain, 1½ miles north of Greenland. At the west end of the doline is a cave that receives the drainage of the area (elevation, 1800 feet). The entrance is a vertical shaft, 40 feet deep, at the top of a bluff 30 feet high. At the base is a small crawlway extending southwest which clogs at times with gravel from the stream. The water flowing into the cave at the base of the bluff resurges ¼ mile east of Scherr. The cave is in the Keyser Limestone.

On the west side of the road to Greenland Gap, 1 mile south of Kessel Cave, is a large opening but no leads could be found that opened to a cave.

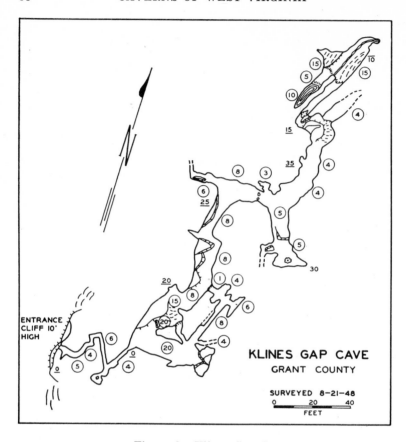

Figure 8.—Klines Gap Cave.

KLINES GAP CAVE 39°05′00″ N.; 79°13′38 W. Greenland Gap Quadrangle.

This cave is 100 yards north of the Kline Gap road, 0.4 mile east of Streby (elevation, 1700 feet). The entrance, in a low limestone bluff, is a crawlway, 3 feet high, 2 feet wide, that follows a sinuous course to the east for 75 feet to a small room. The room, 10 feet wide, 25 feet long, 20 feet high, has a small keyhole type passage leading to the northeast at the end. The main passage trends north from the west end of the room as an opening 15 feet wide, 8 to 10 feet high, floored by breakdown. Two hundred feet from the entrance the passage drops down a mud and rock slope for 35 feet to a stream passage, 40 feet long, blocked by siphons at each end. The roof of the main passage has a considerable amount of loose, shaly material in it and is somewhat dangerous to traverse. The cave is in the Wills Creek-Tonoloway Limestones.

MAYS GAP CAVE 39°07'14" N.; 79°10'16" W. Greenland Gap Quadrangle.

At the east end of Mays Gap, on the north side, ¼ mile northwest of Maysville (elevation, 1450 feet) is a crawlway 100 feet long. The cave is dry but a spring issues below it. The cave is in the Tonoloway Limestone.

MUNSING PIT 39°11'13" N.; 79°12'34" W. Greenland Gap Quadrangle.

Munsing Pit is in the center of a flat on the east flank of Allegheny Front, 1 mile south of West Virginia Highway 42 (elevation, 2640 feet). The pit is 200 feet east of the farm lane along the flat and is reported to be 50 feet deep. It is now partially blocked by timber and trash. A small stream drains into it and a passage probably exists at its base. The pit is in the lower part of the Greenbrier Limestone.

MONGOLD (ELKHORN MOUNTAIN) CAVE 38°54'46" N.; 79°03'46" W. Petersburg Quadrangle.

Mongold Cave is 1.5 miles southeast of Masonville on the north side of the Masonville-Brake road (elevation, 2150 feet). The entrance, in a mixed orchard 200 feet north of the road, is a pit 135 feet deep which ends in an earth slope dropping 30 feet to the south. The passage heads south for 300 feet and rises steeply to near the surface as indicated by a locust root which penetrates the ceiling. To the north it extends for 300 feet. Rimstone pools and large flowstone cascades and draperies line the passage. The passages are 8 to 20 feet wide and up to 60 feet high. A lower level, 60 feet below the base of the entrance slope, is accessible through a small vertical shaft on the side of the upper passage near its center or by a small fissure slope at the north end of the upper passage. The lower passage is narrower and about ⅓ the length of the upper level. The water draining from Mongold Cave is reported to resurge in a spring near Bass. According to the geologic map of Grant County the cave is in the McKenzie Formation (Niagara Limestone). The lithology of the limestone, the fossils (or lack of them) and the immense thickness displayed in the cave indicated it is in the Tonoloway-Wills Creek Formations. The Grant County Report [18] hints at the possibility of faulting in this area. The limestones in Elkhorn Mountain Cave give evidence of a local low-angle overthrust from the east bringing Upper Silurian Limestones to the top of the mountain.

PEACOCK CAVE 38°56'22" N.; 79°13'34" W. Petersburg Quadrangle.

Peacock Cave is in Cave Mountain at the base of a prominent limestone cliff, ½ mile north of Blue Rock (elevation, 1755 feet). The entrance, a crawlway 100 feet long, opens into a small room, 24 feet wide, 50 feet long, and 5 feet high. A crawlway connects with a second room 50 feet beyond. This room is 10 feet high, 35 feet wide, and 100 feet long with a floor covered by breakdown in the center and silt along the edges. The passage continues to the northeast for 230 feet and is 6 to 15 feet wide and 4 to 6 feet high. It then trends northwest in two levels for 240 feet. The lower passage is 12 to 30 feet high, 3 to 10 feet wide, ending in a vertical cliff 18 feet high. Two rooms, 30 feet in diameter and 30 to 35 feet high with moist silt floors, lie at the end of the passage. A crawlway leads to the northeast for 60 feet at the entrance to the room. It forks into passages to the northeast and northwest which are narrow, steeply sloping crevices and crawlways with considerable loose rock, about 100 feet long.

The cave is very dry and formations that line the passages are crumbled and powdered.

Peacock Cave, in the top of the Coeymans Limestone and base of the New Scotland Limestone, follows major joints at N. 30°E., N. 50°W. with a minor joint at N. 70°W. modifying some of the passages.

The cave is named for a Mr. Peacock [19] who obtained clay from the cave in 1808 for use in manufacturing saltpeter.

---

[18] Reger, David B., and Tucker, R. C. Mineral and Grant Counties: West Virginia Geological Survey, 1924, p. 123.
[19] Reger and Tucker, op. cit. p. 702.

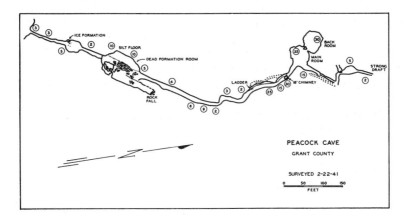

Figure 9.—Peacock Cave.

Remains of the operation consist of an old ladder and wooden platform 600 feet from the entrance.

SMOKEHOLE CAVERNS 38°59'10" N.; 79°16'00" W. Onego Quadrangle.

This cave is one of three commercially developed caves in West Virginia. It is on the north side of West Virginia Highway 28, 300 feet east of Jordan Run (elevation, 1130 feet). The entrance through a stone archway, opens into a straight passage, 10 to 20 feet wide, 8 to 15 feet high, heading N. 20°W., curving gently to N. 20°E., for 500 feet. A stream flows towards the entrance along the east side of the passage. The cave is offset slightly to the west and access to the upper level, 40 feet above, is gained by way of a flight of concrete stairs which lead to the Main Room. The lower level continues northeast for 300 feet as an undeveloped stream passage. The Main Room is 75 feet long, 40 feet wide and averages 65 feet high. The walls are vertical following the bedding-planes. Two pockets open in the ceiling and are over 100 feet above the floor. The ceiling is studded with a myriad of short stalactites lying in rows along the bedding-planes. In addition, flowstone cascades and draperies line the walls and the floor is covered by short stalagmites. At the south end of the room a narrow passage connects with a long, narrow room known as Hades. The cave continues north from the Main Room as a

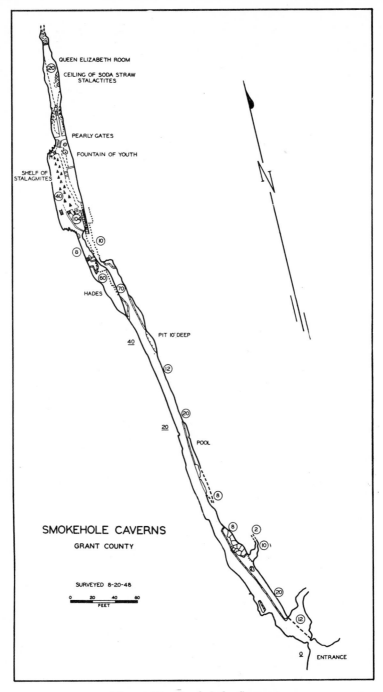

Figure 10.—Smokehole Caverns.

Plate III.—Smokehole Caverns. (Photo by Richard G. Hunter).

passage 10 to 20 feet wide, 30 to 40 feet high, and 100 feet long with formations similar to those in the Main Room. The cave ends in a muddy crawlway sloping steeply upwards for 60 feet. Access to a room lying above the rear passage is through a hole in the ceiling at the north end of the Main Room. The overhead room has the dimensions of the passage

Plate IV.—Smokehole Caverns, Main Room. (Photo by Wm. E. Davies).

below and its floor is 35 feet above the floor of the passage. It is filled with many delicate stalactites.

The cave is well lighted and the pathways are broad and clean. The Main Room, with its abundance of beautiful stalactites, is worthy of the title—"The Room of a Million Stalactites." Smokehole Caverns was opened for commercial purposes May 30, 1940.

The cave is in the Coeymans-New Scotland Limestones which are highly folded and distorted with a general dip to the east at the entrance. The beds quickly assume a vertical attitude north of the entrance. The cave is developed along vertical bedding-planes at N. 20°E.

SPRING RUN CAVE 38°55'08" N.; 79°04'52" W. Petersburg Quadrangle.

Spring Run Cave is in an escarpment on the east side of Spring Run, 0.4 mile southeast of Masonville (elevation, 1400 feet). The entrance is 50 feet north and above the falls of Spring Run. The cave, a passage extending 50 feet north, 4 to 6 feet high and wide, is in the New Scotland Limestone which strikes N. 50°E. and dips 55°W.

VEACH CAVE 30°04'18" N.; 79°04'50" W. Greenland Gap Quadrangle.

Veach Cave is at the head of the hollow in Patterson Creek Mountain, ½ mile southwest of Orr Mountain School (elevation, 2200 feet). It is a single passage 200 feet long, 4 to 8 feet high and wide, with several small rooms. The entrance is at the base of a low cliff of Tonoloway Limestone.

A second cave, 0.4 mile south of Veach Cave on the north side of a hollow at 2200 feet elevation, is a short, low passage in Tonoloway Limestone.

WILLIAMSPORT MARL CAVES 39°12'06" N.; 79°01'41" W. Greenland Gap Quadrangle.

The settlement of Williamsport is built on a large marl terrace 50 to 65 feet above Patterson Creek (elevation, 1030 feet). The edge of the deposit along Patterson Creek is a cliff in which two large and several small shelter caves are developed. The large caves are 6 feet high, 20 feet long and 15 feet wide. The marl deposit is Pleistocene in age and was deposited by a stream from Patterson Creek Mountain on the east. A large spring in the top of the Tonoloway near the marl deposit, accounts for much of the lime deposited.

WOLF DEN ROCKS CAVE 39°09'20" N.; 79°02'30" W. Greenland Gap Quadrangle.

Wolf Den Rocks is a prominent limestone escarpment on the north side of the hollow on Patterson Creek Mountain, 2.2 miles northeast of Forman. A cave (elevation, 1950 feet) opens in the base of the cliff as a crawlway which enlarges to 15 or 20 feet high and wide for 500 feet to the north. At several places the passage widens into small rooms. The floor of the cave is damp clay. Wolf Den Rocks Cave is in the New Scotland Limestone.

WOLFPEN CAVES 38°51′00″ N.; 79°08′00″ W. Petersburg Quadrangle.

Two caves are located at the mouth of the east fork of Wolfpen Hollow (elevation, 1950 feet). The cave on the north side is a vertical pit about 30 feet deep with no opening at the base. On the south side is a ledge in which a low opening leads south as a crawlway for 100 feet. The caves are in the New Scotland Limestone.

GREENBRIER COUNTY

One-quarter of all the caves in the State of West Virginia lie in Greenbrier County. Some 105 caves, varying from short crawlways up to Organ Cave with its miles of passages, are recorded from the county.

Except for two, all of the caves are developed in the limestones of the Greenbrier Series which outcrops in a broad upland, 2 to 4 miles wide, in the central part of the county from Fort Spring north through Lewisburg and Renick. Dips in this section are gentle, mainly to the west. The surface topography is typically that of a subdued karst with little surface drainage and sinkholes that merge one with another. The soil is fairly deep and rock ledges and bands of limestone, so common in more severe karst, are not present. The Williamsburg (Mount Pleasant) Anticline exposes the Greenbrier Series on both flanks of Brushy Ridge. The dips are steep here and a number of large caves are developed in this area.

The two caves not in the Greenbrier Series are near Alvon, one in the McKenzie and the other in the Tonoloway Limestone. The limestones of the Devonian and Silurian Systems outcrop along Beaver Lick Mountain but only those caves cited above have been reported in them. The remote position of these limestones along Beaver Lick Mountain may account for the lack of caves reported.

The Ordovician Limestones, so prominent to the south in Monroe County, do not outcrop in Greenbrier County.

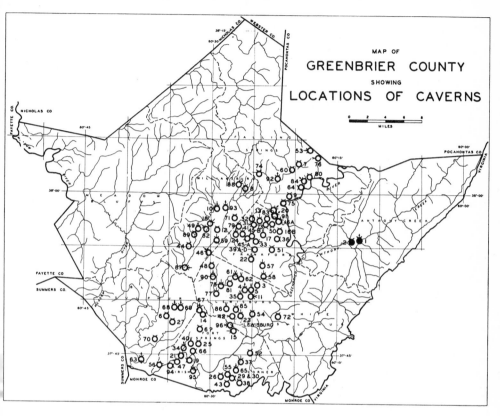

Figure 11.—Greenbrier County Caves

1. Alvon.	18. Cadle.
2. Anthony.	19. Carlisle.
3. Arbuckle.	20. Cave Farm.
4. Arbuckle School.	21. Cliff.
5. Arbuckle Shafts.	22. Coffman.
6. Asbury.	23. Court Street.
7. Ballard Mountain.	24. Culverson Creek.
8. Bob Gee.	25. Davis.
9. Bone.	26. Erwins.
10. Bransfords.	27. Feamster.
11. Brants.	28. Fox.
12. Brushy Ridge.	29. Foxhole No. 1.
13. Buckeye Creek.	30. Foxhole No. 2.
14. Bungers.	31. Fuells Drop.
15. Burnholt.	32. Fuells Fruit.
16. a, b, Burns No. 1 and No. 2.	33. Fuller.
17. Cabble.	34. General Davis.

35. Grapevine.
36. Hanna.
37. Hedricks.
38. Hellems.
39: a,b,c,d, Higginbothams Nos. 1-4.
40. Highlander Ridge.
41. Hinkles Unus.
42. Horse Pit.
43. Hoyt.
44. Hughart.
45. a, b, Jackson No. 1 and No. 2.
46. Jarrets Water.
47. Jewel.
48. Johnson.
49. Judys.
50. Leggs.
51. Levisay.
52. Lewis.
53. Lewis Hole.
54. Lipps.
55. Lipps No. 2.
56. Lost.
57. Ludington.
58. McClung.
59. McFerrin.
60. McMillan.
61. Madison Knob, North.
62. Madison Knob, South.
63. Muddy Creek.
64. Norman.
65. Organ.
66. Parlor.
67. Pecks.
68. Piercys.
69. Piercys Mill.
70. Pollock & Pollock Saltpeter.
71. Poor Farm.
72. Rambows.
73. Rapps.
74. Reinhold.
75. Renick Bridge.
76. Renicks Valley Pit.
77. Richlands.
78. Richlands Northfield.
79. Scout Camp.
80. Seldomridge.
81. Simms.
82. Sinks of Sinking Creek.
83. Spencer.
84. Taylor No. 1.
85. Taylor No. 2.
86. Taylor Falls.
87. Thornbury.
88. Thrasher.
89. Tower.
90. Tuckwiller.
91. U. S. 219.
92. Walton.
93. Water.
94. Wilson Bluff.
95. Wind.
96. Yorks.

ALVON CAVE 37°55′34″ N.; 80°12′36″ W. Callaghan Quadrangle.

A small cave, now concreted up, is on the west bank of Anthony Creek, ½ mile north of Alvon. The cave is 300 feet long, 8 feet high and 6 feet wide. A large stream flows out and is piped to White Sulphur Springs. The cave is in the Tonoloway Limestone.

ANTHONY CAVE 37°55′05″ N.; 80°13′18″ W. Callaghan Quadrangle.

Anthony Cave is a small crawlway developed in the apex of an anticline, one-half mile west of Alvon on the north side of Anthony Creek (elevation, 2200 feet). The mouth is a broad shelter of triangular cross-section, 10 feet wide and high, on the face of a cliff 40 feet high. Ten feet in, the passage reduces to 4 feet high and wide and progressively becomes smaller until it pinches out 20 feet from the entrance. Local residents report that a shaft at the top and to the rear of the ledge in which the cave is developed formerly gave access to a large cave. No evidence of the shaft was observed. The passage is in black calcareous shale (McKenzie Formation) with ceiling and walls formed of white, fine-grained sandstone (Williamsport Sandstone).

ARBUCKLE CAVE 37°51′55″ N.; 80°24′12″ W. White Sulphur Springs Quadrangle.

This small cave is located in a rolling meadow, 0.3 mile east of Maxwelton (elevation, 2220 feet). The entrance, which extends across the base of a low cliff 15 feet high and 30 feet long, is boarded up and entry is through a low, narrow door. The entrance room is 25 feet wide and 50 feet long with a slick clay floor sloping 30° down from the entrance. Near the rear of the room a small hole gives access down a pile of loose rock to a second room, 10 to 15 feet wide, and 30 feet high, which is roughly parallel to the entrance room. This room is 100 feet long and well decorated with flowstone draperies and stalactites on the walls. Water from a small dome pit at the rear of the second room formerly was piped from the cave for domestic use. The floor, below the dome pit, is a large flowstone terrace. Elsewhere, it is wet clay covering small slabs of rock. Arbuckle Cave is in the Patton Limestone, Greenbrier Series, which is horizontal at this point.

ARBUCKLE SCHOOL CAVE 37°51′34″ N.; 80°24′56″ W. White Sulphur Springs Quadrangle.

To the west of U. S. 219 at Arbuckle School is a large compound sink. At the west end of the sink is a low cave opening (elevation, 2200 feet) from which a stream flows. The passage extends west as a water-filled crawlway. Exploration may be possible in dry weather. The stream flows 100 feet to the east where it sinks in a low, swampy meadow. The cave is in the Pickaway Limestone, Greenbrier Series.

ARBUCKLE SHAFTS 37°51'25" N.; 80°24'38" W. White Sulphur Springs Quadrangle.

In the vicinity of Arbuckle School (elevation, 2270 feet) are several deep shafts. One shaft is 200 feet north of the school; one is directly to the rear of the school; and a third is 1000 feet east along the county road. The shafts are now filled with trash and stone. They are in the Pickaway Limestone, Greenbrier Series.

ASBURY CAVE 37°49' N.; 80°34' W. Clintonville Quadrangle.

A large cave with a small entrance is reported to lie in a cultivated field, 0.6 mile west of Asbury (0.3 mile west of W. Va. Highway 12). The cave was not found during field work.

BALLARD MOUNTAIN CAVE 38°03'45" N.; 80°21'00" W. Lobelia Quadrangle.

A small cave lies on the flank of Ballard Mountain, 0.5 mile north of the junction of Robbins Run and Spring Creek (elevation, 2250 feet). The entrance is large enough to permit standing but in less than 20 feet the passage becomes a narrow crawlway extending for over 100 feet. The cave is in the Union (?) Limestone, Greenbrier Series.

BOB GEE CAVE 38°00'45" N.; 80°27'42" W. Lobelia Quadrangle.

The entrance to Bob Gee Cave is at the base of a low, south-facing, limestone escarpment, one-half mile southeast of Trout P. O. (elevation, 2250 feet). The entrance, 6 feet high and 10 feet wide, extends for 20 feet to a low room formed by subsidence over a series of fissure passages. The room is 50 feet square and the floor is cut by a number of narrow fissures up to 20 feet deep. The average ceiling height is 6 to 10 feet. A low tunnel, 6 feet wide and 4 feet high, leads off to the northwest for 100 feet where clay fill reaches to the ceiling. To the southwest and northeast the cave consists of fissure-like passages, 2 to 6 feet wide and 10 to 20 feet high. Formations line the walls of the fissures and those on the southeast passage are large columns and stalactites resembling organ-pipes. At the junction of the entrance passage and the large room, a prominent column, known as the Buttermaid because of its resemblance to a girl churning butter, is found. Local residents report that the cave continues for over 2000 feet to the north as a complicated network of fissure passages, some of them up to 50 feet in depth, which finally emerge as a series of water exits on Carr Branch, Indian Creek. Bob Gee Cave is in horizontal beds of Alderson Limestone, Greenbrier Series, and is developed along a series of joints at N. 60°E. and N. 40°W.

Saltpeter earth was obtained from the cave during the War Between the States. Piles of saltpeter earth with mattock marks, troughs (one or two well preserved), and rotted hoppers remain from this operation. A flat bench at the entrance of the cave was built from the refuse of saltpeter operations. The saltpeter earth was obtained from the dry section in the northwest portion of the large room.

BONE CAVE 37°59′45″ N.; 80°20′08″ W. White Sulphur Springs Quadrangle.

Three cave openings are in the large quarry 1.4 miles east of Renick along the Chesapeake & Ohio Railway (elevation, 2000 feet). The quarry, which is no longer operated, is open to the south. The north face, over 500 feet long and 100 to 150 feet high, has an opening at the level of the quarry floor near the east end. The opening is now very small, being blocked by fallen rock from a blast. The passage was not entered because of the danger from loose rock in the ceiling. A small opening at the same point but 30 feet from the top of the quarry, heads north as a passage 4 feet high and wide. Reports indicate that these openings lead to small but extensive passages totaling over 2000 feet in length. The passages contain numerous speleothems. During quarrying operations the skull of a Pleistocene Peccary was found in soft, loose clay that lined the floor of the upper passage.[20] The cave is in horizontal beds of Patton Limestone, Greenbrier Series

---

[20] Gidley, J. W., A Pleistocene cave deposit of western Maryland: Smithsonian Institution, Annual Report for 1918, pp. 286-288.

BRANSFORDS (RELUCTANCE) CAVES 37°59′25″ N.; 80°28′16″ W. White Sulphur Springs Quadrangle.

A series of small water caves lies on the south side of the country lane, ½ mile northwest of Sunlight (elevation, 2200 feet). The caves consist of a series of four passages from 4 to 15 feet high, 8 to 25 feet wide, and up to 500 feet long. The passages, two of which are traversable, are separated by shallow sinks into which they open. A large stream flows through the caves and comes to the surface in the bottom of the sinkholes. Formations consist of some rimstone and stalagmites scattered in the passages. West of the resurgence in the sinkhole is an opening 3 feet high and 6 feet wide. A 50 foot crawlway opens into a small room from which a low opening leads down to a stream flanked by silt banks. The cave passage is 1700 feet long, averaging 30 feet wide and 12 feet high. Large rooms are on the left side of the passage. The first is 150 feet wide, 200 feet long, and 20 feet high with a gently sloping dry silt floor. An elongate pool at the far side of the room feeds a series of rimstones, culminating in a "frozen waterfall" 60 feet long and 8 feet high. Beyond this speleothem is a section of rapids about 250 feet long with potholes and rugged, fluted canyons. Wading is necessary almost the length of the cave. The cave terminates in a siphon. The caves are in the Union (?) Limestone, Greenbrier Series.

BRANTS CAVE 37°50′03″ N.; 80°25′44″ W. White Sulphur Springs Quadrangle.

Brants Cave is 2.3 miles northeast of Lewisburg on the county road that is to the west of and parallel to U. S. 219 (elevation, 2200 feet). The entrance is in a clump of trees at the southeast corner of a barn, ¼ mile east of the county road. It is a vertical shaft 25 feet deep and 4 feet in diameter with grooved walls typical of a dome pit. At the base, passages lead off to the north and south. The cave is divided into a series of small rooms, 10 to 15 feet in height and width, totaling about 325 feet (50 feet north, 275 feet south of entrance) in length and separated by clusters of formations. Columns, stalactites, and flowstone draperies abound in the south passage and make Brants Cave one of the most beautifully decorated in the State. The cave is in the top of the Sinks Grove Limestone, Greenbrier Series. It is developed along a vertical joint trending N. 10°E. A small, steeply slanting shaft lies just east of the county road, at a point due west of Brants Cave. No passages are reported at its base.

BRUSHY RIDGE CAVE 37°56'40" N.; 80°28'42" W. White Sulphur Springs Quadrangle.

This small crawlway, about 100 feet in length, is located at the east base of Brushy Ridge, 0.9 mile northeast of Bethel School (elevation, 2200 feet). It is in the Alderson Limestone, Greenbrier Series.

BUCKEYE CREEK CAVE 37°58'33" N.; 80°24'03" W. White Sulphur Springs Quadrangle.

This cave is ¼ mile west of Old Rapp School, 5 miles east of Williamsburg (elevation, 1970 feet). It has not been completely explored but 4000 feet of stream passage has been followed. The cave is very wet and in time of heavy rain or snow melt it is dangerous because of flooding. The cave is in the Alderson Limestone, Greenbrier Series.

BUNGERS CAVE 37°50'27" N.; 80°30'20" W. Clintonville Quadrangle.

Bungers Cave is 1.1 miles northwest of Central School on the flank of a low ridge, ¼ mile southwest of Milligan Creek (elevation, 2000 feet). The large entrance is steep and rough and leads to two large rooms, each about 50 feet in cross-section and 150 feet long, at the rear of which is a small stream passage too low for traverse. A few formations are present in the rooms. The cave is in the Union Limestone, Greenbrier Series.

BURNHOLT CAVE 37°47'15" N.; 80°27'48" W. White Sulphur Springs Quadrangle.

This cave is 1 mile southwest of Lewisburg on the county road, ½ mile west of and parallel to U. S. 219 (elevation, 2050 feet). The entrance has steps leading to a small water passage traversable for 600 yards. A concrete dam blocks the stream and formerly provided a reservoir for domestic water supplies. Burnholt Cave is in the Sinks Grove Limestone, Greenbrier Series.

BURNS CAVE NO. 1　37°57′09″ N.; 80°21′52″ W. White Sulphur Springs Quadrangle.

This cave is located 0.3 mile east of Walnut Grove Church (elevation, 2100 feet). It consists of a slanting shaft, 50 feet deep, at the base of which is a narrow, fissure-like room. The shaft, which is in the lower part of the Greenbrier Series, is now filled with fence wire.

BURNS CAVE NO. 2　37°57′34″ N.; 80°21′46″ W. White Sulphur Springs Quadrangle.

On Spring Creek, ½ mile north of Burns Cave No. 1, is a small cave (elevation, 1900 feet). The entrance, a large shelter, is reduced in a short distance to a crawlway over 300 feet in length. The cave is in the lower part of the Greenbrier Series. At one time the large shelter at the entrance is reported to have been used for "moonshine" purposes.

CABBLE CAVE　37°56′20″ N.; 80°23′45″ W. White Sulphur Springs Quadrangle.

One mile northwest of Frankford, at an elevation of 2350 feet, is a vertical pit over 100 feet deep. It is not known if a cave opens at the base. The pit is in the Alderson Limestone, Greenbrier Series.

CADLE CAVE　37°57′26″ N.; 80°29′56″ W. White Sulphur Springs Quadrangle.

Cadle Cave is 0.9 mile southwest of Williamsburg on the road to Sinking Creek (elevation, 2250 feet). The entrance is in a low limestone escarpment in a clump of trees, 100 feet east of the road. The entrance passage is a narrow slot, 2 to 4 feet wide and 6 feet high which leads to a stream passage, 100 feet from the entrance. The stream passage, a fissure, 1 to 2 feet wide and 20 feet high, running to the north and south is 20 feet below the level of the entrance. Its length is not known. It trends S. 20°W. and the stream flows to the south. Cadle Cave is in the Alderson Limestone, Greenbrier Series.

CARLISLE CAVE 37°44'27" N.; 80°32'15" W. Alderson
Quadrangle.

The entrance to Carlisle Cave is directly above the west
portal of the Chesapeake & Ohio Railway tunnel east of Fort
Spring (elevation, 1900 feet). It is in a low escarpment and
is 4 feet high and 10 feet wide. A passage leads S. 70°E. as
a narrow tunnel, sloping steeply down for the first 100 feet,
at which point it is 25 feet high and wide. The cave is level
for the remaining 100 feet and is made up of a room 35 to 40
feet wide with a small pond in the center. Carlisle Cave is in
the Union Limestone, Greenbrier Series.

CAVE FARM CAVE 37°59'06" N.; 80°22'29" W. White
Sulphur Springs Quadrangle.

This cave is at the north end of a long sink, 200 feet west
of U. S. 219, 1 mile southwest of Renick (elevation, 2000 feet).
The entrance, in a low cliff, is 10 feet wide, 4 feet high and
opens into a passage heading west. A deep stream flows out
of the cave. The cave is reported to be of considerable length
but no specific data are available concerning it. The stream
flows south in the sink for 1000 feet where it disappears. It
empties into Spring Creek. The cave is in the Union Limestone, Greenbrier Series.

CLIFF CAVES 37°45'00" N.; 80°33'26" W. Alderson Quadrangle.

A series of small caves is located in the limestone cliffs
(elevation, 1650 feet) along the south bank of the Greenbrier
River, ¾ mile north of Frazier. One of the caves has a large
entrance but, like the others, is reduced to a crawlway after
a short distance. The caves are in the Hillsdale Limestone,
Greenbrier Series.

COFFMAN CAVE 37°55'08" N.; 80°24'56" W. White Sulphur
Springs Quadrangle.

This cave is at the base of Carroll Hill (elevation, 2200
feet), 1.7 miles WSW of Frankford. The entrance, in a large
sink 100 yards west of the Coffman house, is 30 feet wide and
15 feet high, but is reduced to 3 feet in height after a few

Plate V.—Coffman Cave, Rimstone Pool. (Photo by Wm. E. Davies.)

feet. A large stream flows in the entrance and occupies most of the cave floor. One hundred feet from the entrance the passage enlarges to 5 to 8 feet high and 10 to 15 feet wide and continues for 250 feet where the ceiling comes down to within a foot of the stream. Low clay banks and gravel bars make it possible to traverse the cave without wading to the point where the ceiling lowers. Formations occur in a number of places along the walls of the cave. A large rimstone pool, 10 feet long by 5 feet wide and 2 feet deep, is located 70 feet from the entrance. Large flowstone mounds occur along the walls 20 and 50 feet in from the rimstone.

Coffman Cave is in the Union Limestone, Greenbrier Series, which is horizontal. The stream flowing through it connects with Higginbothams No. 1 Cave and rises at the entrance to Coffman Cave, apparently coming from a cave 20 feet to the southeast, the entrance of which is blocked by rock debris. Animal life is abundant in Coffman Cave. The rimstone pool abounds in crayfish and salamanders and throughout the cave crickets and flies are common.

Plate VI.—Coffman Cave, Large Flowstone, 6 feet high. (Photo by Wm. E. Davies).

COURT STREET CAVE 37°48'28" N.; 80°26'30" W. White Sulphur Springs Quadrangle.

At the north end of Lewisburg where Court Street curves to the west, is a shallow sink that has a small entrance opening to the south (elevation, 2150 feet). The entrance is 10 feet high and 8 feet wide with a gently sloping passage leading S. 20° W. Seventy-five feet from the entrance is a small room on the east side of the passage which is filled by a large Dutch Oven formation. The passage narrows from this point until 200 feet from the entrance it is too narrow to be traversed. A small stream flowing south along the passage is encountered 50 feet from the entrance. The cave is in the Sinks Grove Limestone, Greenbrier Series.

CULVERSON CREEK CAVE 37°56'28" N.; 80°27'10" W. White Sulphur Springs Quadrangle.

One-half mile west of Unus (3 miles southeast of Williamsburg), the valley of Culverson Creek terminates in a rock bluff 50 feet high. The creek at this point enters a cave (elevation, 2050 feet). The cavern entrance, 50 feet wide and 20 feet high, is blocked almost completely by an enormous interlocked mound of logs and debris. A hole at the ceiling level of the cave lets one drop down behind the debris to a lake about 10 feet deep, 60 feet long and 50 feet wide. The main portion of the cave trends east along the stream draining this lake. Ten thousand eight hundred feet of passage have been explored; passages are 12 to 35 feet wide and 4 or more feet high. Four hundred and fifty feet from the entrance a large mud floored room is on the south side of the main passage. The cave is extremely dangerous because of flooding and poles 30 feet long are lodged high in the ceiling deep in the cave. Culverson Creek Cave is in the Anderson Limestone, Greenbrier Series.

DAVIS CAVE 37°45'50" N.; 80°31'30" W. Clintonville Quadrangle.

Davis Cave is in a broad hollow ¾ mile north of W. Va. Highway 63 and 1.7 miles northeast of Fort Spring (elevation, 1850 feet). The entrance room, which measures 40 feet in height and width and 200 feet in length, connects with a small crawlway of considerable length. Davis Cave is in the Patton (?) Limestone, Greenbrier Series.

ERWINS CAVE 37°42'42" N.; 80°27'28" W. Ronceverte Quadrangle.

This cave is one mile west of Organ Cave P. O. (elevation, 2250 feet) and is reported to connect with Lipps Cave No. 2. Erwins Cave is in the Hillsdale Limestone, Greenbrier Series.

FEAMSTER CAVE 37°48'24" N.; 80°33'19" W. Clintonville Quadrangle.

This cave is reported to lie 0.9 mile south of Asbury on the edge of Mill Creek Valley (elevation, 2100 feet). The entrance, through a small hole at the base of a tree, opens into a wide, large room which continues for over 300 yards as a high fissure passage several feet wide. Feamster Cave is in the Hillsdale Limestone, Greenbrier Series.

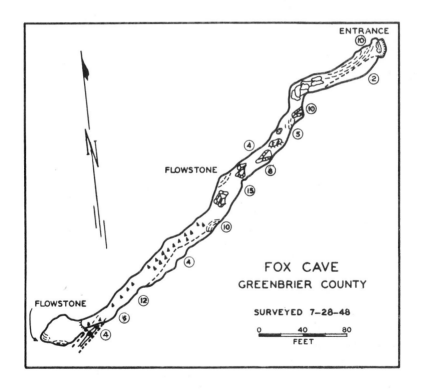

Figure 12.—Fox Cave.

FOX CAVE 38°02'10" N.; 80°19'00" W. Lobelia Quadrangle.

The entrance to Fox Cave is in a shallow sink, 0.5 mile south of Bethel Church and 700 feet northeast of the road to Julia from Bethel Church (elevation, 2340 feet). The cave is a single passage extending 400 feet to the southwest. The passage is 5 to 10 feet wide, 4 to 15 feet high and is quite straight. The floor is of fallen rock covered by a layer of wet clay. Formations are abundant throughout and are very beautiful. Columns, stalactites, and delicate bacon rind practically fill the last 200 feet of the passage. At the rear of the passage is a vertical drop of 10 feet to a lower passage, parallel to and directly beneath the upper level. A swift-flowing stream fills this passage which is 4 feet wide and 6 feet high. The length of the water passage is about 100 feet. The stream flows to the southwest and forms a series of pools 3 feet or more deep. Fox Cave is in the Pickaway Limestone, Greenbrier Series.

FOXHOLE NO. 1 37°43'00" N.; 80°26'28" W. Ronceverte Quadrangle.

This cave is located at the west end of a field 1000 feet northwest of Organ Cave (elevation, 2200 feet). Two entrances lead to the cave. A low crawlway, floored with coarse gravel, which receives a stream in wet weather and a rift-like opening, 20 feet long, 6 feet wide and 15 feet deep, give access to a passage 10 to 25 feet high and wide which extends 1500 feet to the southwest. A dome chamber is 250 yards from the entrance; some small phreatic networks are along the passage 200 yards in. At the end of this passage is a breakdown dome chamber beyond which there is over 1000 feet of dry passage on a higher level. Pits and sumps are developed along this passage. The main passage is essentially straight with a number of small passages branching from it. The cave is in the Hillsdale Limestone, Greenbrier Series.

FOXHOLE NO. 2 37°42′51″ N.; 80°26′28″ W. Ronceverte Quadrangle.

This cave is 600 feet north of Organ Cave P. O. in a deep, wooded sink just east of U. S. 219. It is a single passage, triangular in cross-section, 5 feet high by 8 feet wide, which extends 100 feet in a direction S. 40° W. The cave floor is covered by gravel at the entrance. Towards the rear it is of solid limestone. During wet weather a small stream enters the cave. The cave is in the Hillsdale Limestone, Greenbrier Series.

FUELLS DROP CAVE 37°58′08″ N.; 80°24′27″ W. White Sulphur Springs Quadrangle.

This cave is 4.6 miles east of Williamsburg and south of Buckeye Creek (elevation, 2200 feet). It is a 30-foot pit with a few small crawlways at the base. The pit is in the Alderson Limestone, Greenbrier Series.

FUELLS FRUIT CAVE 37°58′15″ N.; 80°24′30″ W. White Sulphur Springs Quadrangle.

Five hundred feet north of Fuells Drop Cave, in the valley of Buckeye Creek at an elevation of 2050 feet is Fuells Fruit Cave. The entrance room is used for storage of canned fruit. Beyond this the cave follows a small stream for about 1000 feet. The cave is in the Alderson Limestone, Greenbrier Series.

FULLER (THORNY HOLLOW) CAVE 37°56′00″ N.; 80° 25′38″ W. White Sulphur Springs Quadrangle.

Fuller Cave is 0.3 mile south of Thorny Hollow (elevation, 2150 feet). The cave is in two sections separated by a broad shallow sink. The northern section is entered through a vertical sink 20 feet in diameter and 25 feet deep. The passage to the north is a fissure, 1 to 10 feet wide and 1 to 100 feet high, and has been traversed for several thousand feet. 3 waterfalls, the first 25 feet high, the second 10 feet, and the third 40 feet, are about 5000 feet from the entrance. The passage beyond the waterfalls is muddy. About 2000 feet beyond the waterfalls the passage is blocked by fill and breakdown. The passage to the south, 2 to 3 feet high and 10 feet long is 15 feet above the north passage. It is 300 feet long opening at the south in the broad sink that divides the cave. A large stream flows north through the cave. The southern part of the cave is through a small saddle, 100 feet across the sink. The cave is 20 feet wide and 3 to 6 feet high at the north. One hundred feet south it reduces to a small opening 6 feet wide and 3 feet high which receives the stream from the south. The floor of the cave is covered by small slabs of fallen rock. Fuller Cave is in the top of the Alderson Limestone, Greenbrier Series. The drainage of Thorny Hollow is mainly underground, rising to the surface in a few sinks, and follows a series of small caverns eventually joining the underground net of Culverson Creek. The openings are located 1.1 miles southeast of Unus.

GENERAL DAVIS CAVE   37°45'20" N.; 80°33'15" W.
Clintonville Quadrangle.

General Davis Cave is 0.3 mile north of Greenbrier River on the east side of Davis Hollow at the point where the telephone-line crosses the valley (elevation, 1650 feet). The entrance to the cave is in a cliff 75 feet high at the head of a narrow ravine. The entrance passage is 30 feet above the ravine and is a room 20 feet wide, 10 feet high, and 15 feet long, which reduces to a passage of similar width and 4 to 8 feet high. A room 300 feet long, 60 feet wide, and 8 to 10 feet high continues with an axis of N. 40° E. The floor is of silt and sand with large clay and rimstone banks on the west side of the room near the north end. A shallow pool surrounded by columns marks the north end of the room. A short passage, dropping 15 feet over wet clay banks, connects with the stream passage. The stream passage intersects the entrance passages at right angles and has an axis of N. 10° E. It is 20 to 25 feet wide and 25 feet high. Throughout the cave the stream flows in a narrow channel cut through 15 feet of clay. The stream is one or two feet wide and a foot deep. To north and east the stream passage can be followed for over 2000 feet by traversing the top of the clay banks. The passage is somewhat sinuous, alternating between N. 20° E. and N. 80° E. in direction, in stretches 80 to 150 feet long. To the south the stream passage is 4 feet high, 10 feet wide and is blocked by clay fill after 100 feet. A short segment of the stream passage can be reached via a side passage 200 feet

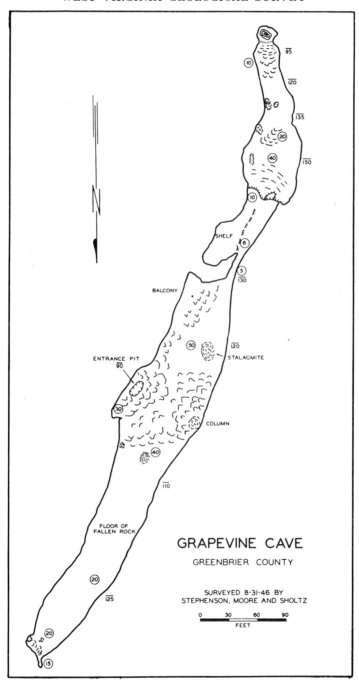

Figure 13.—Grapevine Cave.

Plate VII.—Terraced Column, Grapevine Cave (Greenbrier County). (Photo by W. H. Watkins; copyrighted; published by permission of National Speleological Society).

from the entrance. The stream is reported to emerge in a large spring at the head of a hollow ½ mile to the east. General Davis Cave is in the lower part of the Union Limestone, Greenbrier Series. Crickets are found in abundance in the cave and earthworms occur in great numbers in the clay banks along the stream. The cave is on property originally deeded to John Stuart and is named for General A. W. G. Davis who later acquired the property. It is located 1.1 miles northwest of Fort Spring.

GRAPEVINE CAVE 37°49'50" N.; 80°27'00" W. White Sulphur Springs Quadrangle.

The entrance to Grapevine Cave is on the east flank of the ridge of Weaver Knob at its south end, 2 miles due north of Lewisburg (elevation of cave passage, 2350 feet). A vertical shaft, 115 feet deep, opens into a large room 300 feet long and 25 to 50 feet wide with an axis S. 30° W. The ceiling ranges from 20 to 50 feet high and is relatively flat. The floor is covered by large slabs of fallen rock. 150 feet northeast of the entrance the cave narrows to 8 feet wide and 5 feet high for a short distance after which it enlarges to a broad passage with a slight curve to the north, 200 feet long and 20 to 50 feet wide with ceiling heights of 10 to 40 feet. The formations in the room at the entrance are among the largest and most beautiful in any cave. Terraced stalagmites, up to 30 feet high and 10 feet in diameter, rest on the fallen rock forming the floor. Flowstone cascades and draperies plus many shorter stalactites decorate the ceiling. Similar formations but in lesser numbers decorate the rest of the cave. A small stream can be observed flowing north beneath the rocks along the west wall of the cave. The cave is in the Union Limestone, Greenbrier Series.

HANNA CAVE 37°56'10" N.; 80°21'38" W. White Sulphur Springs Quadrangle.

Hanna Cave is 1.6 miles northeast of Frankford, 1000 feet west of an angular jog in the county road south from Spring Creek to Frankford. The entrance, at an elevation of 2200 feet, is 50 feet north of a wire fence extending west from the road. It is a narrow cleft in a small sink and opens into a passage 200 feet long trending S. 50° W. which is

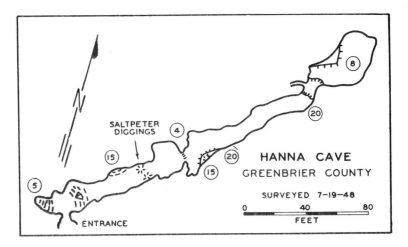

Figure 14.—Hanna Cave.

blocked by clay reaching to the ceiling at the end. The passage is 6 to 12 feet wide and 15 to 20 feet high with a dry clay floor. A few formations are found near the entrance and at the end of the passage. The cave was used for salt-peter operations during the War Between the States and several piles of earth remain in the cave. No hoppers or troughs are in the cave. Hanna Cave is in the lower part of the Greenbrier Series.

HEDRICKS CAVE 37° 43′ 32″ N.; 80°26′02″ W. Ronceverte Quadrangle.

This cave, the largest known in West Virginia, is located 0.6 mile due north of Organ Cave. The entrance, a vertical shaft 30 feet deep, is in a shallow sink (elevation, 2250 feet). A broad passage leads southwest and west for 500 feet. The passage, 10 to 30 feet high, 10 to 50 feet wide, has a shelf along the side that forms an "upper level." A stream flows along the floor of this passage. At one point the passage is blocked by a pinch-down which can be by-passed by way of a labyrinth of side passages to the north. The entrance passage connects at its west end with the main passage of the cave which trends north-south. The main passage is 10 to 50 feet wide and high and the floor, which dips steeply, is covered by a number of fallen rocks. 3,000 feet south of the

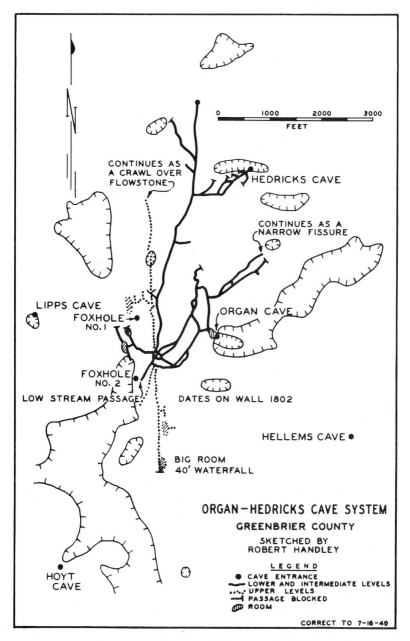

Figure 15.—Organ-Hedricks Cave System.

junction with the entrance passage it joins the main stream passage of Organ Cave. A few hundred feet beyond this junction, the passage is wide but too low for traverse. A stream flows south along the main passage of Hedricks Cave. Several side passages as well as two higher levels are developed near the junction with Organ Cave. These connect with a large passage, similar to the main passage described above, that extends 3,000 feet to the north and 2,000 feet south. Large rooms are found along the south end of the passage. Several side passages lead off but are blocked by breakdown. North of the junction with the entrance passage the main passage extends in several branches for over 2,000 feet. The passages are terminated by breakdown or clay fills except one which opens to the surface.

At the entrance a steeply sloping passage extends south to a stream. The stream passage is blocked by a pool on the north. To the south are two rooms.

For a number of years all that was known of Hedricks Cave was the entrance passage. In 1948-49 work by the Charleston Grotto of the National Speleological Society brought about extensive discoveries including the connection with Organ Cave. Many side passages and upper levels remain to be explored and eventually may tie into the Foxholes and other caves in the vicinity. To the south of the junction with Organ Cave, the upper levels may open to passages extending to Second Creek. At present, the Organ-Hedricks Cave system is the largest known in West Virginia.

Many formations in the form of columns, stalactites, stalagmites, and several small rimstone pools decorate the entrance passage. The main passage lacks formations except for a large flowstone dome near the junction with the entrance passage. Gypsum spikes are found along the main passages and in the upper level near the junction with Organ Cave.

Hedricks Cave is in the Hillsdale Limestone, Greenbrier Series.

HELLEMS CAVE 37°42'40" N.; 80°25'35" W. Ronceverte Quadrangle.

Hellems Cave is 0.8 mile due east of Organ Cave P. O. at an elevation of 2350 feet. The entrance, in a small sink, is a

10-foot pit which opens into a crawlway several hundred feet in length. Hellems Cave is in the lower part of the Greenbrier Series.

HIGGINBOTHAMS NO. 1 CAVE 37°55′58″ N.; 80°24′30″ W. White Sulphur Springs Quadrangle.

This is one of four closely associated caves 1.3 miles west of Frankford at the base of Carroll Hill (elevation, 2250 feet). The entrance is in the face of a low escarpment and opens into two sinuous passages. The east passage can be traversed for 650 feet to a pool where the ceiling is too low for further exploration. The passage is 10 to 40 feet wide and 6 to 35 feet high. A stream flows eastward in the passage. A prominent meander tube occupies much of the ceiling in this passage. The sides of the passage are irregular in shape. Along part of the way they are vertical and straight; in other parts there are shelves and ledges and in one section 400 feet from the entrance, the cave is in two separate passages.

The west passage is over 2200 feet in length and is easier to traverse. It is 10 to 30 feet wide, 6 to 15 feet high and is a series of sinuous meanders. At the end the passage gradually reduces in height until it is too low for traverse. The floor is wet silt and clay and a small stream meanders along sections of it. The stream leaves the main channel a number of times to flow through subordinate side passages. A large side passage trending south leaves the west passage 1000 feet from the entrance. The passage is 2 to 6 feet wide, 8 to 10 feet high, and 500 feet long. An opening to the surface (known as McClungs Cave) in the form of a vertical shaft is 100 feet from the end of the passage. Small formations are found at the rear of the west passage and in portions of the east passage. The cave is in the lower part of the Alderson Limestone, Greenbrier Series.

The stream in the cave has been used since 1769 as a source of power. In that year a grist-mill, the first west of the Allegheny Mountain in this area, was built inside the entrance in the east passage. Some of the larger timbers from this mill and portions of the rock dam still remain in this passage. A millstone from the mill is a part of the historical marker erected at the cave's entrance. A wooden dam and ram were

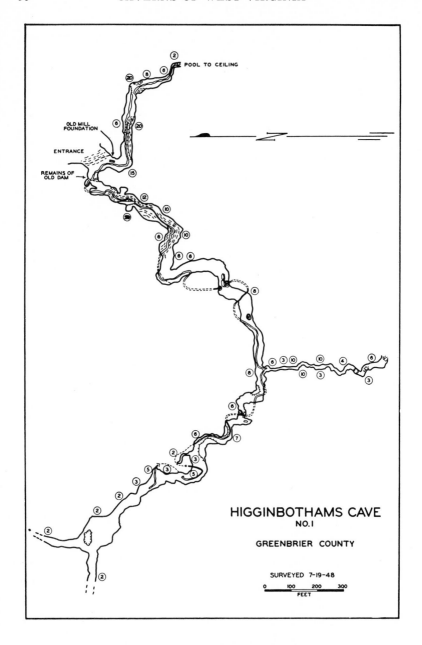

Figure 16.—Higginbothams Cave No. 1.

installed near the entrance in 1909 to provide a domestic water supply.

The stream flowing in the cave sinks at a point ½ mile to the northwest. It comes to the surface, after passing through the cave, in a big spring in front of the Higginbotham's house, 500 feet southeast of the cave entrance, and flows into another cave. It is believed to flow through Coffman Cave.

HIGGINBOTHAMS CAVE NO. 2 37°55'56" N.; 80°24'28" W.
White Sulphur Springs Quadrangle.

This cave is 300 feet southeast of Higginbothams No. 1, in a low ridge 100 feet north of the Higginbotham's house. The entrance (elevation, 2250 feet) is an opening 3 feet high and 10 feet wide which opens into a room 25 feet wide, 6 feet high, and 50 feet long. The floor of the room is soft clay that slopes gently away from the entrance. At the southwest edge of the room and offset to the west another room, with dimensions the same as the entrance room, occurs. The floor of the room is covered with rimstone pools up to a foot deep and a large flowstone formation blocks the west end of the room. A low passage beneath the flowstone opens into a large room with a high ceiling. This room has a dry floor and no formations comparable to the second room. The cave is in the

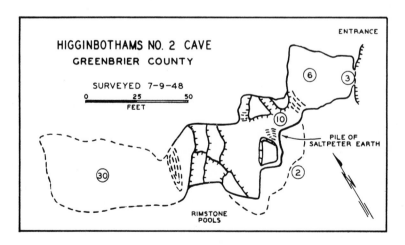

Figure 17.—Higginbothams No. 2 Cave.

Alderson Limestone, Greenbrier Series, which dips 10° to the northwest. A few piles of earth in the second room indicate that the cave may have been used for saltpeter operations.

HIGGINBOTHAMS CAVE NO. 3 37°55'47" N.; 80°24'30" W.
White Sulphur Springs Quadrangle.

Cave No. 3 is situated in a shallow vale, 500 feet south across a low ridge from Higginbothams No. 2. The entrance (elevation, 2250 feet) is a small, vertical sink 10 feet long and wide with a drop of 6 feet to the cave floor. The cave extends both north and south from the sink. The south passage, 10 to 15 feet wide and 4 to 6 feet high, extends for 150 feet to a low crawlway. This crawlway connects with a maze of passages of considerable length. The floor is of wet clay and a few formations are found at the beginning of the crawlway. The north passage is a typical sewer, 10 feet wide and 6 feet high, with an arched ceiling. The passage can be traversed for 200 feet where excavation for saltpeter has been made. The saltpeter earth filled the cave to within 2 feet of the ceiling and has been excavated for a depth of 3 or 4 feet. Beyond the excavations the cave continues as a crawlway 12 to 18 inches high. There are no remains of hoppers or troughs in the cave. The cave is in the Alderson Limestone, Greenbrier Series. Excellent specimens of Blastoids, Crinoids, and Bryozoa can be extracted from the ceiling and walls. Flies and crickets abound in the cave and rats' nests are found in the northern passage.

HIGGINBOTHAMS CAVE NO. 4 37°55'53" N.; 80°24'28" W.
White Sulphur Springs Quadrangle.

This cave is in a low escarpment 100 feet south of the Higginbotham house near the north end of a pond which drains into it (elevation, 2250 feet). The entrance is 10 feet wide and 3 feet high. The passage from the entrance trends south as a crawlway 16 inches high and 15 feet wide. This crawlway is 100 feet long, the last 20 feet of which is floored with liquid mud. For 300 feet more the passage is about 2 feet high. At 400 feet the passage enlarges to 40 feet high and 30 feet wide. The passage trends north with the stream meandering on the floor of a large gallery. At 2400 feet are some well developed stalactites, draperies, and flowstones. At 2700 feet there is a large pool blocking the passage; a muddy crumbly ledge can be used to pass the pool. The cave continues for 375 feet to a 15 - foot waterfall; beyond this is an unexplored passage. Two or three side passages open between the pool and falls; a large stream emerges from one. Four hundred feet inside the cave is an upper level extending south for 300 feet where it terminates in breakdown. A prominent French speleologist, after examining the cave in 1945, washed at an outside spigot at Higginbotham's house and completely clogged the drain—an expressive example of the character of the front part of the cave. The cave is in the Alderson Limestone, Greenbrier Series.

HIGHLANDER RIDGE CAVE 37°45'50" N.; 80°32'00" W. Clintonville Quadrangle.

A large vertical shaft, over 100 feet deep, lies at an elevation of 1950 feet on the east side of Muddy Creek Mountain, 1.4 miles north of Fort Spring. It is not known if a passage exists at the base. The pit is in the Alderson Limestone, Greenbrier Series.

HINKLES UNUS CAVE 37°56'18" N.; 80°26'34" W. White Sulphur Springs Quadrangle.

The cave is ⅛ mile south of the settlement of Unus, 100 feet east of the road. The entrance (elevation, 2150 feet) is in a low cliff and is 30 feet wide and 20 feet high. It heads west into a large room 250 feet long, 60 feet wide, and 30 feet high. The floor is covered by slabs of fallen rock and drops 30 feet to the rear of the room. Several large dome pits occur in the ceiling. At the rear of the large room the cave continues as a narrow passage 2 feet wide and 20 feet high, alternating in direction between S. 60° W. and due north. A stream fills the passage. This tortuous passage slopes steeply to the southwest and at 225 feet it levels off to a low rocky stream crawl. A short passage leads from the stream passage to the bottom of a sink. At the entrance to the cave a low passage, 10 feet wide and 4 feet high, heads S. 20° E. for 60 feet where the ceiling is too low for traverse. A stream enters this passage in a small hole 500 feet to the south and flows through the south passage, the large room and the zigzag channel. The cave is in the Alderson Limestone, Greenbrier Series, with a dip 5° E. and is guided by joints at N. 60° E. (vertical), due N. (dipping 30° E.), and N. 50° W. (vertical).

HORSE PIT 37°48′44″ N.; 80°27′28″ W. White Sulphur Springs Quadrangle.

A vertical pit, 60 feet deep, in the Sinks Grove Limestone, is located ½ mile north of U.S. 60, ¾ mile northwest of Lewisburg (elevation, 2100 feet). No passage opens at the base.

HOYT CAVE 37°42′22″ N.; 80°26′45″ W. Ronceverte Quadrangle.

Hoyt Cave is at the southwest corner of a large sink, ½ mile southwest of Organ Cave P. O. (elevation, 2150 feet). The entrance divides into three passages. The middle lead is blocked after 20 feet. The west passage is a relatively straight sewer, 6 to 8 feet high, 10 feet wide and 150 feet long which heads S. 30° W. This opens into a room 75 feet long, 25 feet wide, and 5 to 15 feet high. At the north end of the room is a massive flowstone mound in the form of a haystack surrounded by stalagmites and rimstone pools. The third passage heads east from the entrance and is a small, sloping crawlway over 100 feet long. The main passage and room are dry and inhabited by skunk and fox. Crickets are common and flies swarm over the walls of the room and are quite annoying to the visitor. The cave is in the Hillsdale Limestone, Greenbrier Series.

HUGHART CAVE 37°54′05″ N.; 80°32′55″ W. Clintonville Quadrangle.

A cave of medium size is located at the settlement of Hughart. The entrance (elevation, 2100 feet) is 500 feet south of the county road along Sinking Creek Valley and opens into a large passage extending over 1000 feet to the north. A short distance from the entrance the passage is reported to be blocked by a recent rock fall. The cave is in the upper part of the Greenbrier Series.

JACKSON CAVE NO. 1 37°56'17" N.; 80°26'03" W. White Sulphur Springs Quadrangle.

This cave is located on the south side of the Unus-Frankford road 0.6 mile southeast of Unus (elevation, 2150 feet). The cave is a crawlway, about 100 yards in length, with a small stream flowing in it. The cave is in the top of the Union Limestone, Greenbrier Series.

JACKSON CAVE NO. 2 37°56'30" N.; 80°25'41" W. White Sulphur Springs Quadrangle.

This cave lies on the north side of the Unus-Frankford road, 0.9 mile east of Unus. The entrance is in a low sink 150 feet north of the road (elevation, 2150 feet) but is filled now with earth and leaves. The cave is reported to be a long passage with no rooms or formations. It is in the Alderson (?) Limestone, Greenbrier Series.

JARRETS WATER CAVE 37°53'52" N.; 80°30'46" W. Clintonville Quadrangle.

This cave is 2 miles east of Hughart at an elevation of 2100 feet. A single passage with a stream has been explored for 630 feet to a pool. The cave is in the Alderson (?) Limestone, Greenbrier Series.

JEWEL CAVE 37°44'30" N.; 80°33'43" W. Alderson Quadrangle.

The entrance to this cave is in a limestone cut on the Chesapeake & Ohio Railway, ¼ mile southwest of the Acme Limestone Company quarry at Fort Spring. The entrance, 25 feet above the railroad grade (elevation, 1650 feet), opens into a passage 300 feet long that trends S. 30° W. and is 15 to 30 feet wide and 7 to 10 feet high. The floor is wet clay and the route of traverse is a sinuous path between mounds of clay. Three hundred feet from the entrance the passage descends steeply for 30 feet and connects with a passage that parallels it. To the south the passage is 15 to 30 feet high and 10 feet wide for 180 feet where it is terminated by the ceiling descending to the surface of a small pool. The floor of the passage is gravel and clay with numerous stream channels

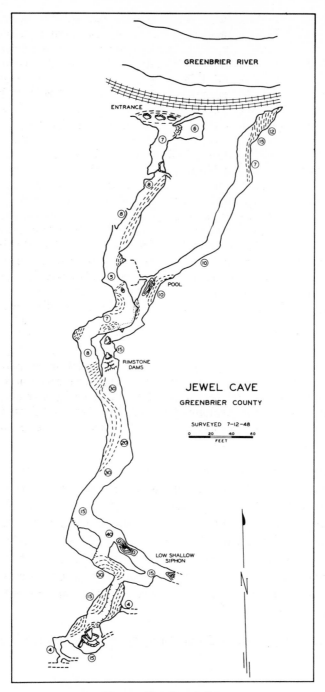

Figure 18.—Jewel Cave.

but no perennial stream. At the south end of the passage a chamber, 20 feet square, opens to the west with breakdown, covered by thick clay, forming the floor. At the northwest corner of the chamber, a passage known as the Cannon's Mouth, 6 feet wide and 4 feet high, connects, after a number of turns, with a fissure passage 4 feet wide and 20 feet high. In places this passage is filled to a considerable depth by water. Several rooms are developed along the fissure and the distance it may be traversed is not known. The crawls and squeezes plus the scaling of slippery clay banks amply justify the taunt—"Cannon's Mouth, Try It"—that is inscribed over the entrance. To the north the main passage is sinuous with a height and width of 15 feet. The 50 feet north of the junction with the entrance passage is floored with rimstone dams. The next 130 feet is floored by bare rock with a few banks of clay. One hundred eighty feet from the junction the intermittent stream channel passes through a narrow crevice that connects with a small room to the west filled with a number of small formations, the only formations in the cave. Continuing northward the main passage gradually fills with clay until 360 feet from the junction it is entirely blocked. This passage, though filled with clay, continues as a crevice that slopes north under the road-bed of the railroad and is connected to the surface by a small hole, at track level, 360 feet north of the entrance to Jewel Cave. This hole gives access to a fissure passage 100 feet long that is floored by wet clay. In March 1943, after prolonged rains, the fissure beneath the railroad bed became waterlogged and caused the grade to slide into the Greenbrier River.

Jewel Cave is probably visited more than any other noncommercial cave in the State. Near the entrance evidence is abundant that it is frequented by "Knights of the Road." Station numbers, painted on the walls, are relics of a survey by the railroad (at which time an inscription—"Eddy's Bear Cave"—was painted over the entrance). A generation ago the cave was honored by the visit of a group of railroad officials while their special train was waiting on the adjacent siding.

The cave is in the Union Limestone, Greenbrier Series.

JOHNSON CAVE 37°52′54″ N.; 80°30′30″ W. Clintonville Quadrangle.

Two and three-tenths miles southeast of Hughart and 0.9 mile north of U. S. Highway 60 on the east side of the county road is a small crawlway about a hundred feet long (elevation, 2100 feet). The cave is in the Alderson Limestone, Greenbrier Series.

JUDYS CAVE 37°56′46″ N.; 80°30′55″ W. Clintonville Quadrangle.

Judys Cave is 0.8 mile due east of Cornstalk on the west side of the valley of Sinking Creek (elevation, 2400 feet). The entrance is a short drop which opens into a small passage and room totaling about 300 feet in length. The cave is very muddy. It is in the Alderson Limestone, Greenbrier Series.

LEGGS CAVE 37°57′30″ N.; 80°22′08″ W. White Sulphur Springs Quadrangle.

Leggs Cave is 0.4 mile south of Spring Creek, 1.2 miles northeast of Spring Creek P. O. (elevation, 2070 feet). The cave is a small crawlway heading east that can be traversed for 300 feet. Local residents report that a man entered Leggs Cave and emerged at Burns Cave No. 2. The cave is in the Pickaway (?) Limestone, Greenbrier Series.

LEVISAY CAVE 37°54′55″ N.; 80°22′38″ W. White Sulphur Springs Quadrangle.

This cave is 0.7 mile southeast of Frankford and 0.4 mile east of U. S. 119 (elevation, 2250 feet). The entrance, on the north side of a farm house in a low escarpment, is 20 feet wide and 6 feet high, opening into a room 30 feet long. At the end of the room, a passage, 6 feet high and 4 feet wide, continues due west but after 100 feet it is too narrow for further progress. The floor of the room is covered with gravel and pools of water which are used for domestic supplies. The cave is in the Patton Limestone, Greenbrier Series.

LEWIS CAVE 37°45′00″ N.; 80°25′34″ W. White Sulphur Springs Quadrangle.

Lewis Cave is in a low hill, ¼ mile south of Holliday-Lewis School, and 600 feet west of the county road (elevation, 2200 feet). The entrance is a narrow, trash-filled fissure at the base of the hill. The cave extends west into the hill as a crawlway which branches into two passages and opens into a small room 15 feet in diameter. The total length of passages is 225 feet. Lewis Cave is in the Hillsdale Limestone, Greenbrier Series.

LEWIS (CROOKSHANK) HOLE 38°04′30″ N.; 80°18′56″ W. Lobelia Quadrangle.

This pit, 90 feet deep, 40 feet in diameter, is at the head of Friars Hole, ¼ mile southwest of the Greenbrier-Pocahontas line (elevation, 2500 feet). A stream flows in the entrance pit. At the base of the pit is a passage recently opened by removal of the gravel fill by stream flushing. This passage is a stoopway for 500 feet to the main passage of the cave. The main passage is 25 feet high, 10 feet wide, trending east for 2600 feet. Logs are lodged in the ceiling as much as 30 feet above the floor of the main passage. Near the entrance pit are several other shafts in the ceiling. Eleven hundred feet from the entrance a side passage trends north for 300 feet. A stream flows along this passage to a lake at the end. The main passage of the cave extends close to Snedegars Cave. Lewis Hole is in the Alderson-Union Limestone, Greenbrier Series.

LIPPS CAVE 37°48′22″ N.; 80°25′48″ W. White Sulphur Springs Quadrangle.

This cave is ¼ mile northeast of Lewisburg and ¼ mile east of U. S. 119 (elevation, 2220 feet). The cave is a small tapering passage, large enough to be traversed by walking that is terminated by a trash-filled sink 200 feet from the entrance. The passage is in the Hillsdale Limestone, Greenbrier Series.

LIPPS CAVE NO. 2 37°43′06″ N.; 80°26′56″ W. Ronceverte Quadrangle.

This cave is in a shallow sink 100 yards north of the road at Chestnut Grove School (elevation, 2300 feet). The entrance is a narrow slit that opens into a low room 10 feet wide, 20 feet long, filled with formations. Considerable water drips from the ceiling of the cave. One hundred feet to the south of this cave is a narrow fissure opening that heads south. It is blocked at the entrance by driftwood. The caves are in the Sinks Grove (?) Limestone which dips 20° S.W. and strikes S. 40° E.

LIZARD CAVE 37°44' N.; 80°40' W. Alderson Quadrangle.

Professor A. M. Reese [21] reported a small cave, known as Lizard Cave, to be 1½ miles west of Alderson on the Alderson-Hinton road. The cave could not be located during field work for this report.

LOST CAVE 37°43'50" N.; 80°35'48" W. Alderson Quadrangle.

Lost Cave is along West Virginia Highway 63, 2.6 miles east of Alderson (opposite Halfway Station on the Chesapeake & Ohio Railway). The entrance is in a shallow sink (elevation, 1650 feet), 100 yards north of the highway, and is just to the north of the telephone-line. A rough path leads to the sink from the highway. The entrance is through a cleft in the base of the sink which drops 9 feet to a chamber 15 feet square. Two small crawl passages lead off the chamber. Saltpeter earth was obtained from the cave in the War of 1812 and Mexican War. The cave receives its name due to the inability to locate it during the War Between the States. Rotted remnants of hoppers still remain in the cave. The cave is in the Union Limestone, Greenbrier Series.

LUDINGTON CAVE 37°53'28" N.; 80°23'22" W. White Sulphur Springs Quadrangle.

This cave is ½ mile north of Gravelpoint School at an elevation of 2150 feet. The entrance is 7 feet high and 10 feet wide. The cave is primarily a stream passage slightly smaller than the entrance. Six hundred and twenty feet from the entrance is a waterfall 40 feet high beyond which the cave continues for 2500 feet. The cave is in the Hillsdale Limestone, Greenbrier Series.

---

[21] Reese, A. M., Fauna of West Virginia Caves: West Virginia Academy of Science, Proceedings, West Virginia University Bulletin, vol. 34, pp. 39-53, 1934.

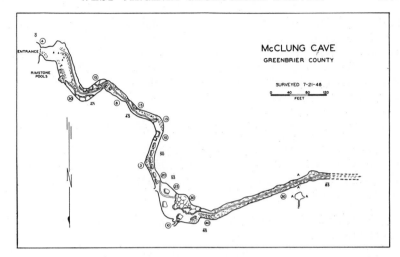

Figure 19.—McClung Cave.

McCLUNG CAVE 37°52′52″ N.; 80°23′24″ W. White Sulphur
Springs Quadrangle.

McClung Cave is 1.5 miles northeast of Maxwelton, 1000
feet southeast of Gravelpoint School (elevation, 2260 feet).
The entrance, in a shallow sink 50 feet to the east of a house,
is a small opening 4 feet high and 10 feet wide which leads
to a large room 30 feet wide, 30 feet high, and 100 feet long.
The room heads N. 20° W. but after 30 feet curves rapidly
until its direction is S. 60° W. The drop from the entrance
to the end of the room is 40 feet. The cave continues as a
passage, 10 to 20 feet high and 10 feet wide trending northwest, which is constricted at the base by shelves and fallen
rocks. A small stream flows along the passage. One hundred
and seventy feet from the entrance room and 20 feet below it,
the passage opens into a room 25 feet high, 60 feet long, and
30 feet wide with a large bank of breakdown and clay on the
south side. Large amounts of water enter the room through
several dome pits. A passage from the room leads S. 80° W.
and is "keyhole" in shape with the stream flowing in a slot
1 or 2 feet wide and 10 to 15 feet deep above which are steeply
sloping banks of clay 25 feet high and 10 feet wide.. This
passage extends for 1900 feet to breakdown beyond which is a
passage 20 feet wide, 25 feet high, and 300 yards long. At the

end of this is a narrow sewer passage, 1 foot high, 90 feet long, which opens into a large, long passage extending to a breakdown. Beyond the breakdown is a dusty crawl 240 feet long after which the passage enlarges and divides. The left (north) branch circles counterclockwise to join the main cave at the end of the first breakdown; the right (south) branch continues as a long silt-floored passage ending in a small room. The ceiling height in this passage is progressively lower towards the rear. Large rimstone pools lie on the east side of the entrance room which also has large flowstone cascades and mounds. McClung Cave is in the Hillsdale Limestone, Greenbrier Series, and is developed along major joints at N. 10° E. and due north.

McFERRIN (SCOUT) CAVE 37°56'04" N.; 80°28'38" W.
White Sulphur Springs Quadrangle.

McFerrin Cave, located 0.6 mile due east of Bethel School (elevation, 2300 feet), is one of the many caves used for saltpeter during the War Between the States. The entrance is on the south side of a broad sink and is an opening 10 feet wide and 4 feet high. A steeply sloping room, 45 feet long,

Plate VIII.—McFerrin Cave, Saltpeter Trough. (Photo by Wm. E. Davies).

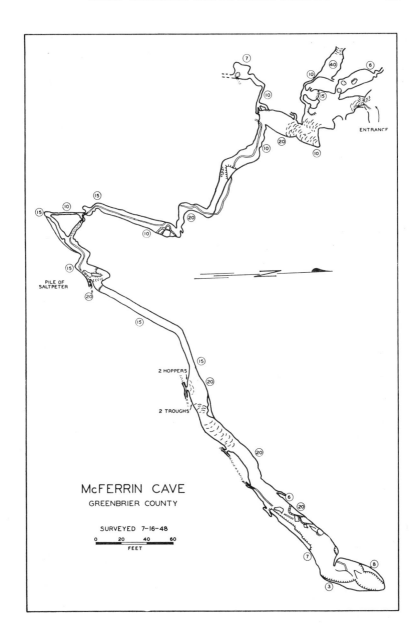

Figure 20.—McFerrin Cave.

heads south and at the southeast corner connects with a rock-strewn, low passage 20 feet long. This passage gives access to the main part of the cave, which is a sinuous passage, 5 to 10 feet wide and 10 to 20 feet high, trending south for 200 feet and then heading northeast for 400 feet. The grade is uniform, dropping 120 feet from the entrance to the end. At the end there is an oval-shaped room 20 feet wide and 40 feet long which is floored by slabs of rock that have scaled from the ceiling. A small stream flows the length of the cave in a channel parallel and often connected to the main passage. Just inside the entrance a passage leads west and north for 40 feet as a low room 20 feet wide, 40 feet long and 6 feet high. Several large pits, 10 to 15 feet deep, lie near the entrance. At the south end of the entrance room a narrow, twisting fissure leads to a room 40 feet long, 15 feet wide and 40 feet high which is blocked at the end by a large wall of clay. The walls are vertical and show, by clay stains, that the room is periodically filled with water to a depth of 8 feet. A circuitous crawlway leaves the main passage 40 feet from the entrance room and trends south for over 300 yards. It is dangerous to traverse as the walls are of argillaceous lime-stone which is in a very crumbly condition.

The saltpeter deposits in the cave are of considerable inter-est as it is one of the few instances where such earth was worked in the vicinity of an active stream. Remains of seven hoppers and four troughs plus numerous piles of saltpeter earth lie along the main passage.

Formations are scattered throughout the cave and a beau-tiful, terraced stalagmite occurs 100 feet from the entrance. McFerrin Cave, in the Union Limestone, Greenbrier Series, which dips 25° E., is developed along joints at N. 30° E. and N. 70° W. modified by subordinate joints at N. 80° E.

McMILLAN CAVE 38°03′30″ N.; 80°21′26″ W. Lobelia Quad-rangle.

McMillan Cave is situated at the junction of Robbins Run and Spring Creek at an elevation of 2250 feet. This cave is reported to be a small crawlway less than 100 feet in length. The cave is in the Alderson Limestone, Greenbrier Series,

MADISON KNOB, NORTH CAVE 37°52′56″ N.; 80°25′45″ W.
White Sulphur Springs Quadrangle.

Madison Knob is an isolated ridge trending northwest-southeast, two miles northwest of Maxwelton. Two caves are situated on the ridge. The North Cave is on the north side of the east end of the ridge at an elevation of 2500 feet. The entrance is a vertical pit 90 feet deep with a diameter of 15 feet at the top and 4 feet at the base. A short passage leads off in a direction N. 65° E. and S. 65° W. at the base for about 20 feet in each direction. The cave is in the Alderson Limestone, Greenbrier Series. It is located 1.3 miles northwest of Maxwelton.

MADISON KNOB, SOUTH CAVE 37°52′52″ N.; 80°25′23″ W.
White Sulphur Springs Quadrangle.

The South Cave is in a low saddle on the south side at the center of the ridge (elevation, 2450 feet). It is a vertical shaft, 70 feet deep and 6 feet in diameter, which opens into a short, narrow crevice heading south. The crevice is well decorated with flowstone. The cave is in the Alderson Limestone, Greenbrier Series. It is located 1.5 miles northwest of Maxwelton.

MUD CAVE 37°46′ N.; 80°37′ W. Clintonville Quadrangle.

Professor Reese [22] reports a small cave on the Alderson-Blue Sulphur Springs road, 2½ miles from Alderson. This cave was not located during field work.

MUDDY CREEK CAVE 37°44′15″ N.; 80°38′04″ W. Alderson Quadrangle.

Muddy Creek Cave is located at the north end of the west leg of the hairpin bend of Muddy Creek, ¼ mile north of Alderson. The entrance is an inconspicuous, small hole (elevation, 1580 feet) in a rocky ledge 50 feet east of the creek. A large spring rises at the base of the ledge. The entrance connects with a large room by a 15-foot vertical drop. The cave extends eastward as a maze of intersecting passages and rooms over 1500 feet in length. Most of the passages are large enough to permit walking but the floors are wet clay and are slippery.

---

[22] Reese, A. M., op. cit.

A small exit hole lies on top of the ridge, 500 feet northeast of the entrance. Formations are numerous and are quite large and beautiful but have suffered severely from wanton vandalism. Part of Muddy Creek sinks at the base of a cliff on the east leg of the bend, opposite the cave entrance, and flows through the cave. During drought practically all the water follows the subterranean course. Beavers residing near the cave have entered it and built dams, at times in the past, that have caused serious flooding in the cave. Muddy Creek Cave is in the Union (?) Limestone, Greenbrier Series.

NORMAN CAVE 38°01′06″ N.; 80°19′12″ W. Lobelia Quadrangle.

This cave is located one mile southwest of Julia. The entrance is at the top of a steep rise (elevation, 2150 feet), 300 feet west of a sharp bend in the county road. It is a low opening, 3 feet high and 10 feet wide and opens into a room 250 feet long, 30 feet wide, and 15 to 40 feet high. The floor is covered by large rock slabs and slopes uniformly downward until 50 feet from the end it is 75 feet below the entrance. At this point is an opening to a small stream channel on the west side of the room. The remaining 50 feet of the room is 20 feet above the low spot on a pile of rock and clay, which closes to the ceiling at the end. Flowstone, bacon rind, and some stalactites decorate the walls. A row of massive columns cuts diagonally across the room 80 feet from the entrance. The cave is in the Hillsdale (?) Limestone, Greenbrier Series.

ORGAN CAVE 37°43′02″ N.; 80°26′14″ W. Ronceverte Quadrangle.

This cave, one of three commercially developed caves in West Virginia, is 0.4 mile north of Organ Cave P. O. The entrance is at the west end of a long valley sink at an elevation of 2200 feet and is in a cliff 100 feet high. The boulder-strewn opening, 20 feet wide and high, leads to a large room 200 feet long and 90 feet wide with a flat ceiling at a height of 30 feet. A small stream enters the cave but disappears in gravel on the west side of the room. At the south end of the room a low sinuous passage, 300 feet long, 6 to 20 feet wide, and 4 to 7 feet high, with a dry clay floor connects with the main stream passage.

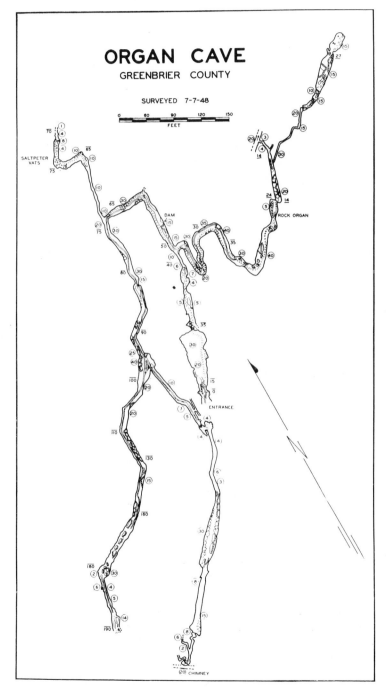

Figure 21.—Organ Cave.

Plate IX.—Terraced Stalagmite, Organ Cave; ending northeast passage. (Photo by Wm. E. Davies).

Plate X.—Organ Cave. Stream Passage. (Photo by Wm. E. Davies).

The stream passage to the east of the junction is an extremely sinuous passage 20 to 30 feet wide, 25 to 40 feet high and is open to the public for 750 feet. The route of traverse is a 'narrow path on ledges of clay high above the stream. Gravel-filled niches close to the ceiling indicate a former, more extensive fill. Near the rear of the lighted passage is a large flowstone mound and columns, known as the Rock Organ, and several small rimstone pools. The undeveloped portion of the passage continues to the northeast over a pile of breakdown for 80 feet to a narrow crawlway. Access is gained to a lower level through one of several pits in the floor. The lower level is a narrow fissure that twists and turns for 300 feet where it opens into a room, 100 feet long, 30 feet wide, and 15 feet high, floored by large slabs of breakdown. At the end of the room are a number of beautiful formations including terraced columns and rimstone pools. The upper level, beyond the pits connecting with the lower passage, continues as a crawlway for 100 feet where it intersects a high vaulted passage which is 20 feet below the crawlway and trends northeast for 1,000 feet. It has a silt floor with a small stream. The passage, 20 feet high and wide, is blocked on the north-

Plate XI.—Organ Cave. Saltpeter Hoppers. (Photo by Wm. E. Davies).

east by a large flowstone formation. A small crevice passage about 1½ feet wide continues beyond the flowstone. To the southwest the passage connects with the commercial part of Organ Cave at the "Rock Organ."

The main channel west of the junction is similar in dimensions to the east portion except that large slabs of breakdown floor the cave in place of clay banks. Three hundred and fifty feet from the junction the portion of the cave open to the public trends north as a narrow passage opening into a low room containing 37 saltpeter hoppers used during the War Between the States. The hoppers are in an excellent state of preservation. A broad crawlway extends for several hundred feet northeast of the hopper room and ends in breakdown. The stream channel, which is uniform in character, can be easily traversed to a point 1750 feet from the junction where the ceiling is too low for further progress. By use of small crawlways lying higher than the stream passage the cave can be followed about 200 feet where it intersects Hedricks Cave.

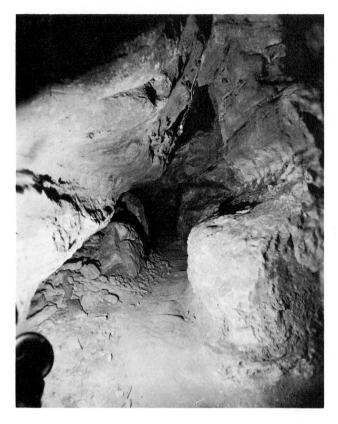

Plate XII.—Organ Cave. Passage to Saltpeter Workings. (Photo by Wm. E. Davies).

It is reported that by crawling the stream channel can be followed for considerable distance beyond this point. This point is 160 feet below the entrance. Nine hundred and forty feet from the junction a small passage leaves the stream passage on the southeast side and trends south. It is 4 to 8 feet high and wide with a small stream, probably the one which flows in the entrance, flowing along it. The stream comes from a small water-filled pit 300 feet from the entrance to the channel. The passage offsets to the east at this point and opens into a very dry section of the cave full of rock that has scaled from the ceiling. This section is dangerous to traverse because of rock fall. The passage continues southwest for 300 feet where it enlarges into a room 250 feet long and 40 feet wide and high. At the end of the room the passage continues for 250 feet where it connects with a maze of small, twisting fissure openings that connect with Hedricks Cave.

The passages described above are believed to be the major ones forming the cave. However, it is probable that a number of the small crawlways may open into large portions of the cave that have not been described. Organ Cave is developed along primary joints at N. 40° E., due North, and N. 80° E. in Hillsdale Limestone, Greenbrier Series, which dips 12° N.W. The walls and ceiling are soft, calcareous clay resulting from solution work on the limestone and small chips are continuously scaling off. The fossil bones of the Pleistocene sloth **Megalonyx jeffersonii** described by Thomas Jefferson in 1799,[23] were found in this cave. The streams in the cave drain to Second Creek.

PARLOR (DEVIL) CAVE 37°45'07" N.; 80°32'00" W. Clintonville Quadrangle.

Parlor Cave is located on the south side of West Virginia Highway 63, 3.3 miles west of Ronceverte (elevation, 1900 feet). The entrances are 10 feet above the road and are two low openings which lead over a pile of rock debris to a large room 8 feet below. The room is 80 feet wide, 120 feet long with a ceiling 15 feet high. A small passage continues for 50 feet beyond the room. The cave trends S. 70° W. in the Patton Limestone, Greenbrier Series, at the crest of an anticline dipping 10° W. and 20° E.

PECKS (BUNGERS NO. 2) CAVE 37°51'00" N.; 80°30'24" W. Clintonville Quadrangle.

Pecks Cave is on the south side of Milligan Creek, 2.4 miles southeast of Alta, at an elevation of 1950 feet. The cave consists of a stream passage 7 feet high and 6 feet wide which heads S. 40° E. for 100 feet and then N. 50° E. for about 200 yards or more. A large stream flows through the cave, enter-

---

[23] Jefferson, Thomas. A memoir on the discovery of certain bones of a quadruped of the clawed kind in the western parts of Virginia: American Philosophical Society. Transactions, vol. IV, pp. 246-260, 1799.

Price, Paul H.; Heck, E. T. Greenbrier County Report: West Virginia Geological Survey, p. 114, 1939.

Plate XIII.—Pecks Cave, Stream Passage. (Photo by Wm. E. Davies).

ing the cave from the east just inside the entrance. A small, brush-filled opening, 300 feet southeast of the entrance, is reported to be the lower end of Pecks Cave. Three hundred feet west of Pecks Cave is a low opening from which a stream flows and disappears just outside the mouth. This stream is seen again in Pecks Cave. Pecks Cave is in the Union Limestone, Greenbrier Series.

PIERCYS CAVE 37°50'37" N.; 80°34'45" W. Clintonville Quadrangle.

Piercys Cave is 0.4 mile west of Piercys Mill Cave. The entrance (elevation, 1650 feet) is in a broad cliff 50 feet high with an overhang on the east side of the cave. There are two openings; the one on the east is the exit for a stream while the west entrance is at the top of a clay bank 40 feet high and connects with the stream passage 40 feet inside. The cave consists primarily of a simple passage trending N. 30° E. and due north for 5000 feet, 20 to 50 feet wide and 10 to 40 feet high. The stream occupies most of the floor with occasional banks of clay along the wall. The first 700 feet from the entrance is straight, one of the longest straight cave passages in the State. A short upper level develops 4100 feet from the entrance. A small side passage opens to the east 4300 feet in. The cave ends at 4800 feet in breakdown which blocks further passage. Piercys Cave is in the Union Limestone, Greenbrier Series, which dips 10° W. and strikes N. 30° E. It is developed along joints at N. 30° E. and due north with modification from joints at N. 50° W. The stream flowing through the cave is apparently from local drainage and not connected with that in Piercys Mill Cave.

Plate XIV.—Piercys Mill Cave. Stream Passage near Entrance. (Photo by Wm. E. Davies).

PIERCYS MILL CAVE 37°50′44″ N.; 80°34′21″ W. Clintonville Quadrangle.

This cave is 500 feet north of the site of Piercys Mill at the head of Muddy Creek (elevation, 1680 feet). The entrance, in a cliff 75 feet high, opens into a stream passage, 30 to 40 feet wide and 20 feet high. The stream varies in depth from 2 to 8 or more feet and traverse is along a series of ledges. The stream channel, which heads N. 30° E., is 900 feet long and is closed at the rear by a dangerous breakdown. The stream enters the cave through a hole ten inches by two feet in size near the ceiling. Two hundred and fifty feet from the entrance a passage leads off to the east which trends N. 80° E. for 100 feet, turning then to N. 30° E. for 500 feet. It is 20 to

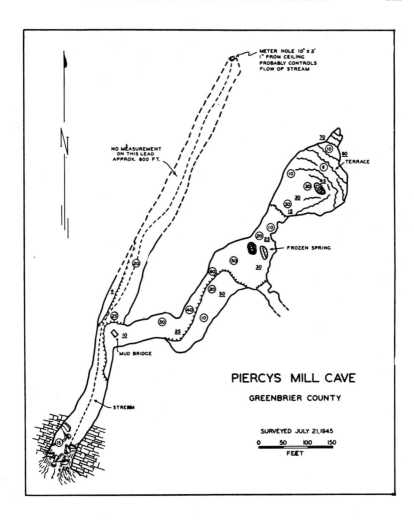

Figure 22.—Piercys Mill Cave.

60 feet high with a ledge 30 feet high on the southeast side
for 50 feet after the turn. The rear 200 feet of this passage is
one of the most beautiful spots in underground West Virginia.
A rimstone terrace floors the passage, which is 100 feet wide
at this point, and a number of large pools, one 20 feet long and
8 feet deep, occur. Flowstone, stalactites, and small columns
lie along the walls.

The cave is developed along two sets of vertical joints at N. 30° E. and N. 80° E. in the Union Limestone, Greenbrier Series, which dips 24° W. and strikes N. 30° E. The stream is a continuation of Hughart and Sinking Creeks which sink to subterranean channels 3 miles to the north. A hundred yards east of Piercys Mill Cave is an opening 3 feet high by 15 feet wide from which a small stream issues. A crawlway passage with a stream is 100 feet long beyond which the cave is a walkway up to 12 feet high and 20 feet wide trending northeast along the strike for 700 feet to a breakdown. Small speleothems, including catenary helictites, are common.

POLLOCK CAVE   37°46'07" N.; 80°36'38" W. Clintonville Quadrangle.

Pollock Cave is situated near the north end of a hollow 0.8 mile due north of Blaker Mills (elevation, 1650 feet). The entrance, on the east side of the hollow, is a pit 18 feet deep, 10 feet in diameter, which opens into a room 30 feet square. A passage, large enough to permit walking, extends for 250 feet to the east and has a small stream flowing in it. The cave is in the Alderson Limestone, Greenbrier Series. This cave is the Saltpeter Cave No. 2 of Prof. Reese.

POLLOCK SALTPETER CAVE   37°46'06" N.; 80°36'38" W. Clintonville Quadrangle.

This cave is 300 feet south of Pollock Cave at an elevation of 1650 feet. The entrance is in a low ledge of rock. The cave is a single passage 350 feet long, heading north and N. 40° E., 4 to 30 feet high and 8 to 10 feet wide. A low stream passage, 5 feet high, 3 feet wide, parallels the main passage, for several hundred feet. Several small rooms are developed along it. The floor is dry clay except at the rear where small slabs of rock have scaled from the ceiling. The cave was used for saltpeter earth extensively during 1862. Twenty piles of earth (probably from hoppers) and two wooden troughs remain as evidence of the activity. Pollock Saltpeter Cave is in the Alderson Limestone, Greenbrier Series, and is the Saltpeter Cave No. 1 of Prof. Reese. Both Pollock Caves have a dip 15° E.

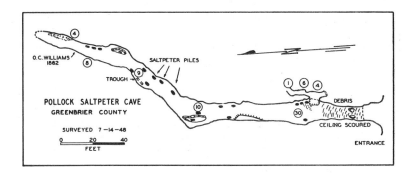

Figure 23.—Pollock Saltpeter Cave.

POOR FARM CAVE (GREENBRIER) 37°57'48" N.; 80°27' 53" W. White Sulphur Springs Quadrangle.

This cave (also referred to as New Poor Farm) is 1.6 miles east of Williamsburg, and 1000 feet south of the Williamsburg-Unus road (elevation, 2200 feet). The entrance is a small, trash-filled opening in the west side of a long doline. The cave is a single passage extending N. 40° E. and S. 40° W. from the entrance. To the northeast it is 15 feet high and 10 to 15 feet wide and is open for 425 feet where it is blocked by

Plate XV.—Pollock Saltpeter Cave. Piles of Saltpeter Earth. (Photo by Wm. E. Davies).

breakdown. Rimstone pools and flowstone decorate the rear of the passage. To the southwest the traverse is over large breakdown covered by formations for 200 feet where it heads west for 150 feet as a broad low, formation-covered passage. At this point it intersects with a long passage running north and south, 20 feet wide and 20 feet high. The south passage, 100 yards long, gradually tapers down until it is too small for traverse. The north passage curves and rejoins the main passage near the entrance. The south side of the cave is painful to traverse because of the large amount of cave coral which covers the walls, floors, and ceiling and inflicts a painful wound on contact. The cave is in the middle part of the Greenbrier Series.

RAMBOWS CAVE 37°48′34″ N.; 80°22′34″ W. White Sulphur Springs Quadrangle.

Rambows Cave is on the east side of the Greenbrier River, 2.2 miles northeast of Caldwell (elevation, 1800 feet). The cave is a wide fissure in a limestone cliff, 200 feet above the river. Legend has it that a pioneer named Rambow took refuge in the cave when pursued by Indians. He entered the cave with a small fortune of money by descending a rope ladder which the Indians cut. History and legend fail to record his method of leaving the cave. The cave is in a small outcrop of Hillsdale Limestone, Greenbrier Series.

RAPPS CAVE 37°58′47″ N.; 80°23′54″ W. White Sulphur Springs Quadrangle.

This cave is on the west side of a hollow 1000 feet due north of Rapps School (elevation, 2050 feet). The entrance, 4 feet high and 10 feet wide, opens into a large room 20 feet high, 80 feet wide, and 100 feet long, with a floor of smooth clay and flowstone. On the east side of the room a number of formations, mainly columns, are developed. The cave continues N. 30° E. as a passage floored with huge slabs of breakdown covered by formations and it is with considerable difficulty that the cave is traversed for 500 feet. The passage may continue but no way through the maze of rock could be found. A large cave entrance, directly opposite Rapps Cave on Spring Creek, may be a continuation of the passage. Rapps Cave is in the Union Limestone, Greenbrier Series.

Plate XVI.—Rapps Cave, Entrance Room. (Photo by Wm. E. Davies).

Plate XVII.—Rapps Cave, Block of Limestone showing Prismatic Joints.
(Photo by Wm. E. Davies).

REINHOLD CAVE 38°01′45″ N.; 80°23′34″ W. Lobelia Quadrangle.

The entrance to Reinhold Cave is on the south side of Dry Run opposite Band of Hope Church (elevation, 2200 feet). The cave is a single passage 4 feet wide and 10 feet high, heading southwest for more than 500 feet. A small stream flows in the rear portion of the passage. The cave is in the Alderson Limestone, Greenbrier Series.

RENICK BRIDGE CAVE 37°59′16″ N.; 80°21′23″ W. White Sulphur Springs Quadrangle.

This cave receives its name from its position at the south end of the highway bridge over the Greenbrier River at Renick. The entrance, at the level of the highway (elevation, 1900 feet), opens into a room 4 to 8 feet high, 20 feet wide, and 70 feet long. The room is irregular in outline with several short crawlways leading off at the rear. The floor is firm, damp clay. Renick Bridge Cave is in the Patton (?) Limestone, Greenbrier Series.

RENICKS VALLEY PIT 38°03′34″ N.; 80°17′48″ W. Lobelia Quadrangle.

A shaft about 50 feet deep is reported at the head of Renicks Valley (elevation, 2600 feet). The shaft is in the Alderson Limestone, Greenbrier Series, and is reported to have been used for "moonshine" operations.

RICHLANDS CAVE 37°52′02″ N.; 80°29′10″ W. White Sulphur Springs Quadrangle.

Richlands Cave is 100 yards from U. S. 60 on the west side of the church at Richlands (elevation, 2020 feet). The cave is a low water passage, 100 yards long, with numerous sections requiring crawls. A large stream flows through the cave. The cave is in the Union Limestone, Greenbrier Series.

RICHLANDS NORTHFIELD CAVE 37°52′09″ N.; 80°28′48″ W. White Sulphur Springs Quadrangle.

This cave, which may connect with Richlands Cave, is ¼ mile northeast of the church at Richlands (elevation, 2050 feet). It is entered through a shaft 10 feet deep opening into a low stream passage over 100 yards long. The cave is in the Union Limestone, Greenbrier Series.

SCOUT CAMP CAVE 37°57'04" N.; 80°27'34" W. White Sulphur Springs Quadrangle.

A small fissure crawlway is in a shallow sink 1.2 miles northwest of Unus, ¼ mile north of Unus-Bethel School road (elevation, 2200 feet). The crawlway is blocked less than 100 feet from the entrance. It is in the Union Limestone, Greenbrier Series.

SELDOMRIDGE CAVE 38°01'14" N.; 80°18'55" W. Lobelia Quadrangle.

Seldomridge Cave is in a rolling meadow, 100 yards south of the county road, 0.7 mile southwest of Julia (elevation, 2100 feet). The entrance is a small rocky sink, 10 feet deep, which opens into a room 10 feet square and high. Several small short crawlways lead off the room. The cave is in the Patton Limestone, Greenbrier Series.

SIMMS CAVE 37°52'28" N.; 80°26'08" W. White Sulphur Springs Quadrangle.

Simms Cave is at the south base of Madison Knob, 1.9 miles northwest of Arbuckle School on the Arbuckle School-Richlands road (elevation, 2275 feet). The entrance, in a low sink 200 feet north of the road, is a 10-foot drop which opens into a passage, 3 to 5 feet high and 3 feet wide, extending north for 50 feet. To the southwest a lead, 4 feet wide and 2 feet high changing to 2 feet wide and 6 feet high, continues for 50 feet, where it curves south. It is reported to continue for a considerable distance. The last 25 feet is occupied by a pool of water. The passage is well decorated. Another passage leads south from the entrance for 35 feet and is 4 to 5 feet wide and 4 feet high. A pool of water occupies the last 10 feet. Simms Cave is in the Union (?) Limestone, Greenbrier Series.

SINKS OF SINKING CREEK 37°57'14" N.; 80°30'05" W.
Clintonville Quadrangle.   37°57'05" N.; 80°30'12" W.

The "Sinks" are located on Sinking Creek, 1¼ miles southwest of Williamsburg (elevation, 2150 feet). Sinking Creek flows under a spur of Brushy Ridge in a passage 750 feet long trending N. 40° E. The south entrance, in a cliff 100 feet high, is an opening 80 feet wide and 40 feet high. For 20 feet inside this entrance the passage is piled high with trees, driftwood, and lumber brought by flood waters. The cave retains a width of 80 feet for most of the way but the ceiling height gradually lowers until the north half is 20 feet high. The passage is floored by large flat slabs of rock that have fallen from the ceiling. The north entrance, at the end of a long ravine and in an escarpment 150 feet high, is 50 feet wide and 20 feet high. The east wall of the passage has large flowstone cascades near the south entrance. Sinking Creek flows beneath the rock slabs along the west side of the passage and is visible near the north end only. Traverse of the cave is best made from south to north keeping close to the east wall at the south and the center for the remainder of the passage. The "Sinks" are in the Patton Limestone, Greenbrier Series, which dips 30° W. and strikes N. 40° E.

SPENCER CAVE 37°59'04" N.; 80°23'18" W. White Sulphur
Springs Quadrangle.

On the south side of the valley of Spring Creek, ¾ mile west of U. S. 219, a large cave entrance opens in a low escarpment. The opening, which is visible from the Esty road, is at an elevation of 1975 feet. The entrance is 30 feet wide and 50 feet high and is rectangular in shape. Just in from the entrance is a passage extending to the west for 100 feet ending as a crawl over rimstone pools. To the east at the entrance is a small sinuous crawlway high above the level of the entrance. The cave is in the Union Limestone, Greenbrier Series.

TAYLOR CAVE NO. 1 38°01'12" N.; 80°19'12" W. Lobelia
Quadrangle.

A large cave opening lies 100 yards north of the county road, 0.9 mile southwest of Julia (elevation, 2050 feet). The

Plate XVIII.—South Entrance, Sinks of Sinking Creek. (Photo by Wm. E. Davies).

entrance, in a low escarpment, is 50 feet wide, 30 feet long, and 15 feet high. A small hole, 1 foot high and 5 feet wide, is filled by a stream that flows from the cave. It is reported that the cave opens into a large passage that can be traversed when the water is low. The water from the cave flows north for 150 feet to a small opening where it sinks. The stream is probably the same as that in Norman Cave. Taylor Cave is in the Patton Limestone, Greenbrier Series.

TAYLOR CAVE NO. 2 37°49'19" N.; 80°27'13" W. White Sulphur Springs Quadrangle.

Taylor Cave No. 2 is 1.5 miles northwest of Lewisburg at an elevation of 2100 feet. The cave is a small water passage with sections large enough for walking and others requiring crawling. The cave is 100 yards or more long. It is in the Patton (?) Limestone, Greenbrier Series.

TAYLOR FALLS CAVE 37°49'34" N.; 80°28'15" W. White Sulphur Springs Quadrangle.

This cave lies one mile southeast of Central School at an elevation of 2000 feet. It is a pit 45 feet deep into which a small stream flows. No passage is open at the base. The pit is in the Patton Limestone, Greenbrier Series.

THORNBURY CAVE 37°52'55" N.; 80°33'30" W. Clinton-ville Quadrangle.

Hughart Creek sinks 1½ miles south of the settlement of Hughart, ¼ mile north of U. S. 60. A passage with a room 50 feet wide and 75 feet long can be traversed for 100 feet at this point. A large pond, 50 feet in diameter, occupies much of the room. The entrance is partially blocked by driftwood. Thornbury Cave is in the Patton (?) Limestone, Greenbrier Series.

THRASHER CAVE 38°00'56" N.; 80°27'46" W. Lobelia Quadrangle.

Thrasher Cave is ¼ mile southeast of Trout P. O. at the base of a low ridge (elevation, 2250 feet). It is reported to be similar in shape but smaller than Bob Gee Cave. The entrance is blocked by a rock fall from a quarry blast. A small stream flows into the cave. The cave is in the Alderson Limestone, Greenbrier Series.

TOWER CAVE 37°56'42" N.; 80°31'00" W. Clintonville Quadrangle.

Tower Cave is 0.7 mile southeast of Cornstalk and 500 feet south across a ravine from Judys Cave (elevation, 2300 feet). The cave is a single passage, 100 feet long, with a room containing a large chimney, 25 feet in diameter and 75 feet high. A small stream enters the cave. Tower Cave is in the Alderson Limestone, Greenbrier Series.

TUCKWILLER CAVE 37°52'32" N.; 80°30'15" W. Clintonville Quadrangle.

An impressive cave opening is located 1.1 miles northwest of Richlands on the Richlands-Williamsburg road. The cave, 10 feet high and 20 feet wide, is open for 20 feet where it is plugged by debris. A small stream flows in. The cave is in the Alderson Limestone, Greenbrier Series.

U. S. 219 CAVE 37°58'43" N.; 80°22'38" W. White Sulphur Springs Quadrangle.

On the east side of U. S. Highway 219, 1.4 miles southwest of Renick, is a small cave opening with a stream flowing out (elevation, 2040 feet). The passage is too low to permit traverse except in very dry weather. The length of the cave is not known. It is in the Pickaway Limestone, Greenbrier Series.

WALTON CAVE 38°01'12" N.; 80°22'23" W. Lobelia Quadrangle.

Walton Cave is on the north side of Spring Creek, ¾ mile northeast of Esty (elevation, 2000 feet). The cave heads northwest as a passage, large enough to permit walking, with occasional long rooms. At the rear the cave is reduced to a crawlway. The cave is 750 feet long and a stream flows out of the entrance. A number of formations are at the rear. The cave is in the Alderson Limestone, Greenbrier Series.

WATER CAVE 37°59'18" N.; 80°28'56" W. White Sulphur Springs Quadrangle.

Two hundred feet west of the Williamsburg-Trout road, 1½ miles north of Williamsburg, is a low, water-filled cave opening. A passage, too low for entry because a dam raised the water-level, heads west from the entrance. The cave is in the Union (?) Limestone, Greenbrier Series.

WILSON BLUFF CAVE 37°44'20" N.; 80°34'28" W. Alderson Quadrangle.

This cave is in a cut on the Chesapeake & Ohio Railway, ¾ mile west of Frazier (elevation, 1620 feet). The entrance, two large openings, 20 feet wide and 10 feet high, quickly narrows to a small passage of considerable length. The cave is known also as Figgs Hole. Figgs was a negro trackwalker who used the cave as a watch station before shanties were built along the railroad. The cave is in the Union Limestone, Greenbrier Series.

WIND (WINDY MOUTH) CAVE 37°43'24" N.; 80°32'00" W. Alderson Quadrangle.

This is apparently the second largest cave in West Virginia but little study has been given it. The cave is difficult to reach as it is at the south end of the river bend two miles south (by river) from Fort Spring. The entrance is a small opening high on a prominent cliff (elevation, 1750 feet). The first 100 yards of the cave is three feet or less in height and 5 to 10 feet wide. Much of it is wet. Beyond this the cave trends southwest for over 5000 feet as a passage 5 to 25 feet wide and 6 to 25 feet high. A stream follows this passage throughout most of its length. Three thousand feet from the entrance a side passage extends over 5000 feet to the west. This passage is 5 feet wide and up to 14 feet high. In several places it is reduced to a crawlway; four waterfalls are along this passage. Gypsum crystals are common in the last 1500 feet of the passage. Several long side passages open from the main passage and the waterfall passage. Most of these openings are small but apparently extend for great distances. The cave is in the Hillsdale Limestone, Greenbrier Series.

YORKS CAVE 37°47'30" N.; 80°27'38" W. White Sulphur Springs Quadrangle.

The entrance to Yorks Cave is a pit, 20 feet deep, located ¼ mile southwest of Lewisburg, ¼ mile west of the country road that is an extension of Court Street. At the base of the pit is a passage 75 feet long. Yorks Cave is in the Sinks Grove Limestone, Greenbrier Series.

Twenty additional caves have been reported in Greenbrier County but details of them are lacking. They are located as follows:

Bethel School Cave—⅜ mile northeast of Bethel School.

Coffmans Well Cave—1.8 miles west of Frankford across road from Coffmans Cave.

Fort Spring Cave No. 1—0.6 mile southeast of Fort Spring above the western tunnel of the C. & O. Railroad. (This cave may be the same as Carlisle Cave.)

Fort Spring Cave No. 2—Small cave ⅜ mile east of Windy Mouth, south bank of Greenbrier River.

Fort Spring Cave No. 3—Small cave ½ mile east of Windy Mouth, south bank of Greenbrier River.

Fort Spring Cave No. 4—Small cave entrance 1 mile east of Perry School, 2 miles south of Fort Spring.

Frog Hollow Cave is reported on the farm of Allen Judy, Raider Valley, between Asbury and Alta. The small entrance which requires stooping leads to a passage 5 feet wide, 8 feet high. The passage has a slope of 5% downwards for several hundred feet ending in a small pool of water.

Harrah Cave—at Hughart, ⅛ mile southeast of school.

Limestone Cliff Cave—½ mile east of Maxwelton at west end of a large sink.

Longanacre Sheep Pit—This pit is 2½ miles southwest of Fort Spring, ¼ mile west of Perry School. Entrance is in a sinkhole; pit is 20 foot drop to room 160 feet long; sheep bones and carcasses cover floor. A pit 25 feet deep is in the floor of the room.

Longanacre Water Cave—This cave is 3 miles southwest of Fort Spring, ½ mile west of Perry School; entrance is 10 feet wide, 20 feet high with a stream flowing in; 12 foot drop 150 feet in; total length of passage 600 feet on several levels; much debris on upper levels; cave flooded during wet seasons.

Millers Caves—2.3 miles southeast of Sunlight; two small caves.

Poorfarm (Greenbrier) Cave No. 2—0.2 mile south of Poorfarm (Greenbrier) Cave.

Powells Lid Cave—Near York Cave; 18-foot drop to a sloping floor.

Rocky Hollow Pit—This pit is on the Monroe-Greenbrier county line 3 miles southwest of Fort Spring on the southeast side of Rocky Hollow. Entrance is 3 feet wide and 6 feet long beyond which is a pit 35 feet deep to a short slope and another pit; total depth is 55 feet.

Spur Cave—3 miles north of Frankford between railroad and Spring Creek. Two entrances in creek bank. Cave is very wet.

Wilsons Cave—2.5 miles west of Lewisburg, ⅛ mile west of Milligan Creek.

Wilsons Cave No. 2—2.5 miles west of Lewisburg, ⅛ mile west of Milligan Creek.

Windmill Cave—1.1 miles south of Trout P. O.

Cave 1.8 miles south of Williamsburg.

Pit 1 mile southwest of Lewisburg, 20 feet deep.

Cave 1.6 miles north of Lewisburg in east edge of sink; low entrance.

Cave 2 miles northwest of Lewisburg, ¼ mile east of U. S. Highway 60; low stream entrance.

Narrow vertical fissure, 1 mile north of Lewisburg.

Reported saltpeter cave ¼ mile north of Sunlight, 2.2 miles northeast of Williamsburg.

A narrow slit opening in a pasture 2 miles south of Fort Spring and 1000 feet west of the Fort Spring-Sinks Grove Road connects with a 25 foot pit; the pit is blocked at the base.

Several large cavern passages and galleries containing considerable quantities of cavern fill have been intersected in mining limestone at the Acme Mine on the Greenbrier River south of Fort Spring.

HAMPSHIRE COUNTY

Although the Silurian-Devonian limestones are of considerable thickness and outcrop over large areas of Hampshire County, only eight small caves are reported in them. Three of the caves are in the Tonoloway Limestone, two in the Ridgeley Sandstone, and one each in the Keyser Limestone and Wills Creek Formation. A shelter type of cave is developed in the Marcellus Shale.

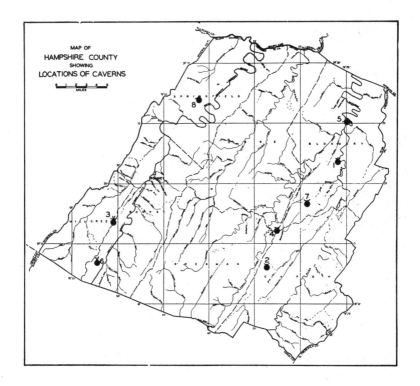

Figure 24.—Hampshire County Caves

1. Castle Rock.	5. Hoagland Indian Caves.
2. Cooper Mountain.	6. Mills (Long Knob).
3. Fairview Mountain Pit.	7. Milslagle.
4. Hanging Rock Shelter.	8. Springfield.

CASTLE ROCK CAVE 39°21'44" N.; 78°26'04" W. Capon Bridge Quadrangle.

A small crawlway is reported to lie in a hollow 1.3 miles south of Castle Rock, 1000 feet south of Cacapon River (elevation, 800 feet). It is probably in the Wills Creek Formation. The cave was not located during field work.

COOPER MOUNTAIN CAVE 39°13'00" N.; 78°33'38" W. Wardensville Quadrangle.

This cave is on Cooper Mountain, ¾ mile west of Millbrook at an elevation of 1450 feet. The opening is a small crawlway which connects with a passage large enough to permit walking. The cave is 100 yards long and is in the Tonoloway Limestone.

FAIRVIEW MOUNTAIN PIT 39°16'44" N.; 78°59'30" W. Keyser Quadrangle.

A pit is reported to exist on the south side of the summit of Fairview Mountain (elevation, 2000 feet). It is about 50 feet deep and opens into a room at the base. Saltpeter is supposed to have been dug from it during the War Between the States. The cave is in the Keyser (?) Limestone.

HANGING ROCK SHELTER 39°16'04" N.; 78°32'32" W. Hanging Rock Quadrangle.

At the east end of the gap at Hanging Rock is a prominent cave opening. It is 50 feet north of U. S. 50 on the west side of the stream that flows in Henderson Hollow (elevation, 950 feet). The shelter is 18 feet in diameter and 15 feet high. The floor is covered to a depth of 16 inches by white sand. Several test holes dug in the sand revealed no archeological material although the cave is an ideal shelter type. It is in a white lime-cemented sandstone in the lower part of the Ridgeley which dips 38° N.W. and strikes N. 70° E.

HOAGLAND INDIAN CAVES 39°25'04" N.; 78°25'00" W. Capon Bridge Quadrangle.

A series of shelter caves open in a bluff on the north side of Cacapon River, 1.1 miles northeast of Forks of Cacapon (elevation, 750 feet). The shelters, in beds of shale, vary from small overhangs to openings 20 feet wide, 6 feet high and 8 feet long. There are seven shelters, of which three are large enough to be of interest. Indians used the shelters for habitation and smoke stains still mark the ceilings. Archeological material has been recovered in large quantities, but no systematic work has been performed. The caves are in the Marcellus Shale which has large concretionary structures. In weathering the spheroidal layers of shale drop out forming shallow recesses. The Indians enlarged the larger recesses into small shelters. In one case a chimney was cut in the ceiling.

MILLS (LONG KNOB) CAVE 39°13′32″ N.; 78°52′12″ W. Moorefield Quadrangle.

A pit is located 0.4 mile north of Long Knob, ¾ mile southwest of Glebe Station (elevation, 1300 feet). The pit is 50 feet deep and opens into a channel. The cave has not been explored. It is in the Tonoloway Limestone.

MILSLAGLE CAVE 39°18′20″ N.; 78°29′19″ W. Capon Bridge Quadrangle.

Milslagle Cave is at the northeast edge of a large doline lying between Cooper Mountain and Timber Ridge, 3 miles west of Capon Bridge (elevation, 1260 feet). The cave can be entered for 15 feet and is a small crawlway heading into breakdown. Maxwell and Swisher [24] report that William Offutt traversed the cave for several hundred feet in 1897. Several small vertical pits, as well as a trough-like sink that receives the drainage of the doline, lie near Milslagle Cave. The water that drains into the doline resurges 2 miles northeast along the west side of Cold Stream in a series of large springs. The cave is in the Tonoloway Limestone.

SPRINGFIELD CAVE 39°27′00″ N.; 78°41′04″ W. Hanging Rock Quadrangle.

Local residents report a small crawlway, less than 50 feet long, at the south end of Valley Mountain, ½ mile east of Springfield (elevation, 800 feet). The cave is in the top of the Ridgeley Sandstone.

---

[24] Maxwell, Hu, and Swisher, H. L. History of Hampshire County, West Virginia: A. B. Boughner, Morgantown, p. 418, 1897.

HARDY COUNTY

Two major groups of limestones outcrop in Hardy County. The Silurian-Devonian limestones outcrop in bands along both sides of Patterson Creek Mountain and Elkhorn Mountain in the western part of the county. On the eastern side they out-crop along Cove Mountain, Warden Ridge, Breakneck Ridge,

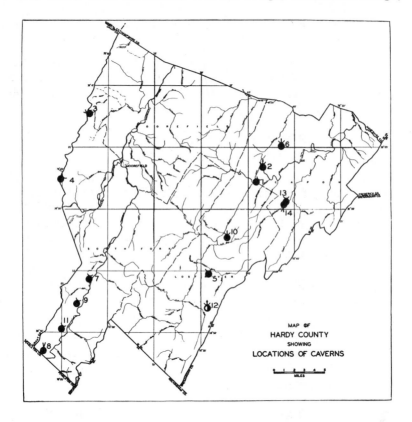

Figure 25.—Hardy County Caves

1. Baker.
2. Baker Quarry.
3. Carpenters Pit.
4. Charles Knob.
5. Cove Mountain.
6. Dyers.
7. Green Hollow.

8. Hinkle School Pit.
9. Joshua.
10. Mill Gap.
11. Randall.
12. Seldon.
13. Thorny Bottom.
14. Thorny Bottom Pit.

Long Mountain, and North Mountain. They form the valley floor and hillsides in Thorny Bottom.

The Chambersburg Limestone outcrops along the Adams Run Anticline at the headwaters of Upper Cove Run.

Of the 13 caves in Hardy County, 7 are in the limestones of the Helderberg Group, 4 are in the Tonoloway, and one each in the Chambersburg Limestone and Ridgeley Sandstone.

BAKER CAVE 39°02′11″ N.; 78°44′05″ W. Wardensville Quadrangle.

Baker Cave is on the east side of Lost River, 0.7 mile southeast of Baker (elevation, 1450 feet). The cave is a single passage, large enough to permit walking, that extends 200 feet to the south. The cave is in the Keyser (?) Limestone.

BAKER QUARRY CAVE 39°03′20″ N.; 78°43′22″ W. Wardensville Quadrangle.

A small cave, opening at road level, opens into a bank at the east end of the large quarry along West Virginia Highway 55 at the gap through Warden Ridge (elevation, 1280 feet). A large stream flows out of the cave but the passage is blocked by loose rock just inside the entrance. It is in the base of the Tonoloway Limestone.

CARPENTERS PIT 39°07′36″ N.; 79°02′04″ W. Greenland Gap Quadrangle.

A vertical shaft lies at the head of Toombs Hollow on Patterson Creek Mountain, 2½ miles southeast of Forman (elevation, 1800 feet). The pit is 2 to 10 feet in diameter and is 110 feet deep. No passage exists at the base. The pit is in the Tonoloway Limestone.

COVE MOUNTAIN CAVE 38°54′38″ N.; 78°49′15″ W. Orkney Springs Quadrangle.

This cave is on Cove Mountain, ¾ mile south of Lower Cove Run, 1.5 miles southeast of Lost City (elevation, 2150 feet). The entrance is through a vertical shaft, 6 feet in diameter and 12 feet deep, which opens into two rooms about 15 feet in length and width. The cave is in the New Scotland (?) Limestone.

DYERS CAVE 39°05′00″ N.; 78°41′26″ W. Wardensville Quadrangle.

Dyers Cave is in the valley between Warden Ridge and Pine Ridge, 3.15 miles northeast of McCauley (elevation, 1700 feet). The entrance, in a valley sink, heads southwest. It is 10 feet high and 16 feet wide, opening into a passage 4 feet wide and 6 feet high. The cave consists of a series of passages 2 to 6 feet wide and 3 to 10 feet high which alternately trend southwest and southeast. There are a number of small drops in the passage and the average slope of the floor is 15° down from the entrance. Three hundred and seventy-five feet from the entrance a stream flowing southwest joins the passage. From here the cave is on two levels. A dry passage is parallel to and 15 feet above the stream passage which lies on the north. The passages, 3 feet high, 2 to 4 feet wide, are connected at several points and slope 5° to 8° in this section. The passages are blocked by clay fill and a small pool to the ceiling 675 feet from the entrance. A number of side passages, clay filled or too narrow to permit traverse branch from the main passages and apparently form a maze which is rectangular in plan. The cave, in the Tonoloway Limestone, which dips 28° W. and strikes N. 30° E., follows joints at S. 30° W. and S. 40° E. A subordinate joint running due east modifies the trend in places.

The Moorefield (W. Va.) Examiner (issue of April 15, 1942) indicates in an article on Dyers Cave that saltpeter was mined in the cave during the latter part of the eighteenth century. No evidence remains to indicate such an operation.

GREEN HOLLOW CAVE 38°54′20″ N.; 70°02′00″ W. Petersburg Quadrangle.

Green Hollow is one mile northeast of Brake on the west side of South Fork. A cave consisting of two small rooms is developed at the base of sandstone cliffs on the north side of the entrance to the hollow (elevation, 1060 feet). The cave is in the Ridgeley Sandstone.

HINKLE SCHOOL PIT 38°48'30" N.; 79°07'02" W. Petersburg Quadrangle.

One hundred yards south of Hinkle School on South Fork Mountain, at an elevation of 2075 feet, is a vertical pit over 100 feet deep. It is filled partially with logs and trash. Local residents report that a stream flowing at the base of the pit resurges in Trumbo Gap, one mile south. The pit is in the Keyser (?) Limestone.

JOSHUA CAVE 38°52'16" N.; 79°03'24" W. Petersburg Quadrangle.

Joshua Cave is in a large hollow on the east side of South Fork Mountain, 1.6 miles southwest of Brake (elevation, 2100 feet). The cave is a series of small muddy crawlways a couple hundred feet long. The cave is in the top of the Helderberg Series.

MILL GAP CAVE 38°57'42" N.; 78°47'12" W. Orkney Springs Quadrangle.

This cave is on the east side of Hommon Mountain, 1¼ miles northeast of Lost River (elevation, 1750 feet). The entrance is a small sloping crawlway that drops steeply to a room. The cave extends north for about 500 feet as a series of rooms, 10 feet wide, 9 feet high, alternating with crawlways and narrow fissure passages. A stream flows for a short distance along the passage and drops down a narrow crevice, 10 feet deep, 100 feet from the entrance. The cave is in the Tonoloway Limestone.

RANDALL CAVE 38°50'16" N.; 79°05'00" W. Petersburg Quadrangle.

Randall Cave is on the east side of South Fork Mountain, ⅝ mile southwest of Peru (elevation, 1600 feet). The cave is a crawlway 400 feet long that has one room, 20 feet in diameter and 20 feet high, developed near the entrance. The floor and walls are wet clay. A pit, 20 feet deep, leads to a lower level that has not been explored. The entrance clogs periodically with surface wash and it is necessary to clear it out to gain entrance. The cave is in the New Scotland (?) Limestone.

SELDON CAVE 38°52′00″ N.; 78°49′25″ W. Orkney Springs Quadrangle.

This cave is ½ mile northeast of Basore, on the east side of the road north to Lower Cove Run (elevation, 1850 feet). A spring-house has been built over the entrance which is in a low ledge of limestone 100 feet east of the road. A passage heads northeast and east for 178 feet. Near the entrance it is a wide crawlway for a short distance which opens into a passage 4 to 6 feet high and 10 feet wide. A short side passage heads north 75 feet from the entrance. A large stream flows through the cave but clay banks make it possible to traverse the cave without wading except at the entrance where the water covers the floor to a depth of a foot. At the end the passage is blocked by a siphon. The water from the cave is the source of the north segment of Upper Cove Run.

The geologic map of Hardy County indicates that the cave lies in the Martinsburg Formation. The limestone exposed at the entrance to the cave, however, should be assigned to the Chambersburg.

THORNY BOTTOM CAVE 39°00′34″ N.; 78°40′52″ W. Wardensville Quadrangle.

A cave is located on the west side of Thorny Bottom, 0.7 mile southwest of Shady Grove School (elevation, 1500 feet). The cave is a crawlway sloping 60° down for 35 feet to a 10-foot drop which opens into a room 15 feet in diameter and 10 feet high. Three small wells up to 30 feet deep and clogged at the base, open in the floor of the room. The cave is in the Keyser Limestone.

THORNY BOTTOM PIT 39°00′27″ N.; 78°41′08″ W. Wardensville Quadrangle.

On the west side of Thorny Bottom, one mile southwest of Shady Grove School, is a pit 50 feet deep. No opening occurs at the base. The pit is in the Keyser Limestone at an elevation of 1700 feet.

HARRISON COUNTY

Harrison County lies west of the area in which cavernous limestones outcrop and no caves large enough to warrant description have been recorded. One small shelter cave, however, is of considerable interest because of the pictographs it contains.

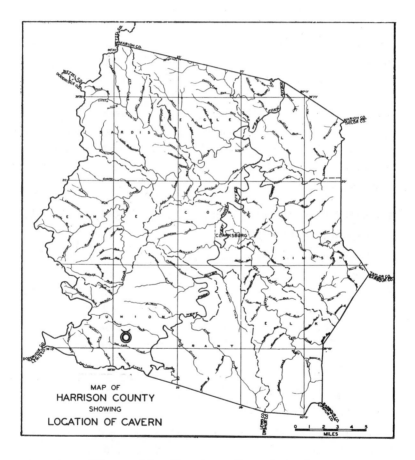

MAP OF
HARRISON COUNTY
SHOWING
LOCATION OF CAVERN

Figure 26.—Harrison County Cave

1. Indian.

INDIAN CAVE 39°10'40" N.; 80°29'00" W. Weston Quadrangle.

This small, but interesting, shelter cave is 2.3 miles west of Goodhope and 0.7 mile N.N.W. of Two Lick School. It is in a low hill on the west side of a fork of Two Lick Creek (elevation, 1180 feet.) The shelter, oval in shape, 20 feet wide and 4 to 5 feet high, extends into the hill for 12 feet. On the walls are numerous pictographs, apparently of Indian origin. The pictographs, depicting turtles, foxes, rattlesnakes, birds, fish,

Plate XIX.—Indian Cave, Two Lick Creek, Harrison County, showing Pictographs. (Photo by Wm. E. Davies).

are in two rows, 2 and 3 feet above the floor on the rear wall of the shelter. Several special symbols, including a human hand, are mixed with the animal figures. Some of the drawings were tinted with colors which are now barely discernible.

The shelter is in a soft buff-colored sandstone in the middle of the Monongahela Series.

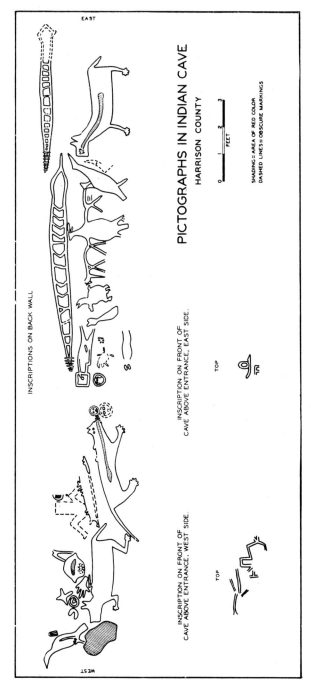

Figure 27.—Pictographs in Indian Cave.

Plate XX.—Indian Cave, Two Lick Creek, Harrison County.
(Photo by Wm. E. Davies.)

JEFFERSON COUNTY

The greater part of Jefferson County is underlain by lime-stones of the Cambrian and Ordovician Systems. Considering such extensive outcrops it is surprising that only 16 caves are reported from the county and that, with two exceptions, they are little more than small rooms or short crawlways.

BRIAR SINK 39°16′40″ N.; 77°54′20″ W. Middleway (Martinsburg) Quadrangle.

A small, vertical sink, 10 feet deep, opens into a steeply sloping passage, 3.5 miles northeast of Summit Point, 100 feet north of the Charles Town-Summit Point road (elevation, 530 feet). The passage is 20 feet long and ends in a clay fill. The cave is in the Chepultepec (?) Limestone.

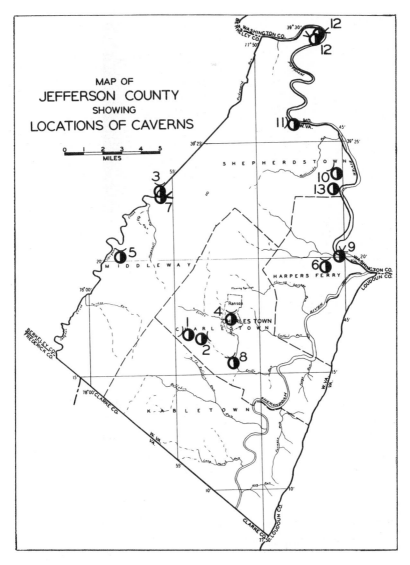

Figure 28.—Jefferson County Caves

1. Briar Sink.
2. Byrd Orchard.
3. Chapman.
4. Charles Town (Crystal Lake, Lakeland).
5. Dead Dog.
6. Ditmer Caves.
7. Duffys Cavern
8. George Washington.
9. John Browns.
10. Molers.
11. Shepherdstown Caves.
12. Terrapin Neck Caves.
13. Unnamed Caves (3).

BYRD ORCHARD CAVE 39°16′25″ N.; 77°53′20″ W. Middleway (Martinsburg) Quadrangle.

This cave is 800 feet south of the Charles Town-Summit Point road, 2 miles west of Charles Town (elevation, 540 feet). The entrance is a small hole that drops 5 feet to a low room. A passage leads 10 feet to the north and south of the room as a crawlway. The cave is in the Conococheague Limestone.

CHARLES TOWN (CRYSTAL LAKE, LAKELAND) CAVE 39°17′27″ N.; 77°51′33″ W. Charles Town (Martinsburg) Quadrangle.

This cave is in the center of Charles Town at an elevation of 510 feet. The entrance is in the cellar of a bakery and leads down 10 feet to a small passage 50 yards long. At the end of the passage is a large pool of water, 25 feet in diameter. The cave is in the Elbrook Limestone.

CHAPMAN CAVE 39°23′00″ N.; 77°55′46″ W. Martinsburg Quadrangle.

Chapman Cave is on the east side of Opequon Creek at the boundary line between Berkeley and Jefferson Counties (elevation, 480 feet). The entrance, at the base of a low cliff 50 feet east of the county road, opens into a sinuous crawlway, 40 feet long. The passage enlarges to a width of 5 feet and a height of 5 to 15 feet trending south with offsets to the west. The cave ends in a room 10 to 15 feet wide, 20 to 25 feet high, and 60 feet long with flowstone and columns along the walls. The cave is in the Chambersburg Limestone.

DEAD DOG CAVE 39°20′20″ N.; 77°58′07″ W. Middleway (Martinsburg) Quadrangle.

This cave is in a low hill 2 miles southwest of Leetown, 800 yards south of Opequon Creek, at an elevation of 500 feet. The entrance, a pit, 2 feet in diameter and 15 feet deep, opens into a narrow passage, 4 to 6 feet wide and 3 to 10 feet high, extending 250 feet to the southeast. At the end a small opening connects with the surface. A lower level in the form of a crawlway with a stream develops in the last 200 feet of the cave. Seventy feet from the entrance a side passage 50 feet long leads west dropping vertically 30 feet to the lower level.

The cave continues north of the entrance for 35 feet in a room, 7 feet wide and 7 to 15 feet high. The entrance pit has been used by a local dog catcher as a dumping place for dead dogs but the carcasses, which at one time were quite an obstacle to overcome, are now little more than piles of bones.

Dead Dog Cave, in the Chambersburg Limestone, is developed along joints at N. 40° E. and N. 70° W.

DITMER CAVES 39°19'55" N.; 77°46'18" W. Charles Town (Martinsburg) Quadrangle.

On the west side of the county road leading northeast from U. S. 340, one mile west of Bolivar, are three large sinkholes (elevation, 400 feet). The sinks are 400 yards west of the

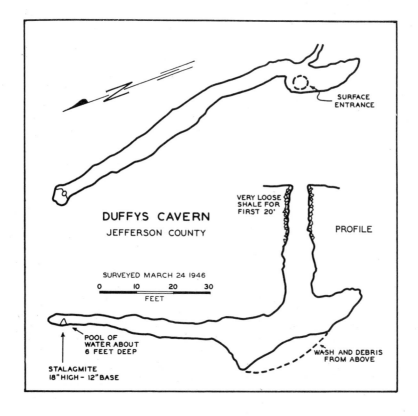

Figure 29.—Duffys Cavern.

county road and ¾ mile north of U. S. 340. At the base of the sinks are small rooms that apparently connect via small passages as a small stream flows north through them and resurges 800 yards to the north. The caves are in the Waynesboro Formation.

DUFFYS CAVERN 39°22'50." N.; 77°55'50" W. Martinsburg Quadrangle.

A pit, 40 feet deep, lies in the center of an orchard 200 yards east of Opequon Creek, ⅛ mile south of the Berkeley-Jefferson county line (elevation, 530 feet). The pit is 6 feet in diameter with a passage at the base 3 to 8 feet high and 4 feet wide, heading N. 10° W. for 60 feet. The cave is in the Chambersburg Limestone.

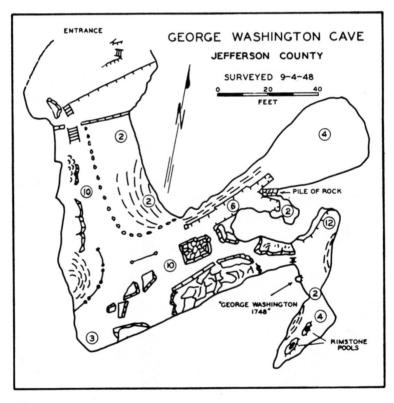

Figure 30.—George Washington Cave.

GEORGE WASHINGTON CAVE 39°15′25″ N.; 77°51′40″ W.
Charles Town (Martinsburg) Quadrangle.

This cave is 2.3 miles south of Charles Town, ¾ mile southeast of U. S. 340, and 100 yards south of Evitts Run (elevation, 460 feet). The entrance, in a shallow sink 100 feet north of the county road along Evitts Run, opens into a broad chamber heading S. 20° E., 40 feet long and 30 feet wide. The ceiling follows the bedding-planes, being 10 feet high on the west and 2 feet high on the east side. The chamber divides into two smaller ones with ceiling heights of 4 to 8 feet. The one on the southeast has a small alcove on the east side, 5 feet above the floor, on the walls of which is George Washington's signature, dated 1748. Mr. Washington visited the cave during the first of his western survey journeys.

The cave was formerly opened for commercial purposes and remnants of iron railings and electric wires are scattered about the floor. The crushed stone pathways are still in good condition.

Plate XXI.—George Washington's Signature in George Washington Cave. (Photo by Wm. E. Davies).

The cave, in the Elbrook Limestone (strike, N. 10° E., dip, 34° E.), is along joints at N. 10° E. (vertical to beds), N. 80° W. (vertical to beds), and N. 30° W. (vertical).

JOHN BROWNS CAVE 39°20′01″ N.; 77°45′06″ W. Charles Town (Martinsburg) Quadrangle.

The entrance to John Browns Cave is at track level of the Baltimore and Ohio Railroad, 300 yards east of the mouth of Elks Run (elevation, 330 feet). The entrance, 7 feet wide and 4 feet high, after 40 feet, opens into a crevice passage, 4 to 6 feet wide, 10 to 30 feet high, extending south for 225 feet. The passage ends in a clay bank at the top of which is a small crawlway leading steeply upwards. The cave continues on the east as a stream passage, 3 to 15 feet high, 10 to 20 feet wide, 250 feet long. At the rear the ceiling descends into a small pool blocking further traverse. In dry seasons the siphon can be passed by descending a shoot for 10 feet to a series of small rooms. The stream flowing through the passage is offset beneath the entrance passage at the small slot connecting the two passages.

John Brown is supposed to have used the cave to store arms in preparing his raid on Harpers Ferry.

John Browns Cave, in the Tomstown Dolomite which strikes N. 30° E., dips, 68° E., is developed along the bedding-planes, modified by a joint trending north-south.

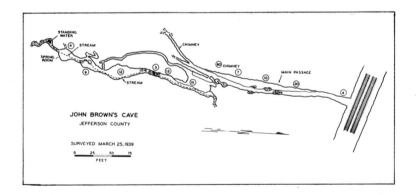

Figure 31.—John Browns Cave.

Plate XXII.—John Browns Cave. (Photo by Wm. E. Davies).

MOLERS CAVE 39°23′38″ N.; 77°45′20″ W. Shepherdstown (Martinsburg) Quadrangle.

Molers Cave is 800 yards southeast of Bethesda Church (Moler Crossroads) at an elevation of 415 feet. The entrance, 8 feet high and 15 feet wide, at the junction of two shallow ravines, opens into a sewer passage of similar dimensions 60 feet long. Rolls of fence wire and other debris have been carried into this part of the cave. The cave continues northeast for 1500 feet as a passage 5 to 15 feet high and 4 to 10 feet wide. For most of this distance it is on two levels although the lower level is not large enough to permit continuous traverse. The levels are connected at a number of places by vertical pits. The upper level is blocked by clay 400 feet from the entrance. Two hundred feet from the end of the cave is a large room, 135 feet long, 20 to 30 feet wide, and 6 to 20 feet high. The cave ends in a pool and siphon.

Molers Cave is in the base of the Elbrook Limestone with a strike of N. 20° E. and dip of 10° E. It is developed along vertical joints at N. 20° E., N. 70° E., and due north. Torrents of water flood much of the cave, including the upper

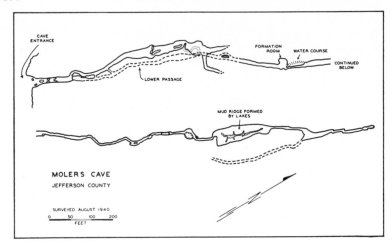

Figure 32.—Molers Cave.

level, to the ceiling and caution should be exercised in entering it in rainy weather.

A small cave lies 400 yards northeast of Molers Cave and consists of a short crawlway leading to a small, low room. It is in the Elbrook Limestone.

SHEPHERDSTOWN CAVES 39°25'40" N.; 77°47'30" W.
Shepherdstown (Martinsburg) Quadrangle.

Several short passages, either crawlways or crevices, less than 100 feet in length, open into the cliffs along the Potomac east of Shepherdstown. The passages are in the Elbrook and Conococheague Limestones.

TERRAPIN NECK CAVES 39°29' N.; 77°46' W. Shepherdstown (Martinsburg) Quadrangle.

Several small, pit-like openings lie in the fields at the northeast end of Terrapin Neck. They are now filled with fence wire and no data are available as to their size. They are in the Conococheague Limestone.

Three unnamed caves are reported near Molers Crossroad. In an old quarry 1 mile southeast of Molers Crossroad is a small passageway 40 feet long. One thousand feet northwest of this cave are two large sinks. In the smaller sink is a shaft 40 feet deep. A crawlway leads down from the shaft at a point

20 feet down. One and one-half miles southeast of Molers Crossroad in an old quarry is a passage 35 feet long which is probably a remnant of a more extensive cave. The passage has numerous speleothems. The caves are in the Waynesboro Formation.

MERCER COUNTY

The Ordovician limestones outcrop in Mercer County along East River Mountain from Bluefield to the Narrows. The limestones dip steeply to the east and are bounded on the west by the St. Clair Fault. Six caves are developed in the lime-

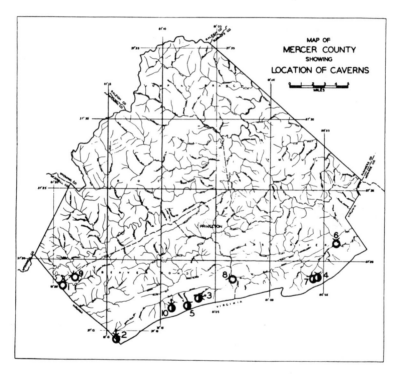

Figure 33.—Mercer County Caves

1. Abbs Valley.
2. Beaver Pond.
3. Big Spring.
4. Caldwell.
5. Dyepot.
6. Hales Gap.
7. Honacker.
8. Ingleside.
9. Nemours.
10. Thompson School.

stones. The Greenbrier Series, on the west side of the St. Clair Fault, parallels the Ordovician Limestone outcrops. The Abbs Valley Anticline, trending northeast through Nemours, brings the Greenbrier Series to the surface along the southwest part of the county. Four caves lie in the Greenbrier Limestone in Mercer County.

ABBS VALLEY CAVE 37°17′56″ N.; 81°19′04″ W. Bramwell Quadrangle.

This cave is on the south side of the creek, 0.9 mile west of Nemours, near the West Virginia-Virginia State line (elevation, 2350 feet). The entrance, in a shallow sink, opens into a passage 1500 feet long. For most of the way the passage is large enough to permit walking and only short sections require crawling. The passage enlarges to form small rooms in several places. A stream flows through the cave.

Abbs Valley Cave is in the lower portion of the Union Limestone at the crest of the Abbs Valley Anticline.

BEAVER POND CAVE 37°14′20″ N.; 81°14′00″ W. Bluefield Quadrangle.

At Beaver Pond Spring, on the West Virginia-Virginia State line, 2 miles S.S.W. of Bluefield, is the entrance to a cave (elevation, 2500 feet). The cave, reported to be quite large, extends south for over 1000 feet and passes into the State of Virginia. A large stream flows from the cave and is a source of water for the City of Bluefield. The cave is in the Stones River Limestone which dips 35° to 40° S.E.

BIG SPRING CAVE 37°17′26″ N.; 81°06′30″ W. Bluefield Quadrangle.

This cave, at the headwaters of Big Spring Branch, is 2.2 miles east of the town of Ada (elevation, 2250 feet). The cave consists of a large passage over 2000 feet long extending along the St. Clair Fault. A large stream flows through the cave and is used as source for the water supply of Bluefield by the West Virginia Water Service. Big Spring Cave is in the Beekmantown Limestone and lies along the St. Clair Fault.

CALDWELL CAVE 37°18′54″ N.; 80°55′38″ W. Narrows Quadrangle.

Caldwell Cave lies 1.6 miles southeast of Pigeon Creek School, in a saddle on a spur of East River Mountain (elevation, 2270 feet). The cave is reported to be a large passage in the Stones River Limestone.

DYEPOT CAVE 37°16′52″ N.; 81°07′45″ W. Bluefield Quadrangle.

Dyepot Cave is at the head of Dyepot Branch, 1½ miles southeast of Ada (elevation, 2550 feet). The entrance, in a small sink on the north side of the road along East River Mountain, opens into a passage 100 yards long and large enough to permit walking. The cave is in the Stones River Limestone.

HALES GAP CAVE 37°21′12″ N.; 80°53′45″ W. Narrows Quadrangle.

Hales Gap Cave is in a limestone ledge on the Norfolk and Western Railway, 0.6 mile northwest of Wills Station (elevation, 1700 feet). The cave extends southwest for 300 yards, consisting of a large passage with minor side passages. The cave, in the Alderson Limestone, Greenbrier Series, is on the flank of an overturned fold dipping 45° S.E.

HONACKER CAVE 37°18′48″ N.; 80°55′42″ W. Narrows Quadrangle.

Honacker Cave lies at the head of the west fork of Big Spring Branch, 1.3 miles southeast of Pigeon Creek School (elevation, 2300 feet). The cave is reported to be a large passage extending over 1000 feet in the Stones River Limestone.

INGLESIDE CAVE 37°18′40″ N.; 81°03′23″ W. Bluefield Quadrangle.

In a limestone ledge on the west side of East River, ¼ mile southwest of Ingleside (elevation, 2000 feet), is a large cave extending southwest for 2000 feet. The passages are large enough to permit walking and are developed in the base of the Greenbrier Series which is overturned, dipping 60° S.E.

NEMOURS CAVE 37°18′42″ N.; 81°18′00″ W. Bramwell Quadrangle.

This cave is 0.7 mile north of Nemours (elevation, 2350 feet). The entrance, in a small hollow, opens into a passage 100 yards long. Crawlways alternate with sections large enough to permit walking. The cave, in the top of the Union Limestone, Greenbrier Series, is at the crest of the Abbs Valley Anticline.

A deep vertical pit lies near the cave. No passage is reported at the base of the pit.

THOMPSON SCHOOL CAVE 37°16′30″ N.; 81°08′42″ W. Bluefield Quadrangle.

At Thompson School, on East River Mountain, 4 miles east of Bluefield (elevation, 2500 feet), is a large cave opening out of which a large stream flows. The cave is a single passage over 2000 feet long, averaging 30 to 40 feet high and wide. The passage is occupied by the stream which flows 1,000,000 gallons a day. It is used by the West Virginia Water Service as a part of the water supply of Bluefield. The cave is in the Stones River Limestone.

MINERAL COUNTY

Seven caves are known in Mineral County. One of these is in the Greenbrier Limestone which forms a narrow band along the east side of Allegheny Front. The six other caves are in the Silurian-Devonian limestones which outcrop along Knobly Mountain, the southern part of Patterson Creek Mountain, and Patterson Creek Ridge. The dip in the Greenbrier is slight and to the west but it is interrupted by minor flexures. In the Silurian-Devonian outcrops the dips are steep.

HIGH ROCKS FISSURE CAVE 39°28′05″ N.; 78°56′17″ W. Keyser Quadrangle.

This cave is in an escarpment on the west side of the summit of Rock Hill, 3 miles northeast of Keyser (elevation, 1650 feet). The entrance, at the end of a small recess in the cliff, is an opening 4 feet wide, 10 feet high and enlarges into a fissure passage 2 to 8 feet wide, 15 to 75 feet high, extending

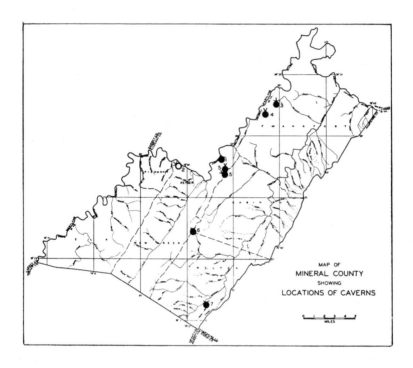

Figure 34.—Mineral County Caves

1. High Rocks Fissure.
2. Kites (Flaherty).
3. Knobly Mountain.
4. Knobly Mountain
   Vertical Shaft.
5. O'Neil Gap Pits.
6. Ridgeville.
7. Saltpeter.

S. 30° E. for 70 feet to a vertical drop of 30 feet. At the base of the drop the cave continues S. 60° W. as a fissure sloping gently upwards for over 500 feet to a point where it is too narrow for traverse. A small side passage runs parallel to the main passage 50 feet from the entrance. Flowstone and cave coral line part of the passage walls. The cave is in the top of the Coeymans Limestone and the base of the New Scotland Limestone (strike, N. 60° E., dip, 24° E.) and is along vertical joints at S. 60° W. and S. 30°E.

KITES (FLAHERTY) CAVE 30°27′35″ N.; 79°01′00″ W. Elk Garden Quadrangle.

Kites Cave is at the north end of Allegheny Front, 0.6 mile east of Powder House Run (elevation, 1510 feet). The entrance, in a steep-sided sink, 30 feet deep and 4 feet wide, is in a dense woods and a guide is necessary to locate it. The cave trends south as an irregular passage, 4 to 20 feet wide and 10 to 20 feet high, with occasional sections low enough to require crawling. It is 400 feet long and ends in a small room with a waterfall on the south side. The water flows from a crawlway, reported traversable over 100 feet, and disappears under a rock and clay bank after plunging to the floor. It does not flow in the front part of the cave. The rear part of the cave is 47 feet above the entrance sink. Kites Cave is in the top of the Greenbrier Limestone, with a strike N. 70° E. and dip 10° to 18° W. The cave is along vertical joints at N. 10° E., N. 20° W. and a joint at N. 20° E. which slopes 50° S.E.

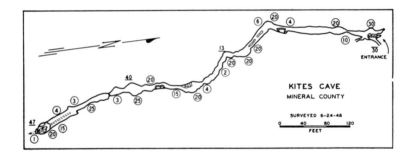

Figure 35.—Kites Cave.

KNOBLY MOUNTAIN CAVE 39°32′33″ N.; 78°50′15″ W. Frostburg Quadrangle.

This cave is in a large sink on Knobly Mountain, 1¼ miles south of Short Gap, 200 feet west of the road along the top of the mountain. The entrance is a small steep-sided depression, 20 feet deep, now filled with logs, trash, and dirt. The opening is reported to have been a vertical drop of 20 feet to a passage extending north and south, averaging 8 feet high. Several small chambers, as well as sections of crawlway, are developed along the passage. A stream flows along the floor from south to north emerging in Short Gap. Local residents report a rock fall blocked the cave close to the entrance in recent years. The cave is in the Tonoloway Limestone.

Several vertical shafts are developed in this section of Knobly Mountain in the Tonoloway Limestone. None are reported to open into caves.

O'NEIL GAP PITS 39°27′17″ N.; 78°55′55″ W. Keyser Quadrangle.

Several small pits are located along the summit of Knobly Mountain on the west side of O'Neil Gap. The largest, 4 feet in diameter and 60 feet deep, is on the northwest side of the gap (elevation, 1700 feet). The short passage at the base of the pit was used for storage of moonshine liquor at one time. On the south side of the gap are several small shafts sloping at steep angles. No passages exist at their base. The pits are in the Tonoloway Limestone.

RIDGEVILLE CAVE 39°22′08″ N.; 78°59′15″ W. Keyser Quadrangle.

Ridgeville Cave is on the north side of the gap in Knobly Mountain, 1.4 miles north of Ridgeville (elevation, 1330 feet). The entrance, a crawlway in a ledge of limestone 25 feet below an old logging road trending west through the gap, enlarges after 8 feet to a crevice sloping down for 55 feet at an angle of 60° to the west. The passage at the base extends north for 75 feet as a fissure, 4 to 20 feet wide and 30 feet high, to two pits 30 feet deep. The floor of the passage is covered by large blocks of fallen rock. At the base of the pit is a room running east-west, 100 feet long, 40 feet wide, and 20 feet high, with narrow crevice passages at each end. The east passage leads to a pit 60 feet deep which is plugged at the base.

At the base of the entrance drop a crawlway extends south for 35 feet beneath fallen rock. The end, close to the surface, is plugged by fallen rock and soil.

Ridgeville Cave is in the Keyser Limestone (strike, N. 40° E.; dip, 24° E.; pitch, 30° N.) and is developed along joints at N. 40° E. sloping 60° W. and N. 30° W. which is vertical.

SALTPETER CAVE   39°16′20″ N.; 78°57′56″ W.   Keyser Quadrangle.

Saltpeter Cave is on the north side of Cave Run, Patterson Creek Mountain, 0.8 mile east of Welton School (elevation, 1150 feet). The entrance, at the base of a prominent cliff 1000 feet from the entrance to the hollow, is 10 feet high and wide. Twenty feet from the entrance the passage reduces to a narrow slot, 4 to 8 feet high, 2 to 6 feet wide, extending north. Five hundred feet from the entrance the passage is offset 20 feet to the west and continues north as a crawlway swinging to the west and south to emerge on the cliff 100 feet to the west of the entrance. The passage is constricted at places by partitions and shelves. Saltpeter earth was dug in the cave in the first half of the nineteenth century and piles of earth remain at the entrance. An initial dated 1842 was observed at the offset 500 feet from the entrance. The cave, in the Coeymans Limestone which strikes N. 10° E., dips 20° E., is developed along a joint at N. 40° E. A strong draft of air blows in the eastern opening of the cave and out the western opening.

MONONGALIA COUNTY

Four caves are known in Monongalia County. Three are in the Greenbrier Series which is brought to the surface along Cheat River and Deckers Creek by the Chestnut Ridge Anticline. The fourth cave is in the Pottsville Series at Cooper Rock.

BEAVERHOLE, LOWER (EAGLE) CAVE   39°37′08″ N.; 79°47′50″ W. Morgantown Quadrangle.

Lower Beaver Hole Cave is on the north side of the Cheat River, 0.2 mile west of the Preston-Monongalia county line, at an elevation of 1500 feet. The entrance, directly below a high tension power line in a low ledge of limestone, is 6 feet high and 3 feet wide. The cave opens to the east as a single, high, fissure passage over 1000 feet long. The floor slopes gently downwards for the first 150 feet but is level in the rest of the passage. A stream flows along the passage. The cave is in the upper part of the Greenbrier Limestone.

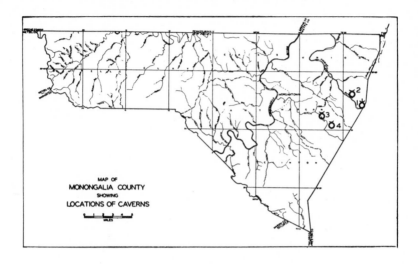

Figure 36.—Monongalia County Caves

1. Beaverhole Lower (Eagle).   3. Dellslow.
2. Cooper Rock.   4. Maiden Run.

COOPER ROCK CAVE 39°38′04″ N.; 79°48′58″ W. Morgantown Quadrangle.

At the base of Cooper Rock (elevation, 2000 feet) is a narrow cleft passage that extends into the cliff for 100 feet. It is in the Upper Connoquenessing Sandstone (Pottsville Series).

DELLSLOW CAVE 39°36′10″ N.; 79°52′26″ W. Morgantown Quadrangle.

Nine-tenths of a mile southeast of Dellslow, on the north side of West Virginia Highway 7 (elevation, 1360 feet), is a small shelter cave, 20 feet square in plan and 10 feet high. It is in the Greenbrier Limestone.

MAIDEN RUN CAVES 39°35′57″ N.; 79°51′34″ W. Morgantown Quadrangle.

A high fissure passage opens into the valley of Maiden Run 1200 feet northeast of West Virginia Highway 7. The passage, about 100 feet long, is wet and slopes steeply. In a quarry where West Virginia Highway 7 crosses Maiden Run is a small cave opening. The caves are in the Greenbrier Limestone.

MONROE COUNTY

Forty-nine caves are recorded in Monroe County. Of these, the majority are in the Greenbrier Series and the remainder are in the Ordovician limestones.

The Greenbrier Series, covering the central and northern part of the county, forms a rolling plateau. Structurally, it is made up of gentle to moderate, broad, symmetrical anticlines and synclines. A band of Greenbrier limestones, overturned and dipping steeply east, lies along Little Mountain in the southeast part of the county. Most of the caves in this series are in the Union Limestone although a relatively large number also are found in the Patton Limestone.

The Ordovician limestones outcrop in two bands in the eastern part of the county occupying the valley floor on the west side of Peters Mountain and Back Valley. The limestones along Peters Mountain are on the southeast side of the St. Clair Fault and have a dip to the southeast averaging 40° to 60°. In Back Valley the limestones are found in a similar position with respect to the Sugar Grove Fault except the dip is to the northwest.

The limestones of the Helderberg Group, conspicuous in the counties to the north, are reduced to less than 50 feet in thickness in Monroe County and no caves have been reported in them.

ARGOBRITES CAVE 37°38'20" N.; 80°35'10" W. Alderson Quadrangle.

Argobrites Cave is located 600 yards northeast of the site of Lady Hall School, on Broad Run, 2.8 miles southeast of Wolf Creek P. O., at an elevation of 2250 feet. The entrance is in a cliff 60 feet high and 150 feet wide. The stream issuing from the cave drops over a series of four beautiful waterfalls each about 15 feet high in front of the cave. The old road up Swoopes Knob to the east passes across the top of the cliff. The entrance is 15 feet wide and 20 feet high with a large

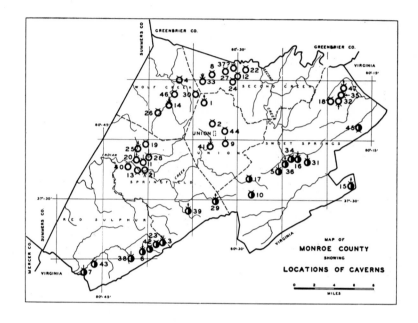

Figure 37.—Monroe County Caves

1. Argobrites.
2. Bear Hole.
3. Bradley.
4. Broad Run.
5. Chambers.
6. Clarence Simms.
7. Coburn.
8. Cold Hole.
9. Cold Spring.
10. Crosier.
11. Cross Road.
12. Crowder.
13. Doan Ballard.
14. Elmhurst.
15. Ewin Run.
16. Fletcher.
17. Fulton.
18. Galford.
19. Greens.
20. Greenville Saltpeter.
21. Greenville Pit.
22. Haynes.
23. Hilton.
24. Hinkle.

25. Indian Draft.
26. Irons.
27. Johnsons.
28. Laurel Creek.
29. McClung Zenith.
30. McGraw.
31. Miller.
32. Mitchell.
33. Mott Hole.
34. Neel.
35. Owens.
36. Patton.
37. Purgatory.
38. Rich Creek.
39. Rock Camp.
40. Shanklin.
41. Steeles.
42. Thompson.
43. Trigger Run.
44. Union (Caperton).
45. Wickline.
46. Wolf Creek.
47. Wylie.

stream flowing out. From the entrance a stream passage 30 feet high and 15 feet wide trends south for 50 feet where a large side passage opens to the east. The stream passage continuing south beyond the junction is 4 to 6 feet high and 10 to 15 feet wide and can be traversed for about 200 feet where the ceiling comes within a foot of the water. The pools of water along the passage are a foot to three feet deep. The side passage is a dry passage and is floored with silt about 6 feet higher than the stream passage. It trends east for 117 feet and then south for 150 feet. The first 80 feet of the passage is 25 feet wide, 40 feet high with a ceiling niche developed by two migrating dome shafts. These dome pits are now on the south side of the passage 80 feet from the junction. They are 50 to 60 feet high and have been breached on one side where they intersect the passage. They are 10 feet in diameter. The dry passage beyond the dome pits is 5 to 20 feet high and 25 feet wide with two small rooms along it. The last 60 feet of the passage is filled with old rimstone to within a foot of the ceiling. The pools are now dry and contain large kidney-shaped calcareous concretions. A small hole about a foot in diameter at the end of the rimstone is reported to open to a passage 2000 feet long averaging 25 feet in height and width. The cave is developed in the Union Limestone which dips gently to the west. The stream that issues from the cave forms one of the main tributaries of Broad Run and was formerly blocked by a dam at the cave entrance for water-power for a gristmill and sawmill. A decade or so ago the cave was used for extensive "moonshine" operations.

BEAR HOLE 37°36'27" N.; 80°32'34" W. Ronceverte Quadrangle.

One mile north of Union, ½ mile west of West Virginia Highway 3 is a sinkhole 45 feet deep with a small, muddy crawlway about 100 feet long at the base (elevation, 2050 feet). The cave is in the Union Limestone, Greenbrier Series.

BRADLEY CAVE 37°26'40" N.; 80°38'13" W. Pearisburg Quadrangle.

Bradley Cave is located ½ mile southwest of Shires School, 2000 feet south of the dirt road along Peters Mountain, at an elevation of 2600 feet. The entrance is through a narrow vertical pit, 35 feet deep, which opens into a small room at the base. It is reported by local residents that saltpeter was dug from this cave but no other evidence supports this assertion. The pit is developed in the lower 100 feet of the Stones River Limestone.

BROAD RUN CAVE 37°39′58″ N.; 80°37′00″ W. Alderson Quadrangle.

In a meadow 100 feet north of West Virginia Highway 3, 0.4 mile east of Wolf Creek P. O., is a small cave (elevation, 1650 feet). The entrance, a small pit 10 feet deep, is at the base of a dead, scrub oak tree. At the base of the pit a crawl passage leads east for 100 feet, and is 4 feet high and 6 feet wide. The cave is in the Patton (?) Limestone, Greenbrier Series.

CHAMBERS CAVE 37°32′04″ N.; 80°25′00″ W. Ronceverte Quadrangle.

The entrance to Chambers Cave is at the base of a 20-foot cliff on the north side of a low rise in the west end of a large sink 1.8 miles south-southwest of Gap Mills (elevation, 2350 feet). The entrance is 10 feet wide, 5 feet high but the ceiling lowers to less than 4 feet in a short distance. After 50 feet the passage enlarges and divides. To the southwest are a series of crawlways and stoopways to a large room 450 feet from the entrance. Breakdown, pools, and a few speleothems are in the room. The cave continues upstream to the southwest for 2000 feet to breakdown. Several large rooms 200 feet long, 40 to 50 feet wide and up to 70 feet high are along this passage. A few large speleothems decorate these rooms. Four hundred feet from the entrance is a passage to the east, 100 feet long. It is a muddy tortuous crawlway leading to a room 200 feet long, 30 feet wide, and 60 feet high. The far end of the room is blocked by flowstone but a small crawl passage with a stream leads off from the side of the room and is 250 feet long. Chambers Cave is in the Stones River Limestone.

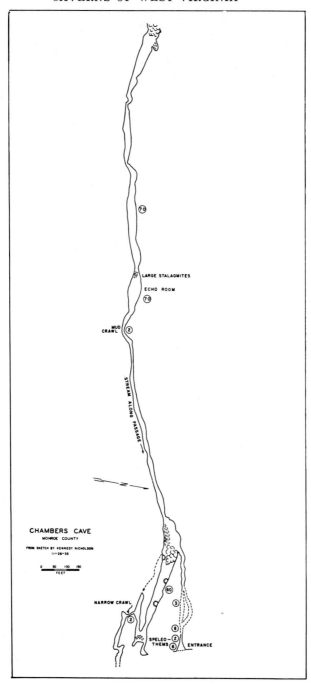

Figure 38.—Map of Chambers Cave.

CLARENCE SIMMS CAVE 37°25'20" N.; 80°40'36" W. Pearisburg Quadrangle.

This cave is located 100 yards south of the road at the base of Peters Mountain, 1.2 miles southwest of Spruce Run School (elevation, 2150 feet). The entrance is in a cliff 40 feet high and is low with water flowing in. No traverse of the cave was possible. The cave is developed in the Upper Stones River Limestone.

COBURN CAVE 37°23'00" N.; 80°46'34" W. Narrows Quadrangle.

Located at the head of Scott Branch, 1.6 miles southeast of Peterstown, Coburn Cave has the distinction of extending under West Virginia and Virginia. The entrance, at an elevation of 1870 feet, is just to the east of the St. Clair Fault. The passages are somewhat constricted and for the first 550 feet trend east across the strike, turning then to the south along the strike for about 100 feet. A stream flows in the cave and pools having water 20 to 40 inches deep are numerous. Formations are plentiful and include a number of well-developed catenary helictites. The cave is developed along primary joints in the Beekmantown Limestone, which, near the entrance, dips 25° to 30° to the east. The entrance is near the St. Clair Fault at the base of a thin, sandy chert (Huntersville ?).

COLD HOLE 37°40'37" N.; 80°33'23" W. Alderson Quadrangle.

This is a small cave in broken limestone ½ mile northwest of Sinks Grove (elevation, 2050 feet). The cave is in the Patton (?) Limestone, Greenbrier Series.

COLD SPRING CAVE 37°34'24" N.; 80°30'52" W. Alderson Quadrangle.

Burnside Branch of Indian Creek rises from a large spring 2 miles southeast of Union (elevation, 2100 feet). The spring issues from a cave which consists of a main passage trending east for 200 feet and minor, small side passages. The main passage is 10 to 15 feet high with occasional short crawlways and, except at the rear, is occupied by the stream. The cave is developed in the Sinks Grove Limestone, Greenbrier Series.

CROSIER CAVE   37°30'38" N.; 80°28'49" W.   Ronceverte Quadrangle.

This cave is located 100 feet east of the road along the west base of Peters Mountain, ¾ mile east of the site of Zenith School. The entrance is in a shallow sink and is a broad opening at the base of a low escarpment facing west (elevation, 2500 feet). The cave was formerly used as a milk cooler and the entrance was walled up. The door now is blocked with clay and other debris which prevents entry. The cave, which is developed at the base of the Stones River Limestone, is reported to be quite extensive.

Plate XXIII.—Cross Road Cave. (Photo by Wm. E. Davies).

CROSS ROAD CAVE 37°33′14″ N.; 80°40′00″ W. Alderson Quadrangle.

Cross Road Cave is a part of the Laurel Creek-Greenville Saltpeter cave system and is located on the Laurel Creek road 0.4 mile south of Laurel Creek Cave and 1.2 miles northeast of Greenville (elevation, 1700 feet). The entrance, which is 15 feet wide, 5 feet high, is in a low escarpment 25 feet east of the road and leads 15 feet down a slope of rock debris to a small room 15 feet square. The cave trends S. 60° E. The east passage is keyhole in shape with a width of 10 feet and a height of 15 feet. The slot of the keyhole is formed by a trench 8 feet deep and 4 feet wide through which a large stream flows to the west. The western passage is a broad stream passage 20 feet wide and 5 feet high with a level gravel floor. In both directions the passages are closed 100 yards from the entrance by low ceilings which reach water-level. The east passage is beautifully decorated with terraced rimstone pools developed on shelves adjacent to the stream channel. In addition a few stalactites are found near the entrance. The cave is developed in the Union Limestone, Greenbrier Series.

CROWDER CAVE 37°40′56″ N.; 80°30′08″ W. Alderson Quadrangle.

This cave is located on the road from Sinks Grove to Patton via Spider Den School, 0.35 mile northeast of the site of Patent School. The entrance is in a large sink surrounded by a grove of trees, 300 yards southeast of the road, in a rolling, sink-studded pasture. The sink, which is 60 feet deep, 125 feet long and 75 feet wide, is elongated in the direction N. 20° W. The walls are vertical, except on the east side where debris and wash have filled the sink within 20 feet of the surface. A ladder at this point gives easy access to the cave. (Elevation at base of sink, 2000 feet.)

At the north side of the sink, a short passage leads off but is blocked by breakdown 20 feet in. To the south is a large chamber 180 feet long, 75 feet wide, and 60 feet high with an axis N. 50° E. The floor is strewn with large, fallen rock slabs. A large flowstone formation 10 feet in diameter and stretching to the ceiling, occurs on the east wall 80 feet from the entrance. Twenty feet in from this formation, a small sinuous passage, 8 to 10 feet wide and 4 to 8 feet high, trends N. 30° W. for

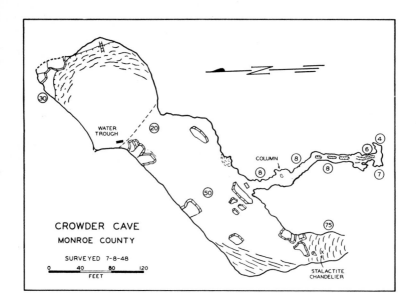

Figure 39.—Map of Crowder Cave.

185 feet and then N. 10° E. for 120 feet where it ends in a small, low rectangular room, blocked at each end by flowstone. At the end of the large, main chamber the cave abruptly turns due south forming a gallery, 45 feet wide and 75 feet high which is blocked after 80 feet by a huge flowstone "altar" which is the largest formation found in a West Virginia cave. Stalactites, columns, and large flowstone draperies (one in the form of a huge chandelier) decorate the walls and ceiling adjacent to the "altar."

Crowder Cave is developed at the top of the Patton Limestone which dips 4° E. with a strike of N. 50° E. The main passages lie along a series of vertical joints trending due north and N. 50° E. with modifications from a series of minor joints at N. 80° W. and N. 30° W. Ice has been collected by local residents as late as July from under the rocks in the chamber at the north end of the entrance sink.

DOAN BALLARD CAVE 37°32′22″ N.; 80°40′12″ W. Alderson Quadrangle.

A cave of small size, in the Union Limestone, lies along Indian Creek ¾ mile east of Greenville (elevation, 1650 feet). It is 75 feet long and consists of a small passage widening in places to small rooms. The cave is very dry and saltpeter was dug, in small quantities, during the War Between the States.

ELMHURST CAVE 37°38′00″ N.; 80°37′49″ W. Alderson Quadrangle.

At a point 2.3 miles south of Wolf Creek P. O. (0.2 mile south of Elmhurst) Wolf Creek flows into a cave (elevation, 1690 feet) and continues underground for one mile. The entrance, near Elmhurst, is 100 yards west of the road and is 6 feet wide and 4 feet high. Ten feet in the cave is blocked by a large amount of driftwood and similar debris. The cave is developed in the Patton Limestone, Greenbrier Series.

EWIN RUN CAVE 37°31′50″ N.; 80°17′30″ W. Ronceverte Quadrangle.

Ewin Run rises from a cave near the site of Sugar Grove School, 3.1 miles southwest of Paint Bank, Virginia (elevation, 2270 feet). The cave trends east for a short distance as a low crawl in water after which it opens up somewhat and it is possible to walk for a short distance to a pool, more than 20 feet deep, that blocks the passage. The cave is developed in the Stones River Limestone (dip, 58° N.W.) and the entrance faces on the Sugar Grove Fault.

FLETCHER CAVE 37°33′24″ N.; 80°23′30″ W. Ronceverte Quadrangle.

One mile east of Gap Mills, a branch of Kitchen Creek flows westward into Fletcher Cave (elevation, 2430 feet). The entrance is in a long, shallow sink. The water entrance is low and turns abruptly from west to north where a pit 15 feet deep and 10 feet in diameter opens to the surface. The cave trends southwest along the strike for 2100 feet as a single passage averaging 10 feet wide and high with occasional small rooms 20 feet wide and long. The passage terminates in breakdown.

A large room is 500 feet from the entrance. Formations of considerable size and beauty occur a short distance inside the entrance; elsewhere speleothems are small but numerous. The cave is in the Beekmantown Limestone which dips 45° N.W. and strikes N. 50° E.

FULTON CAVE 37°31′42″ N.; 80°28′15″ W. Ronceverte Quadrangle.

This cave is at the end of a low spur separating the tributaries of Turkey Creek, 1.25 miles northeast of McGlone. The entrance (elevation, 2300 feet) is at the end of a long, vertical-walled sink that parallels the spur. The cave is a narrow passage, 20 feet high and 5 to 10 feet wide which, after 300 feet, pinches down to a crawl and is soon impassable for further traverse. The passage changes direction often, varying from due east to N. 40° E. The first 50 feet at the entrance drops rapidly 40 feet over fallen rock. The cave is well decorated with flowstone, columns, and stalactites throughout. The limestone in which the cave is developed is uppermost Stones River in age with a dip of 20° E. and strike N. 40° W. It is part of a small outcrop lying on the west side of the St. Clair Fault. The cave follows two sets of major vertical joints. Another cave, reputedly of large size, is across the valley.

GALFORD CAVE 37°38′12″ N.; 80°19′56″ W. Ronceverte Quadrangle.

A small crawl cave with a stream flowing in it is developed in the south end of the limestone outcrop, 0.3 mile southeast of Wylie Church (elevation, 2600 feet). The entrance is 5 feet square but rapidly reduces to a crawl. The cave is in the lower part of the Greenbrier Series.

GREENS CAVES
   37°35′16″ N.; 80°40′26″ W. (West Cave)
   37°35′17″ N.; 80°40′24″ W. (East Cave)
   Alderson Quadrangle.

In a large sink, 0.8 mile east of Indian Draft School, are two openings that lead to small caves (elevation, 2250 feet). Each cave consists of narrow, tapering tunnels that are high enough for walking at the entrance but are reduced rapidly to small crawlways. The West Cave is 75 feet long and the East Cave is 30 feet long. Small streams flow into each cave. The caves are in the Alderson Limestone, Greenbrier Series.

GREENVILLE SALTPETER (HEAD OF MILL POND) CAVE 37°32′56″ N.; 80°40′49″ W. Alderson Quadrangle.

Of the many West Virginia caves bearing the connotation "saltpeter," the Greenville Cave, with its four entrances, is the largest. The southern entrance (elevation, 1680 feet) is on the stream that feeds the mill-pond at Greenville and is located 0.4 mile northeast of the town. The other entrances occur in a shallow valley sink 2000 feet to the north.

The cave, as far as known, is among the largest in West Virginia. Over 13,000 feet of main passages have been explored which makes it more than twice as large as Laurel Creek Cave. The southern entrance, near the mill-pond, is 5 feet high and 20 feet wide and opens into a broad, sloping room on the north side of which is a low passage with a floor composed of large rimstone pools. The main passage trends east for 1200 feet and then north. The northern half of the cave consists of three parallel passages trending northeast-southwest, interconnected by subordinate passages. The entrance to the eastern passage, which is 25 feet high and wide, is a water entrance with a large stream flowing in, 15 feet wide and up to a foot deep. The stream flows along the floor of a large room 75 feet wide, 50 feet high, and 500 feet long and sinks in a pool in a small passage to the east of this room.

The central passage reaches the surface in an entrance 20 feet wide by 6 feet high, which lies about 200 feet west of the Water Entrance. The western entrance is 1000 feet west of the central one and leads to a passage in which are the remains of extensive saltpeter operations. Cart ruts, burro tracks, mattock marks, and other relics of saltpeter operations are found in the passage leading southwest from this entrance as well as in subordinate passages to the west and east.

The floor of the cave is made up of damp clay except in the east end of the passage connecting the saltpeter and central passages where a large area of breakdown occurs. Similar breakdown is found at the south end of the large room at the Water Entrance and in adjacent passages. Formations are rather scarce and consist of rimstone pools found near the

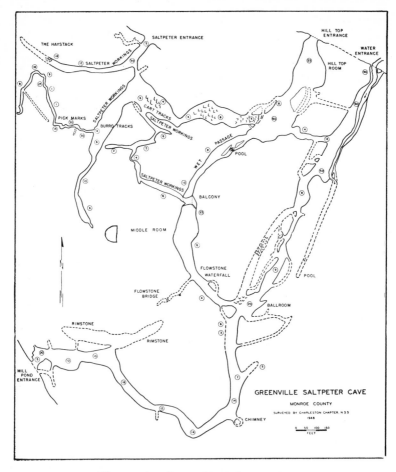

Figure 40.—Greenville Saltpeter Cave.

Mill Pond Entrance and occasional flowstone scattered throughout various passages. A large flowstone dome, the Haystack, is found near the end of the passage leading west from the Saltpeter (West) Entrance. The cave occurs in the Union Limestone, Greenbrier Series, and is developed along a series of major joints trending N. 25° E. in horizontal beds with subordinate joints at N. 50° W. and due east. The stream which flows through the cave is a part of the underground drainage net of Laurel Creek and is discussed in the section on Hydrology.

GREENVLLE PIT 37°32'30" N.; 80°39'58" W. Alderson Quadrangle.

A pit, 50 feet deep, opening into a narrow room 60 feet long at the base, is located in the Union Limestone, one mile east of Greenville on Indian Creek. A few formations decorate the room.

HAYNES (BURWELL) CAVE 37°41'13" N.; 80°29'00" W. Ronceverte Quadrangle.

Haynes Cave lies ½ mile south of Second Creek near the site of Patton (2.2 miles north of New Lebanon Church, formerly Monitor, on the Patton road) at an elevation of 2120 feet. The cave is 1000 feet long and consists of two sinuous passages, one 10 feet above the other, and connected at a number of points. Throughout most of the cave passages average 10 to 15 feet in height and 10 feet in width. Except for the first 100 feet near the entrance, the cave is very dry and dusty with the floor of the upper passage made of dusty clay mixed with gypsum and considerable quantities of rat and bat manure Few formations remain in the cave because of its dryness. Fifty feet from the entrance is a large flowstone formation on the north wall. Opposite this, in the center of the passage, is

Plate XXIV.—Haynes Cave. Dripstone-covered Trough near Entrance. (Photo by Wm. E. Davies).

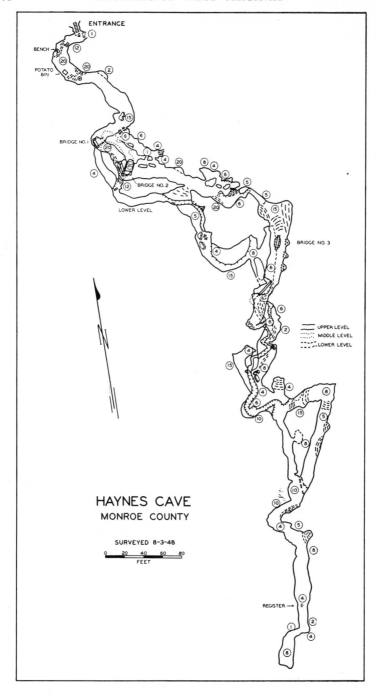

Figure 41.—Haynes Cave.

Plate XXV.—Haynes Cave. Bridges. (Photo by Wm. E. Davies).

a trough resting on a mound of flowstone. The trough was placed by saltpeter miners to collect water from a drip in the ceiling and now is covered by 1½ inches of flowstone. Fibrous gypsum crystals occur in beds up to 3 inches thick in many places in the cave and coarse gypsum flowers cover most of the cave walls. Haynes Cave is in the Patton Limestone, Greenbrier Series, and is developed along a series of joints at N. 60° W. and N. 20° E. Subordinate joints at N. 30° W. and due north modify these trends.

Relics from saltpeter operations during the War Between the States are numerous and well preserved in the cave. A number of bridges over shallow pits, troughs, and similar remains are found scattered along the main passage. The prize feature, however, is the winch found on the lower level. The winch, made of roughly hewn saplings, was used to lift material from a deep pit and is in perfect state of preservation. At the far end of the upper passage is a guests' register dating back to 1915. Signatures and comments of hundreds of persons who have explored the cave form a vivid, humorous and, at times, a pathetic record. Such comments as "It is wonderful to observe the wonderful works of God in developing the world in which we live" followed by the pert statement of another cave explorer—"Lord, What a trip" amply suggest that caving does not produce like impressions on all individuals. A note of pathos is found in the entry of January 1, 1920— "A Watch Meeting was held this New Year's Eve; Good-bye dear Rosa."

Plate XXVI.—Haynes Cave. Trench Dug by Saltpeter Workers. (Photo by Wm. E. Davies).

Plate XXVII.—Haynes Cave. Windlass. (Photo by Wm. E. Davies).

HILTON CAVE 37°26'38" N.; 80°38'30" W. Pearisburg Quadrangle.

The entrance to Hilton Cave lies at the base of a low lime-stone escarpment, 800 feet east of the road along Peters Mountain, 1.7 miles southeast of Lindside near the Red Sulphur-Springfield District line (elevation, 2400 feet). The cave is narrow, 2 to 4 feet wide and about 10 feet high, extending for a few hundred feet. Shallow pools of water cover part of the cave floor. The fissure-type cave bears S. 70° W. along a joint vertical to the bedding. A minor joint at S. 30° E. modifies the pattern slightly. The upper Beekmantown Limestone in which the cave is developed dips 40° south.

HINKLE CAVE 37°40'30" N.; 80°31'30" W. Alderson Quadrangle.

Hinkle Cave is a small cave, a few hundred feet in length, located 1.1 miles northeast of Sinks Grove (elevation, 2200 feet). The passages are large enough to permit walking and are dry. The cave is in the Sinks Grove Limestone, Greenbrier Series.

INDIAN DRAFT CAVE 37°34'58" N.; 80°41'13" W. Alderson Quadrangle.

Located on the east side of Indian Draft, 2.8 miles north of Greenville (elevation, 1795 feet), Indian Draft Cave is one of the most difficult in West Virginia to traverse. The entrance is small and rocky with a stream flowing out. About 400 feet from the entrance the cave divides into two passages. The left or north passage is about 1200 feet long and is an alternation of low sections, 4 feet high and 10 feet wide, and high fissure sections up to 30 feet high and 20 feet wide. The passage is steeply inclined throughout its length and the last 200 feet of the traversable section is an alternation of rimstone pools and wet clay floors with a low ceiling that requires crawling, ending at a 15-foot waterfall beyond which a small crawlway extends 100 yards to a pinch down. The right or south passage is 1200 feet long and is similar in nature to the other passage. It ends after a difficult crawl at a chamber 25 feet long, 10 feet wide, 30 feet high, that has a crystal pool. An upper level leads off the south passage but it is small and difficult to traverse. This upper level ends in a small chamber 4 feet square. A number of beautiful formations occur throughout much of the cave; the south passage has the greater number. Indian Draft Cave is in the Alderson Limestone, Greenbrier Series.

IRONS CAVE 37°37'19" N.; 80°39'00" W. Alderson Quadrangle.

Irons Cave is at the foot of Patricks Peak, 1 mile west-northwest of Johnsons Crossroads (elevation, 1850 feet). The entrance passage, measuring 3 by 8 feet, leads to a small room averaging 10 feet in height and somewhat larger in length and width. The entire cave measures 75 feet in length. The cave is extremely dry, and is developed in the Union Limestone (?), Greenbrier Series.

JOHNSONS CAVE 37°41'10" N.; 80°31'10" W. Alderson Quadrangle.

On the farm of M. A. Johnson, 1.8 miles northeast of Sinks Grove (0.4 mile east of Spider Den School), is a small cave with an entrance in a low hollow 100 yards northwest of the barn. The cave is at an elevation of 2150 feet, and heads due south through a low saddle for 600 feet, emerging in a small sink. The first 100 feet is 10 feet wide and high enough to permit walking. The remaining 500 feet require difficult crawling. Formations are small except for a large stalagmitic bowl near the entrance. This cave is in the Sinks Grove Limestone, Greenbrier Series.

LAUREL CREEK CAVE 37°33′32″ N.; 80°39′56″ W. Alderson Quadrangle.

On the west side of Laurel Creek, 1½ miles northeast of Greenville, is the entrance to Laurel Creek Cave. The entrance is on the east slope of a low hill and is a flat arched opening, 110 feet wide and 30 feet high (elevation, 1680 feet). A broad

Plate XXVIII.—Entrance to Laurel Creek Cave. (Photo by David P. Cruise).

Plate XXIX.—Inside Entrance Laurel Creek Cave Looking Out.
(Photo by David P. Cruise).

passage curves gently to the south and for over 300 feet is of dimensions comparable to the entrance. At this point the passage is divided into two parts by a partition, the west section being strewn with breakdown, while the east section is an open passage 20 feet wide and 15 feet high. On the northwest edge of the breakdown is a small exit to the top of the hill. At the end of the divided section the passage resembles the entrance section except that the width is about 50 feet. One thousand feet from the entrance is a large room that has been designated the Theater Room. The room is 160 feet long and has a ceiling height of 50 feet. From this room the cave is made up of two parallel passages. The upper level leads off from the southwest edge of the upper part of the room and is 40 feet above the lower passage. Three hundred feet from the Theater Room the passages are connected by a broad corridor. Three hundred and fifty feet beyond this the upper level is full of breakdown for 225 feet after which it changes direction to the south and crosses the lower level, continuing for 900

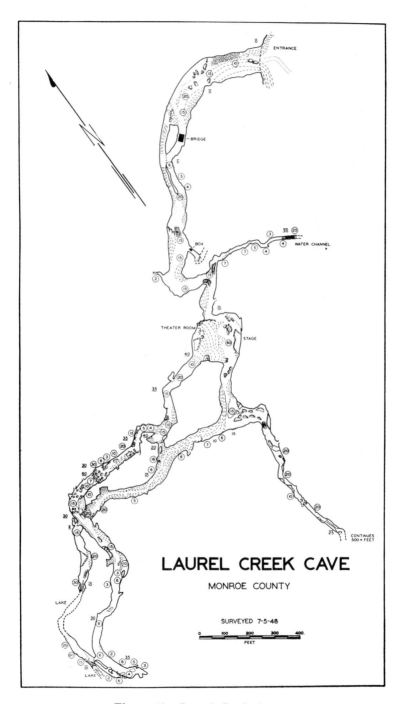

Figure 42.—Laurel Creek Cave.

Plate XXX.—Recharging Carbide Lamps at Entrance to Laurel Creek Cave. (Photo by David P. Cruise).

feet where further passage is blocked by silt and flowstone that reaches to the ceiling. Throughout its entire length the upper level is rather uniform in size averaging 20 to 30 feet wide and 6 to 15 feet high except in the breakdown area and near the end of the passage. The lower level is less uniform in nature. From the Theater Room the passage is 25 feet wide and 15 feet high for 100 feet where a large passage develops to the southeast. The passage turns abruptly to the west and for 420 feet is 20 feet wide and 4 to 7 feet high. Here the passage passes beneath the upper level and is connected to it by a pathway along the south wall. The passage is traversable for 250 feet where a lake is encountered which continues for 100 feet more at which point it narrows to a thin crevice. The lake can be reached from the upper level, 250 feet from the end. The lower level (Lake) at this point is floored with breakdown. To the north the lake is encountered again and is open for 100 feet where the ceiling comes down to water-level. To the south the passage is floored with large rocks lying in a deep pool of water which has not been traversed.

Plate XXXI.—Pendants on Roof of Laurel Creek Cave, Monroe County. Pendants Due to Differential Erosion and Solution Along Concentric Stress Lines; Greenbrier Limestone. (Photo by David P. Cruise).

A number of passages lead off from the lower level. All of them are on the south or east side and the largest is that which develops 100 feet south of the Theater Room. This passage is very irregular, ranging from 10 to 20 feet wide and averaging 20 feet high. The passage is very long but has been mapped for 900 feet only. In this section there are a large number of boulders blocking the passage and shallow pools of water are found throughout. It is reported to end at an exit to the surface 10 yards north of Cross Road Cave.

The floor of the cave, except near the entrance, is underlain by deep, fine-grained, olive-drab silt. On the upper level it is dry but compact. On the lower level it is damp and in some places the high clay content makes it sticky. Near the end of the upper level a slump pit exposes 15 feet of silt resting on rock, a thickness that is average for this level. On the west side of the Theater Room the thickness reaches 40 feet but in the remainder of the lower level the thickness ranges from a

Plate XXXII.—Gravel Fill in Laurel Creek Cave, Monroe County. (Photo by David P. Cruise).

Plate XXXIII.—Laurel Creek Cave, Lower Level Passage with Deep Silt Fill. (Photo by Wm. E. Davies).

Plate XXXIV.—Laurel Creek Cave. Bridge Washed in.
(Photo by Wm. E. Davies).

Plate XXXV.—Laurel Creek Cave. Lake at End of Lower Level.
(Photo by Wm. E. Davies).

Plate XXXVI.—Vertical Solution Grooving, Laurel Creek Cave.

thin veneer to 6 or 7 feet. From the entrance to the Theater Room the floor is covered with coarse gravels made of cobbles from 4 to 10 inches in size in a matrix of finer sand and gravel. Banks of stratified clay reaching to the ceiling occur in this section in niches along the wall.

Laurel Creek Cave is developed in the Union Limestone, Greenbrier Series. Joints at N. 40° E. and N. 70° W. control the development of the cave from the entrance to the Theater Room. Beyond this point the cave is developed along joints at N. 80° W. and N. 80° E. The rear part follows joints at N. 40° E. and due north. A minor joint at N. 10° E. is visible in many parts of the cave but exerts little influence on the pattern.

Laurel Creek Cave is an integral part of the subterranean drainage connecting Laurel Creek with Indian Creek, via Greenville Saltpeter Cave. In normal periods of precipitation Laurel Creek sinks before entering Laurel Creek Cave but scoured channels in the floor indicate that in high water the creek enters the cave and follows the main passage to the junction beyond the Theater Room where it follows the east passage. The undisturbed, dry silt on the upper level indicates that the water does not reach that level and the lower level beyond the junction is not disturbed by torrents as the channels in the clay are typically those of small, gentle streams. The entrance section shows evidence of torrential flooding to the ceiling. A wooden highway bridge wedged into the passage 900 feet from the entrance and the debris anchored securely in cracks in the ceiling are good evidence of these torrents.

McCLUNG ZENITH CAVE 37°30'08" N.; 80°31'17" W. Alderson Quadrangle.

A quarter of a mile east of the settlement of Zenith is a large water cave. The entrance (elevation, 2300 feet) is 1000 feet east of the grist-mill which uses the stream flowing from the cave as a source of power. The mouth of the cave is at the top of a pile of rock debris, 20 feet high, on the face of a low escarpment. The stream discharges at the base of the debris. The entrance passage is 20 feet wide and 15 feet high with a flat arched ceiling and the stream occupies the floor. Fifty feet from the entrance the passage turns abruptly to the northeast and divides into two parts. The stream follows the east passage while the north passage is dry. The dry passage is floored with deep silt clay while the stream passage is in gravel with banks of clay. The stream passage is 100 yards long beyond which it is a crawl through deep water and dangerous breakdown for 50 to 75 feet; beyond this it is a very low crawl. The dry passage is several hundred yards long. The cave is developed along joints at S. 50° E. and due east, with minor jointing at N. 10° E. The cave is in the Beekmantown Limestone (dip, 18° E., strike, N. 40° E.) along the east side of the St. Clair Fault.

McGRAW CAVE 37°38'56" N.; 80°35'56" W. Alderson Quadrangle.

A short cave of small cross-section is located on the Wolf Creek-Knobs road, 1.8 miles southeast of Wolf Creek P. O. (elevation, 1950 feet). The cave, which is in the Union Limestone (?), Greenbrier Series, is traversed by difficult crawling.

MILLER CAVE   37°33′26″ N.; 80°22′08″ W.   Ronceverte Quadrangle.

In a hollow at the base of Peters Mountain, 2¼ miles east of Gap Mills, a large stream issues from Miller Cave (elevation, 2440 feet). The entrance is a room 15 feet square in cross-section which, after a short distance, is reduced in size to a crawlway extending a considerable distance to the east. A large amount of fallen rock is encountered throughout the cave. Miller Cave is in the Stones River Limestone which dips 20° east.

MITCHELL CAVE   37°38′26″ N.; 80°19′03″ W.   Ronceverte Quadrangle.

Mitchell Cave is located one mile east of Wylie Church at the head of the hollow formed by the east branch of Cove Run (elevation, 2640 feet). It is reported to be 2000 feet long with spacious passages and rooms. A stream flows into the cave and in 1948 the entrance was blocked by debris of timber. The cave is in the upper part of the Greenbrier Series.

MOTT HOLE   37°40′04″ N.; 80°34′45″ W.   Alderson Quadrangle.

Mott Hole is located ½ mile northwest of West Virginia Highway 3, 2¼ miles due west of Sinks Grove. The vertical entrance shaft is 20 feet in diameter and has a depth of 203 feet. The deepest single vertical drop is 39 feet. Ledges and slopes break the shaft at several points. A horizontal stream passage at the base of the shaft is 500 feet long. The entrance to the shaft is at an elevation of 2530 feet and the cave is in the Alderson and Union Limestones, Greenbrier Series.

NEEL CAVE   37°33′08″ N.; 80°23′50″ W.   Ronceverte Quadrangle.

Neel Cave is developed in a low sink in gently rolling hills, 0.9 mile southeast of Gap Mills (elevation, 2450 feet). It consists of a large entrance chamber, about 30 feet square in cross-section and length, which narrows and divides at the rear into two small passages that pinch out after a short distance. The cave is in the Beekmantown Limestone.

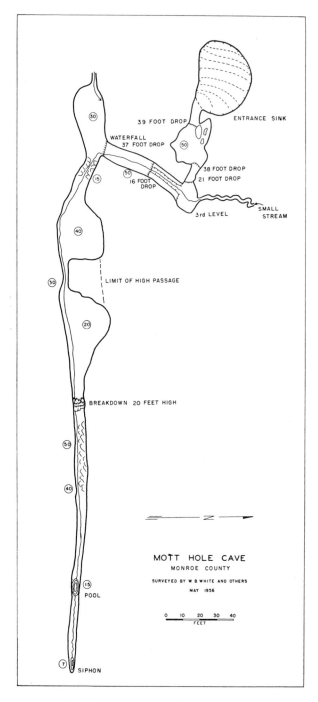

Figure 43.—Map of Mott Hole.

OWENS CAVE 37°38'38" N.; 80°19'00" W. Ronceverte Quadrangle.

Located 1000 feet north of Mitchell Cave, near the head of the east branch of Cove Run, the entrance to Owens Cave is in a shallow sink (elevation, 2550 feet). The main passages of the cave, totaling over 1000 feet, are 12 to 15 feet square in cross-section except for short stretches that are narrow crawlways. A few rooms 50 feet high and wide are developed as a result of increase in size of passages. The floor of the cave is composed of wet silt and clay and a stream which enters the cave at the mouth flows through most of the cave. The stream is reported to emerge in Wylie Cave, 1000 yards to the north. A few formations are found scattered throughout the cave. Owens Cave is in the lower part of the Greenbrier Series.

PATTON CAVE 37°32'36" N.; 80°23'56" W. Ronceverte Quadrangle.

Patton Cave, which is among the largest in the county, is located at the head of a branch of Second Creek, 1.4 miles southeast of Gap Mills (elevation, 2400 feet). The entrance is in a sink 30 feet deep, 200 feet southwest of a large spring that forms a major branch of Second Creek. The cave is developed as a disrupted rectangular pattern in a series of intersecting "T"-shaped passages. It has over 5000 feet of passages which vary from broad, low-arched tunnels, 30 to 40 feet wide and 6 to 15 feet high, to those with rectangular cross-section, 10 to 15 feet wide and 8 to 20 feet high. Breakdown is extensive 3500 feet from the entrance and consists of huge blocks on the east side of the passage. The floor in the front part of the cave is of coarse silt and gravel scoured by a number of stream channels. Throughout the rear portion the floor is of ochre-brown silt and clay. Formations of considerable size are found at a number of places throughout the cave.

The stream which issues below the entrance, while apparently related to the cave, was not observed in any of the passages although numerous stream channels in some sections indicate that the stream occupies a portion of the cave in wet weather. The available evidence indicates that the stream flows on the same level as the cave but in channels not readily accessible from the dry sections.

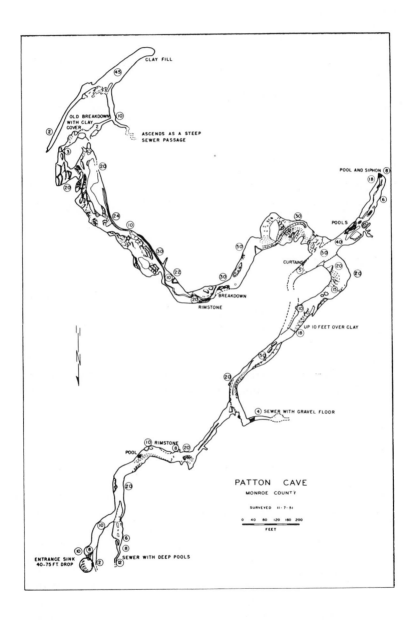

Figure 44.—Patton Cave.

Plate XXXVII.—Flowstone Mounds in Patton Cave.

The main passages are developed along joints at N. 60° E., S. 40° E., and S. 40° W. in the Stones River Limestone which, at the entrance, is a contorted syncline but assumes a horizontal structure just above the entrance. At the rear of the cave the beds are vertical.

PURGATORY CAVE 37°41'20 N.; 80°30'34" W. Alderson Quadrangle.

Purgatory Cave is reported to lie on the south side of Second Creek in Purgatory Hollow opposite the site of Nickells Mill. The cave was not located during field work and no definite information is available on it.

RICH CREEK CAVE 37°24'59" N.; 80°42'04" W. Pearisburg Quadrangle.

Rich Creek Cave is located at the head of a branch of Rich Creek, 1.3 miles southeast of Brick Church (elevation, 1900 feet). The entrance is in a cliff, at the head of a hollow, a quarter of a mile east of the county road along the base of Peters Mountain. The entrance is a low crawl which opens into a passage several hundred yards long and large enough to permit walking. A large stream flows through the cave and occupies much of the floor. Occasionally deep pools are encountered. At one time the stream was dammed near the entrance to the cave and the water operated a grist-mill half a mile to the east. The cave is silted considerably from the impounded waters. Rich Creek Cave is in the Beekmantown Limestone.

ROCK CAMP CAVE 37°28′34″ N.; 80°35′16″ W. Pearisburg Quadrangle.

The entrance of this cave is in a low escarpment on the east side of the road up Rock Camp Creek, 1.9 miles southeast of Rock Camp (elevation, 2280 feet). The mouth of the cave, 4 feet high by 8 feet wide, is at the top of debris 15 feet high. The main passage at the base of the debris trends N. 60° E. for several hundred yards and averages 10 to 15 feet wide and high. A large stream, which emerges at the base of the debris to form Rock Camp Creek, occupies the passage floor. Deep pools are encountered occasionally. Rock Camp Cave is in the Beekmantown Limestone which dips 28° S. and strikes N. 60° E. The main passage follows a set of master joints at N. 60° E., with minor joints at N. 30° W. which modify it. The joints are vertical to the bedding.

SHANKLIN CAVE 37°32′25″ N.; 80°40′19″ W. Alderson Quadrangle.

This cave is located along Indian Creek 0.6 mile east of Greenville (elevation, 1680 feet). The entrance to the cave is low and narrow but opens into a passage large enough to permit standing. A large room which makes up most of the cave is situated a short distance from the entrance. The total length of the cave is 300 feet. Soldiers are reported to have used the cave as a camping place during the War Between the States. Shanklin Cave is in the Union Limestone, Greenbrier Series.

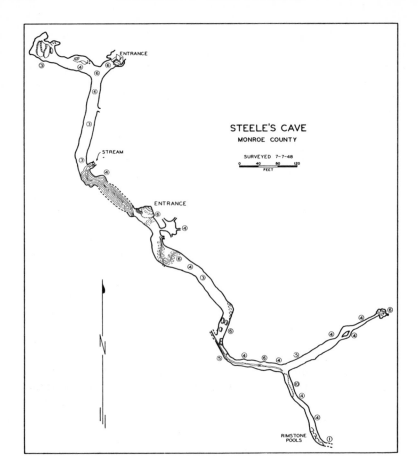

Figure 45.—Map of Steeles Cave.

STEELES CAVE 37°33′53″ N.; 80°33′00″ W. Alderson Quadrangle.

Indian Creek rises in a large spring two miles south of Union. The spring is fed in turn by a subterranean stream flowing through Steeles Cave. The entrance to the cave is in a 55-foot deep, vertical-sided sink (elevation, 1900 feet), 1.1 miles southeast of Salt Sulphur Springs at the point where the valleys of Burnside and Taggart Branches join to form Indian Creek. The cave extends to the east from the entrance sink as a broad, low passage, 10 to 20 feet wide and 4 to 6 feet high, which trends S. 40° E. curving gently to S. 80° E. Six hundred feet from the entrance a small side passage, 2 to 10 feet wide and 4 feet high, trends S. 20° E. This passage continues for a considerable distance but after 100 feet decreases in size to a small crawlway. The main passage beyond the junction with the side passage continues for 250 feet at N. 60° E. with a height of 4 to 5 feet and a width of 6 to 15 feet. At the end is a room 15 feet in diameter with breakdown blocking further passage. The floor of the cave is dry clay or gravel except in the side passage which is floored with rimstone.

On the west side of the entrance sink the cave is a low water-filled passage, 8 to 10 feet wide, with a lake 150 feet long and over 6 feet deep. The ceiling is 4 feet above the water. The stream entering the lake is seen in the east passage at only one point which is just inside the entrance where it cuts diagonally across the passage.

At the west end of the lake the stream exits through a narrow, rock-strewn passage to the north. The main passage continues on for 200 feet as a gravel-strewn tunnel, 3 to 6 feet high and 10 feet wide. An entrance in the end of a long, shallow valley sink gives access to the cave at this point. Forty feet from this entrance a side passage bears west into a maze of breakdown. A third entrance is at the spring forming Indian Creek but is now blocked by waters impounded by a dam.

Salamanders, crayfish, and crickets abound in this cave. In the lake a dark-colored fish up to 6 inches long was observed. Water walkers are abundant on the surface of the lake.

Steeles Cave is in the lower part of the Union Limestone, Greenbrier Series.

THOMPSON CAVE 37°25′37″ N.; 80°39′56″ W. Pearisburg Quadrangle.

This cave is located in a field 100 yards south of the county road along the base of Peters Mountain at a point 1.9 miles south of Lindside (elevation, 2340 feet). The cave is in a low sink and is a single room 30 feet long, 10 feet wide, and 20 feet high. The cave is in the Stones River Limestone which dips 25° S.E.

TRIGGER RUN CAVE 37°23′30″ N.; 80°45′12″ W. Narrows Quadrangle.

Trigger Run Cave is at the head of Trigger Run (elevation, 2100 feet), 2.6 miles east of Peterstown. The entrance is in a low ledge of rock 100 yards south of the road along the base of Peters Mountain. The cave is a small crawlway blocked by breakdown 100 yards in. It is in the Beekmantown Limestone along the St. Clair Fault.

UNION (CAPERTON) CAVE 37°36′05″ N.; 80°30′58″ W. Alderson Quadrangle.

Union Cave is located in a large open field (elevation, 2200 feet) on the side of a low hill, 1.7 miles E.N.E. of Union. The entrance is in a small sink and opens into a long main passage with numerous side passages. Along the main passage in several places and in some of the side passages large rooms are developed. The main passage and most of the side passages are large enough to permit walking except for occasional short sections of crawlways. Rope is needed in some of the passages as vertical drops of 10 feet occur. No stream is encountered in the cave but in the rooms shallow pools often cover the floor. The cave is in the Patton (?) Limestone, Greenbrier Series.

WICKLINE CAVE 37°36′10″ N.; 80°16′30″ W. Ronceverte Quadrangle.

This small single passage crawlway, less than 100 feet in length, is located on the flank of Peters Mountain, 2.7 miles southwest of Sweet Springs (elevation, 2280 feet). It is in the Stones River Limestone.

WOLF CREEK CAVE 37°38′46″ N.; 80°37′20″ W. Alderson Quadrangle.

Wolf Creek, for much of its length above Broad Run, flows along subterranean courses. For occasional stretches it comes to the surface in seeps or from caverns. At a point 1.4 miles south of Wolf Creek P. O. (elevation, 1650 feet) several sewer-like openings occur with dimensions up to 4 feet in height and 6 feet in width. During normal conditions these sewers are filled with water. However, in drought it is apparent they can be traversed to the subterranean channel of Wolf Creek. The caverns are in the Patton Limestone, Greenbrier Series.

WYLIE CAVE   37°39'12" N.; 80°19'00" W.   Ronceverte Quadrangle.

Wylie Cave is located on the east branch of Cove Creek, 1.4 miles northeast of Wylie Church, and 1000 feet south of the entrance to the hollow (elevation, 2450 feet). The cave is a crawlway several hundred feet in length and a stream flows out of the cave. It is in the lower part of the Greenbrier Series.

Eight other caves have been reported in Monroe County but details on them are lacking. They are:

Deales Hole—¼ mile south of Crowders Cave.

Destitute Cave—⅛ mile south of U. S. Highway 219 and Greenbrier-Monroe county line.

Dicksons Cave—½ mile east of U. S. Highway 219, 1 mile north of Second Creek; reported to be 400 feet long.

Maddys Cave—0.7 mile northeast of Greenville.

Mitchells Cave—Small cave 1.2 miles south of Union on west side of U. S. Highway 219.

Steeles Pit—Pit in ridge across Burnside Creek from Steeles Cave now covered with no entry possible.

Sugar Tree Cave—Muddy crawlway 1.4 miles west of Sinks Grove in sinkhole just north of road.

Union Church Cave—Small cave about 100 feet long near Union Presbyterian Church.

MORGAN COUNTY

Only one cave, in the Tonoloway Limestone at Rock Gap, Warm Spring Ridge, has been reported in Morgan County. The Tonoloway Limestone and Helderberg Group outcrop in two bands in the County. The eastern band is along the west side of Warm Spring Ridge extending across the county from south to north. The western band is similar in extent and lies along Little Mountain and Tonoloway Ridge.

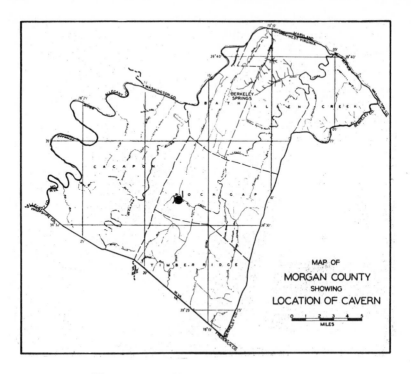

Figure 46.—Morgan County Cave

1. Rock Gap.

ROCK GAP CAVE 39°31'31" N.; 78°17'21" W. Paw Paw Quadrangle.

Rock Gap Cave is at the north end of a small quarry on the southwest side of Rock Gap (elevation, 860 feet). The entrance, in a narrow ravine at the northeast edge of the quarry, is 8 feet wide and 4 feet high with a mound of clay and leaves partially blocking it. Just inside the entrance is breakdown that reduces the passage to a narrow crawlway for 15 feet after which it enlarges to 13 feet wide and 2 to 6 feet high. Forty-five feet from the entrance the floor drops 10 feet over a clay slope to a siphon filled with 10 feet of water. Local residents report that there are four rooms about 20 feet long, 15 feet wide, along the passage 150 feet south of the siphon. The cave heads S. 20° W. curving to due south. In wet weather a stream flows out of the cave which forms the drainage channel for two large sinks, one mile to the south. The northern sink has a low crawl opening that heads north, apparently connecting with Rock Gap Cave.

The cave is in the Tonoloway Limestone in the center of a syncline with a strike N. 30° E. and dip 50° W. (east side) and 90° (west side).

NICHOLAS COUNTY

Limestones in Nicholas County are thin and discontinuous in the Pennsylvanian formations. Only two caves are known in the county.

BROCKS BRIDGE CAVES 38°16'20" N.; 80°49'08" W. Summersville Quadrangle.

At the west end of Brocks Bridge carrying West Virginia Highway 39 over the Gauley River is a crawlway 15 feet long in limy sandstone. A second cave is 100 feet north of the east end of the bridge and it consists of several small rooms and pits. The caves are in the Pottsville Series.

PENDLETON COUNTY

There are 55 significant caves recorded in Pendleton County. The majority of the caves (36) are in the Devonian-Silurian limestones that outcrop in several northeast-southwest bands in the central part of the county. The structure is typical Appalachian folds with a number of overthrusts disrupting the symmetry. It is interesting to note that most of the caves in this group are developed in limestones at or close to the junction of the New Scotland-Coeymans Limestones.

The Ordovician limestones are brought to the surface by the Wills Mountain Anticline in the area of Germany Settlement. Eight caves are in the Lowville and Lenoir Limestones and are generally characterized by having deep pits.

The remaining caves are in the Greenbrier Limestones which outcrop along the western edge of the county and dip gently west.

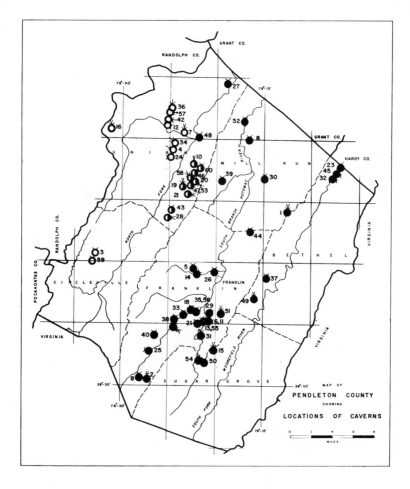

Figure 47.—Pendleton County Caves

1. Allen Pitzenbargers.	12. Ferris.
2. Arbegest.	13. Flute.
3. Back Ridge.	14. Friends Run.
4. Blowhole.	15. George Eye.
5. Bill Hendricks.	16. Graveyard.
6. Bruce Rectors Drop.	17. Gypsum.
7. Butcher.	18. Hamilton.
8. Cave Mountain.	19. Harper.
9. Cove Knob.	20. Hellhole.
10. Cowhole Well.	21. Hoffman School, Hoffman
11. Deer Lick Pits.	Cliff, Hoffman Pit.

22. Hourglass.
23. Indian.
24. Keel Spring.
25. Kenny Simmons.
26. Keys.
27. Kisamore.
28. Lambert No. 1.
29. McCoys Mill.
30. Mill Run.
31. Minor Rexrode.
32. Mitchells.
33. Moyers.
34. Mystic.
35. New Trout.
36. Onego Mill Stream.
37. Propst.
38. Quarry.
39. Reeds Creek.
40. Rexrode.
41. Rexrode Drop.

42. Roaring Creek Mill.
43. Ruddle.
44. Ruddle No. 2.
45. Saltpeter.
46. Schoolhouse.
47. Seneca.
48. Seneca Rock.
49. Sinkhole Hollow.
50. Sinnit.
51. Sites.
52. Smokehole.
53. Stratosphere Balloon.
54. Thorn Mountain, Thorn Mountain Pit.
55. Torys.
56. Trout.
57. Vance.
58. Warners.
59. Warners No. 2.
60. Warren Harpers Drop.

ALLEN PITZENBARGERS CAVE 38°43'17" N.; 79°12'34" W. Fort Seybert Quadrangle.

The entrance to this cave is a shaft 60 feet deep located 1.2 miles east of Deer Run Community and 0.8 mile southwest of Egypt School (elevation, 2510 feet). At the base of the shaft is a talus slope extending 50 feet west to a deep pool 5 feet wide and 18 feet long. On the far side of the pool, 25 feet above the water, is a short lead. The cave is in the Tonoloway Limestone.

ARBEGEST CAVE 38°30'04" N.; 79°28'53" W. Circleville Quadrangle.

Arbegest Cave is on the southwest end of High Knob, 1.4 miles southwest of Harper (elevation, 2750 feet). It is a vertical pit about 25 feet deep that is blocked at the base by a low fill. A passage is reported to exist beneath the clay fill. The cave is in the base of the Keyser Limestone.

BACK RIDGE CAVE 38°40'48" N.; 79°33'40" W. Spruce Knob Quadrangle.

This cave is at the head of Back Run on the west side of Spruce Mountain (elevation, 3950 feet). It is a short crawlway opening into a large room in the base of the Greenbrier Limestone.

BLOWHOLE 38°49′40″ N.; 79°24′53″ W. Onego Quadrangle.

This cave is located on the west side of Timber Ridge, 0.8 mile southwest of Teterton (elevation, 2250 feet). The entrance is a small crawlway in a low limestone ledge which opens into a channel 6 to 12 feet high and 20 to 30 feet wide, extending east for 350 feet. It then heads south and southeast for 2000 feet narrowing to an average width of 4 to 12 feet. Twelve hundred feet from the entrance, a second passage develops and heads south parallel to the main passage. Near the entrance to this passage is a section 35 feet long, with formations that hang from the ceiling and reach the surface of a pool to form a siphon. Beyond this the passage continues rather large and connects with a series of rooms. Two low waterfalls are developed along it. The passage is over 1000 feet in length and ends in a pile of broken rock. A large crevice passage opens about midway along this passage and heads east for 500 feet. Several side passages lead off in the first 300 feet from the entrance and, except one, are blocked by siphons after a short distance. One passage trends N. 30° E. and N. 50° E. for 300 feet ending in a small chamber. Two small pits are in this section of the cave. Formations are plentiful in the cave but are scattered. Flowstone, some rimstone, stalactites, and bacon rind form the bulk of the decorations.

A stream flows north through the cave and in several places deep pools are developed. Blowhole, in the Greenbrier Limestone, is developed along joints at N. 35° W., N. 10° E., and due east.

BILL HENDRICKS CAVE 38°39′46″ N.; 79°22′36″ W. Circleville Quadrangle.

This cave is on the south end of Brushy Mountain 0.9 mile northeast of Friends Run School (elevation, 3000 feet). The cave trends N. 40° E. and the main passage is 10 to 15 feet wide and 7 to 11 feet high. It is about 150 feet long. Forty feet from the entrance a small crawlway slit on the west side of the passage gives access to a room 40 feet long, 25 feet high, and 10 to 15 feet wide. Several small passages lead off the main passage and the room. The cave is in the New Scotland-Coeymans Limestones.

BRUCE RECTORS DROP CAVE 38°35′20″ N.; 79°20′53″ W. Circleville Quadrangle.

This pit is one mile northeast of Hoffman School on the west side of Neds Mountain (elevation, 2150 feet). The entrance is 3 x 4 feet in size and the pit is 30 feet deep with a narrow fissure about 70 feet deep at its base. The cave is in the Keyser-New Scotland Limestones.

BUTCHER CAVE 38°50′33″ N.; 79°23′25″ W. Onego Quadrangle.

This cave is a half mile north of U. S. Highway 33, one mile west of Mouth of Seneca. The entrance is 8 feet above a stream (elevation, 2250 feet). It is a 2-foot hole opening to a shaft 10 feet in diameter, 30 feet deep with a stream passage 30 feet long at the base. In the southeast corner of the pit is a passage 3 feet wide dropping 10 feet to a room 10 feet long, 5 feet high, and 20 feet wide. The cave is in the Greenbrier Limestone.

CAVE MOUNTAIN CAVE 38°49′44″ N.; 79°17′02″ W. Onego Quadrangle.

Two large caves are located on Cave Mountain. At the south point of the ridge, in the base of the limestone escarpment (elevation, 2450 feet), is the entrance to one of the caves. This cave consists of two parallel passages trending N. 30° E. The entrance is 4 feet high and wide but enlarges to 10 to 35 feet high and 10 to 50 feet wide. This passage extends for 2100 feet, ending in breakdown. Several pits up to 50 feet deep are developed in the floor of the passage. One of the pits, 1100 feet from the entrance, leads 35 feet down to the second passage which averages 15 to 65 feet wide, 10 to 40 feet high and is over 1700 feet long. The cave has been a source for saltpeter since Colonial days and was worked extensively during the War Between the States. A set of initials with a date of 1769 is stenciled on the wall in soot. Its authenticity is questionable. A few columns and flowstone are scattered along the passages. The cave is in the New Scotland Limestone near the crest of an anticline with a slight dip to the east. It is developed along a bedding-plane and a joint vertical but parallel to the bedding-plane.

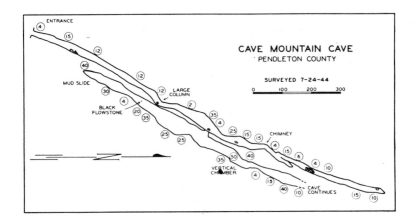

Figure 48.—Map of Cave Mountain Cave.

A second but much smaller cave parallels the large cave 200 yards south and 50 feet above it. The passage is large enough to permit walking and is about 1500 feet long with several rooms and side passages. Another small cave consisting of a single room entered through a very small tubular passage is near Cave Mountain Cave.

COVE KNOB CAVE 38°30′10″ N.; 79°29′13″ W. Circleville Quadrangle.

Cove Knob Cave is on the south spur of Cove Knob, 1.5 miles southwest of Harper, at an elevation of 2800 feet. The entrance is a narrow crevice that drops 12 feet to a low, broad, sloping passage through large fallen rocks for 30 feet. A drop over rocks and flowstone opens into a room 40 feet long, 25 feet wide, 5 to 8 feet high, with a clay floor sloping steeply to the south. Saltpeter earth was dug from the clay in this room during the War Between the States and mattock marks are clearly visible in the excavated area. A large cluster of columns and flowstone is at the center of the cave on the north side of the room. The cave, in the Keyser Limestone, which dips 5° to 10° west, heads S. 40° W. along a series of joints.

COWHOLE WELL 38°47′43″ N.; 79°22′33″ W. Onego Quadrangle.

A vertical shaft, 15 feet in diameter and 105 feet deep lies at the base of a sinkhole on the north side of Harpers Gap road, 0.8 mile north of the site of Cave School (elevation, 2050 feet). A short passage exists at the base of the shaft. Cowhole Well is in the Lenoir Limestone.

DEER LICK PITS 38°35′36″ N.; 79°20′48″ W. Circleville Quadrangle.

These pits are south of Deer Lick Draw, Thorn Run (elevation, 2150 feet). One pit is 35 feet deep; another within 150 feet of the first is a 4-foot hole 250 feet deep. The pits are in the Keyser-New Scotland Limestones. These pits may be the same as Bruce Rectors Drop Cave.

PHARIS CAVE 38°51′28″ N.; 79°25′00″ W. Onego Quadrangle.

This cave is in a cliff, 0.7 mile north of Onego on the west side of Roaring Creek (elevation, 2000 feet). It is a small sewer passage less than 150 feet long that follows joints at N. 80° W., N. 60° E., and due north. It is in the base of the Greenbrier Limestone and is 40 feet above the creek.

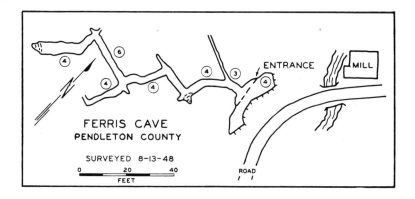

Figure 49.—Map of Pharis Cave.

FLUTE CAVE 38°34'46" N.; 79°21'39" W. Circleville Quadrangle.

The entrance to this cave is at the east end of the limestone escarpment ¼ mile east of Hoffman School, 50 feet above the road along Thorn Creek (elevation, 2200 feet). There are two openings, the south one is a narrow fissure 1 to 2 feet wide, 15 feet high, 100 feet long, leading west to the cave. The north opening is small and pinches out in a short distance. The cave is a series of pits and domes 20 to 40 feet deep connected by crawlways and stoopways. Total length is about 600 feet. The cave trends south with several short side passages and offsets to the east. Flute Cave is in the New Scotland Limestone.

FRIENDS RUN CAVE 38°39'06" N.; 79°22'15" W. Circleville Quadrangle.

The entrance to Friends Runs Cave is in a cliff 75 feet high on Friends Run 2.4 miles northwest of Franklin (elevation, 2050 feet). The entrance is 25 feet above the stream and opens to a crawlway 50 feet long. At the end of the crawlway is a small passage trending east to a pit. Another small passage at the end of the crawlway trends west to a flowstone terrace beyond which are several small passages and pits. The cave is in the Tonoloway Limestone.

GEORGE EYE CAVE 38°32'26" N.; 79°19'58" W. Circleville Quadrangle.

The entrance to this cave is in the middle of a field ½ mile due east of Mitchell at an elevation of 2700 feet. The entrance is a pit 30 feet deep at the base of which is a room 100 feet long, 6 to 8 feet high, and 10 feet wide, to the southwest. There are numerous speleothems at the end of the room. To the northeast from the base of the pit are two rooms, the first is 20 feet square while the second is 80 feet long, 20 feet wide, and 5 to 25 feet high. In this section the cave slopes downward to the northeast. The cave is in the Tonoloway Limestone.

GRAVEYARD CAVE 38°50′43″ N.; 79°31′42″ W. Horton Quadrangle.

This cave is near the head of White Run, ½ mile east of the Randolph-Pendleton county line and ¼ mile south of the county road (elevation, 3150 feet). A graveyard, in the middle of a pasture, is about 100 yards from the cave. The cave entrance, in a low sink, is a 40-foot pit. The passage at the base, a crevice over 200 feet long, is intersected by a chimney 150 feet from the entrance. The cave is very dangerous because of loose rock on the walls and ceiling. It is in the Greenbrier Limestone.

GYPSUM CAVE 38°45′00″ N.; 79°23′22″ W. Onego Quadrangle.

Entrance to this cave is a small pit 6 feet deep located two miles south of Judy Spring. It is at the east edge of a clearing about 4500 feet east of the road from Riverton to Seneca Caverns (elevation, 2300 feet). At the base of the pit is a talus slope in a room about 50 feet long, 15 feet wide, and about 30 feet high. At the end of this room is a passage to the left over and through a breakdown. This passage is 2 to 3 feet wide and 15 to 20 feet long. Anthodites are on the walls and under ledges. At the end of this passage is a dome room 15 feet in diameter and 12 feet deep. Flowstone is on the walls and floors of the pit. A passage 6 feet high leads from the pit 20 feet to an opening above a flowstone mound which bounds a pit 3 feet in diameter and 90 feet deep. At the base of the pit is a room 10 feet in diameter with no passage off it. Twenty feet from the bottom of the pit is a narrow passage leading to the bottom of a canyon passage 30 feet long and as narrow as 8 inches in places.

The passage leading from the 12-foot pit has white gypsum crusts on the walls and in a side passage. Adjacent and at the top of the flowstone cascade in this pit is a small hole connecting to an 86-foot dome pit. The cave is in the zone of contact between the Trenton member of the Martinsburg Shale and the Chambersburg Limestone.

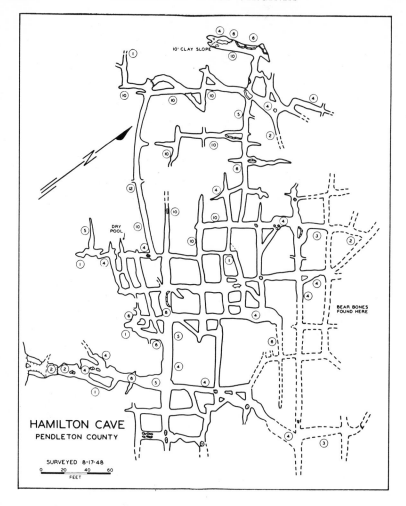

Figure 50.—Map of Hamilton Cave.

HAMILTON CAVE 38°36′20″ N.; 79°22′15″ W. Circleville Quadrangle.

The entrance to Hamilton Cave is at the west end of a low cliff above U. S. 220, 3.5 miles southwest of Franklin (elevation, 2025 feet). The entrance is a low crawl that opens into a maze of passages intersecting at right angles. The longer passages of the cave trend N. 40° W. On the northeast side are low crawlways but in the rest of the cave the passages average 3 to 4 feet in width and 5 to 10 feet high. The floor throughout the cave is damp clay. Formations are numerous with delicate soda-straw and "carrot-shaped" stalactites hanging from the ceilings, and columns and flowstone lining the walls.

Horizontal projections, the remains of less soluble lenses of limestone, are found in most of the passages. The cave is in the New Scotland Limestone which has a slight dip to the east. It is developed along major joints at N. 40° W., and N. 50° E. with subordinate joints at N. 60° W. and N. 80° E. modifying the passage. Persons entering the cave should use a map or provide proper markings of their traverse as the unusual pattern of the passages makes it easy to become lost.

HARPER CAVE 38°45'52" N.; 79°23'45" W. Onego Quadrangle.

Four-tenths of a mile due south of Key, at an elevation of 2050 feet, is a pit 80 feet deep. It opens into a passage, 30 to 70 feet high and 20 to 40 feet wide, that circles and joins itself. A second level, 30 feet below this passage, is not extensive. The cave is in the Lenoir (Stones River) Limestone.

HELLHOLE 38°46'18" N.; 79°22'49" W. Onego Quadrangle.

Hellhole is 600 feet west of the Harper Gap-Riverton road, 0.9 mile south of the site of Cave School (elevation, 2200 feet). The entrance is in a compound valley sink. Two large openings, with a third small hole between them, develop into a large entrance room 300 feet long, 160 feet wide, and 167 feet high. The entrance, at the top of the room, is a sheer drop of 180 feet to the floor. Two passages lead from the entrance room. One trending north is in two levels connected at several points by pits, 20 to 30 feet deep. After 400 feet the lower level is cut out but the upper level continues for 425 feet averaging 25 to 40 feet high and wide. The last 150 feet slopes steeply upward and is covered by a deposit of bat guano over 5 feet deep. The passage is blocked by wash from a surface sink.

One hundred and thirty-eight feet from the entrance to the north lead, a small opening on the lower level drops for 20 feet to a series of passages, 5 to 20 feet wide, and 4 to 15 feet high, which connect with a pit 54 feet deep known as Little Hellhole.

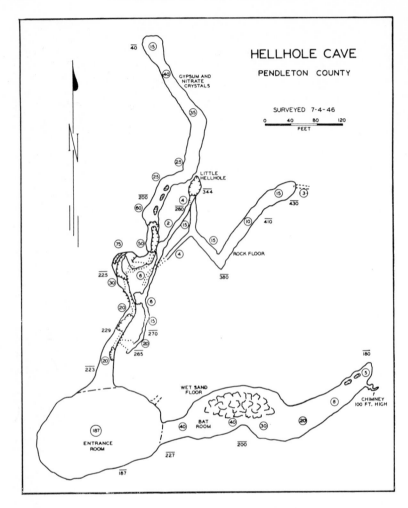

Figure 51.—Map of Hellhole.

From the base of the pit, sewer-like passages up to 15 feet high and wide trend south, southwest, and northeast. The northeast passage ends in a small room which is choked with driftwood, sand, and similar material. This point is over 300 feet below the entrance. The east passage is a large vaulted chamber 150 feet wide and 50 feet high extending for 500 feet. One hundred feet from the entrance room is a pile of break-

Plate XXXVIII.—Entrance Room, Hellhole (Pendleton County). Copyrighted; pub-
ﬂed by permission of National Speleological Society. (Photo by W. H. Watkins).

down covered by deep bat guano. The passage narrows towards the end and the ceiling lowers until slabs of breakdown block it. Several small pits near the end of the east passage lead to a small passage below. The floor of the entrance room is large slabs of fallen rock while along the north passage it is sand and wet clay.

Hellhole is in the Lenoir (Stones River) Limestone at the crest of the Wills Mountain (Cave School) Anticline.

HOFFMAN CLIFF CAVE 30°34′38″ N.; 79°21′50″ W. Circleville Quadrangle.

This cave is in the limestone cliff about 60 feet above and 100 feet east of Hoffman School Cave (elevation, 2235 feet). It is a vertical fissure several feet wide and 12 feet high and 75 feet long. The cave is in the New Scotland Limestone.

HOFFMAN PIT CAVE 38°34′37″ N.; 79°21′50″ W. Circleville Quadrangle.

This cave is 150 feet west of and 120 feet higher than Hoffman School Cave (elevation, 2295 feet). It is a circular pit 2 feet in diameter and 40 feet deep. At the base is a small passage grading into a fissure. The cave is in the New Scotland Limestone.

HOFFMAN SCHOOL CAVE 38°34′38″ N.; 79°21′49″ W. Circleville Quadrangle.

In the west end of a limestone escarpment on Horner Mountain, just west of the site of Hoffman School, is a small shelter-like opening, 15 feet high and long and 20 feet wide (elevation, 2175 feet). A small crawlway enlarges to a fissure passage, 10 feet wide, 10 to 30 feet high, and 100 feet long heading N. 30° E. Seventy-five feet from the entrance a passage opens to the west as a low crawlway excavated by saltpeter miners and after 50 feet turns N. 30° E. for 180 feet over considerable breakdown, as a passage 10 to 30 feet wide, and 10 feet high. A clay slope and several small chimneys connect with a passage 10 feet above and to the east. The upper passage continues N. 30° E. for 500 feet ranging from 6 to 20 feet wide and 6 to 15 feet high. The last 210 feet of the passage has high clay banks on the east side. In this section pendants

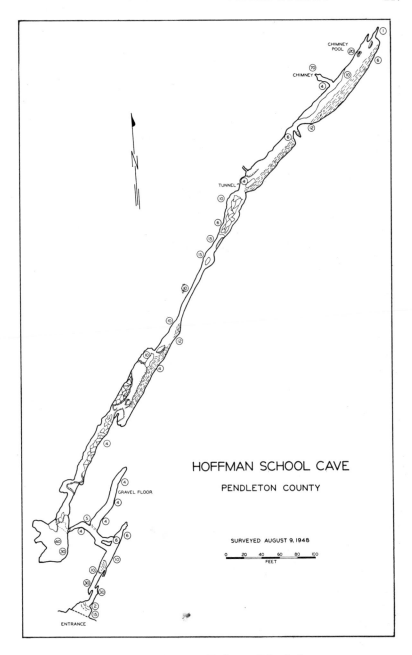

Figure 52.—Map of Hoffman School Cave.

are clustered on the ceiling and two large dome pits are on the west side of the passage near the end. The cave ends by clay sealing off the passage. Considerable bat guano covers the floor of the cave. Hoffman School Cave, in the New Scotland Limestone, which dips 10° W., is developed along joints at N. 30° E., N. 40° W., and N. 80° E. Fossils from the New Scotland Limestone weather out in large quantities and are found free of the limestone matrix near the rear of the cave. A strong blast of air blows out the entrance.

HOURGLASS CAVE 38°45'37" N.; 79°23'32" W. Onego Quadrangle.

This cave is 3 miles northeast of Riverton near a small cemetery (elevation, 2250 feet). The entrance is through a well shaft 20 feet deep that was opened into a cave 45 feet below. There are two rooms, one 25 feet long, 15 feet wide, and 25 feet high; the other is 39 feet long, 15 feet wide, and 25 feet high. The cave contains a profusion of white speleothems and a thin vein of carbonaceous material is reported interbedded with the limestone in the cave. The cave is in the limestones of the Stones River Group.

INDIAN CAVES 38°47'44" N.; 79°06'54" W. Petersburg Quadrangle.

These caves are on the northwest side of the South Fork, 0.1 mile west of the Hardy-Pendleton county line (elevation, 1425 feet). The caves are in a high limestone cliff and are reached by dropping down from the top of the cliff. The largest cave is a winding fissure about 50 feet long ending in a small room. To the south, on another cliff, is the remains of an old ladder that gives access to a short, dry crawlway. The caves, though named Indian, have nothing to indicate they were occupied by Indians. The caves are in the New Scotland (?) Limestone.

KEEL SPRING CAVE 38°48'53" N.; 79°24'58" W. Onego Quadrangle.

The entrance to this cave is in a low ledge of rock, 100 yards west of the road along Timber Ridge, at Keel Spring School (elevation, 2550 feet). The opening is through fallen rock which connects with a room 100 feet long, 20 feet wide and high. A narrow stream passage leads north for 100 yards. Stalactites and flowstone decorate the room. The cave is in the Greenbrier Limestone.

KENNY SIMMONS CAVE 38°32'54″ N.; 79°26'53″ W. Circleville Quadrangle.

This cave is in a low, rounded hill, 100 yards west of U. S. 220, 0.4 mile north of Cave P. O. (elevation, 2175 feet). The entrance is man-made (dug 1895) and opens into a room trending N. 40° E. for 450 feet. At the entrance the room is 30 feet wide and 20 feet high while near the rear it broadens to 150 feet. At the rear the room divides into two sections. Along the east side of the room breakdown is banked to the ceiling. Beneath the breakdown is a series of crawlways extending the length of the cave. An extension of these passages opens on the hillside 20 feet below the main entrance. It was through this passage that the cave was first entered. Numerous stalactites (including soda straws) and columns are developed near the entrance, along the east wall of the main room and in the crawl passages. The floor of the room is deep clay and is smooth. At the point where the room divides is a chasm can be traversed in a boat and is entered through a twisting channel with low ceiling for 30 feet. The pond is 25 feet in

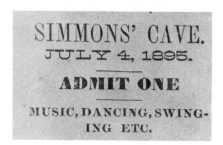

Plate XXXIX.—Kenny Simmons Cave—Copy of ticket.
(Photo by Wm. E. Davies).

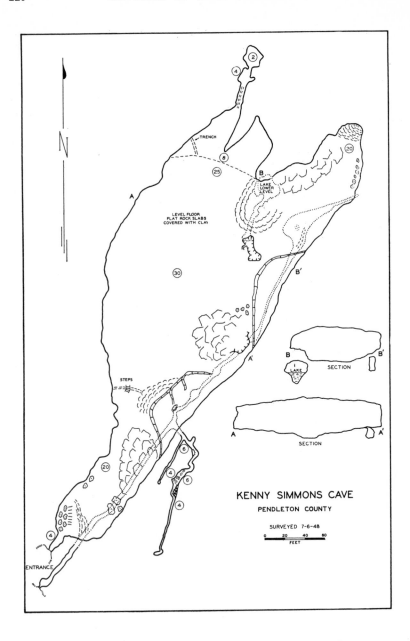

Figure 53.—Map of Kenny Simmons Cave.

diameter with a ceiling 20 feet above the water. The water is 10 feet deep in the room and crystal clear with a white silt bottom. In the passage it is 30 feet deep. The cave is in the Keyser Limestone which strikes N. 30° E. and dips 22° W.

Dances, boat rides, and similar entertainment were held in the cave on July 4 of each year at the turn of the century. The present owners of the cave have tickets from such events. Initials and dates are abundant in the cave and on a rock on the east side of the room, near the middle, is a set of names dated 1847, the oldest found in the cave.

A small cave, consisting of a crawlway 40 feet long, lies near the base of the hill directly below the entrance to the large cave.

KEYS CAVE 38°39'18" N.; 79°20'38" W. Circleville Quadrangle.

Keys Cave is along U. S. Highway 33, 1 mile west of U. S. Highway 220 (elevation, 1850 feet). The entrance is a crawlway 8 feet above the creek. The crawlway goes beneath the highway and opens into a small maze of passages on three levels. The levels are 8 to 45 feet apart and the passages are mostly low stoopways 2 to 10 feet wide. A few speleothems are in the rear part of the cave and chert lenses projecting from the walls are common. Keys Cave is in the New Scotland Limestone. A 75-foot pit is reported near by.

KISAMORE CAVES 38°54'30" N.; 79°18'45" W. Onego Quadrangle.

Along West Virginia Highway 28, ¼ mile north of Zeke Run is a cliff with a number of cave openings (elevation, 1500 feet). The cliff is 150 feet high and the openings are in groups 20 feet (2 large openings); 40 feet (2 large and 4 small openings); and 90 feet (8 small openings) above the North Fork River. The caves trend north and the larger ones show passages at N. 30° W., N. 20° E., and N. 70° E. Most of them are crawlways less than 100 feet long. The large caves are 5 to 10 feet high and 5 feet wide. One is in the center of the cliff, the others at the west end. The caves on the second level are floored with river gravel. Those on the other levels have clay floors. The caves are in the Keyser Limestone which dips 10° E.

LAMBERT CAVE NO. 1 38°43'54" N.; 79°25'12" W. Circleville Quadrangle.

Lambert Cave is on a small flat, 1.2 miles southeast of Riverton (elevation, 2250 feet). The entrance is a pit, 30 feet deep, now filled with rock. A passage, 15 feet wide, 30 to 40 feet high, extends south for 300 feet. An interesting calcite encrusted wooden trough rests on a dome of flowstone near the entrance. The cave is in the Lowville Limestone.

LAMBERT CAVE NO. 2 Circleville Quadrangle.

A cave is reported along Smith Creek south of Franklin. No specific data could be obtained in the field concerning it.

McCOYS MILL CAVE 38°36'06" N.; 79°21'07" W. Circleville Quadrangle.

Three hundred yards south of the Reunion Grounds (Thorn Spring Park), in a high cliff along the Thorn Creek road, is a large shelter cave at road level (elevation, 1800 feet). The opening is 15 feet wide and long and 10 feet high. Ten and 30 feet above the road, two passages open on the face of the cliff. The lower one (southernmost) is a crawlway 200 feet long ending in a room 10 feet wide, 20 feet long, and 10 feet high. The other passage, 3 to 6 feet wide and 2 to 4 feet high, parallels the southern passage for 150 feet. Near the end a cross passage connects the two. The cave is in the New Scotland Limestone which strikes N. 50° E. and dips 30° S.E.

MILL RUN CAVE 38°46'20" N.; 79°13'26" W. Petersburg Quadrangle.

This cave is in the cliffs on the south side of Mill Run, 0.4 mile south of Kline (elevation, 2050 feet). The cave is a single passage (except for a fork near the rear), 1000 feet long, with an average height of 30 feet and width of 15 feet. A few short crawlways, one at the entrance, 20 feet long, interrupt the passage. Several rooms develop along the passage where it widens. The floor of the passage is fallen rock and clay. Legend indicates that the cave was used for saltpeter in the early part of the nineteenth century. The cave is in the Coeymans-New Scotland Limestones.

MINOR REXRODE CAVE 38°33′52″ N.; 79°21′38″ W. Circleville Quadrangle.

This cave is on the north side of Thorn Run, at the south end of Neds Mountain, 3½ miles north of Moyers P. O. (elevation, 2200 feet). The entrance, at the base of a low cliff, opens into a shelter 20 feet long, 6 feet high, 10 feet wide, with a crawlway leading west. The crawlway is 30 feet long and opens into a room 90 feet long, 30 feet wide, 10 feet high with a floor of breakdown sloping steeply west. The main passage of the cave, 50 feet below the entrance, is a fissure 3 to 20 feet wide, 4 to 20 feet high trending N. 40° E. for 600 feet. The passage ends in a steeply sloping clay-covered crevice with a number of chimneys opening in the ceiling. The last half of the passage is floored by slabs of rock that have scaled from the ceiling. Beyond the sloping clay crevices the cave continues on a level 18 feet above the main cave. The upper level is 250 feet long, the first 80 feet of which is a fissure 20 feet high, 10 feet wide, sloping 45° to the southwest. Beyond this fissure is a narrow fissure 2 to 5 feet wide extending 100 feet above the floor. In the rear this fissure is blocked by debris from the surface that has slumped into the cave. Several domes are on the southwest side of the fissure near the end of the cave. The cave, in the New Scotland Limestone which strikes N. 40° E. and dips 30° W., is developed along joints at N. 40° W. A strong current of air blows out of the entrance.

MITCHELLS CAVE 38°46′50″ N.; 79°07′56″ W. Petersburg Quadrangle.

Mitchells Cave is on the west side of Sweedlin Hill, 1.6 miles southwest of the Pendleton-Hardy county line (elevation, 1550 feet). The entrance to the cave is at the base of a low ledge of limestone, 300 feet above the river. The opening is a crawlway sloping 50 feet downwards to the north. It opens into the main passage which extends 1800 feet to the northeast with a ceiling height of 10 to 50 feet and a width of 30 to 80 feet. At the end it is blocked by a mud bank. South of the entrance it extends less than 100 feet. Beneath the main passage are two lower level ones about 500 feet long. The junction between the main passage and the entrance crawlway is difficult to find and should be well marked on entry. The cave is in the Keyser Limestone.

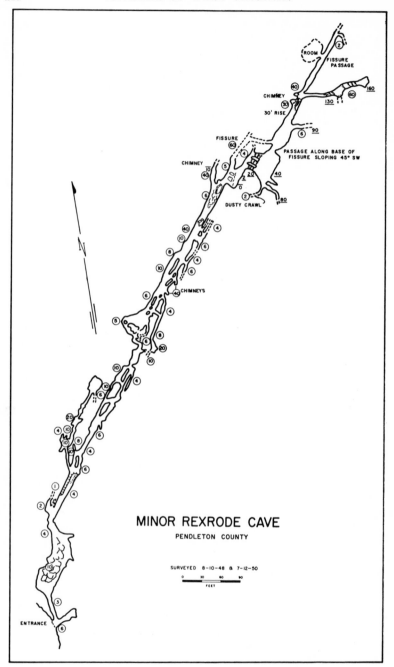

Figure 54.—Map of Minor Rexrode Cave.

MOYERS CAVES 38°36'08" N.; 79°22'45" W. Circleville Quadrangle.

Moyers Caves are 50 feet west of U. S. 220, 1.6 miles southwest of McCoys Mill (elevation, 1850 feet). They are two small crawlways on the north side of a small gully. The west hole is 50 to 75 feet long and slopes steeply downwards. The other hole is 150 feet to the northeast and is 15 feet long. The passages are in the New Scotland Limestone.

MYSTIC CAVE Onego Quadrangle.
38°49'50" N.; 79°24'42" W.
38°49'50" N.; 79°24'52" W.
38°49'26" N.; 79°24'45" W.

Mystic Cave (north entrance) is in a shallow valley sink 100 yards west of Timber Ridge road, 0.4 mile southwest of Teterton (elevation, 2280 feet). The entrance is a low crawl, 20 feet wide for 20 feet where it enlarges to 8 feet high. A stream flows into the cave at the entrance. Eighty feet from the entrance is a vertical drop of 18 feet to a junction of two passages. One passage heads west and receives the streams entering the cave. The main passage heads S. 20° W. for 2000 feet with minor offsets and varies in width from 10 to 35 feet with occasional narrower areas. The ceiling averages 6 to 30 feet high with occasional short crawls. Four rooms open along the passages at several points. At the beginning of the passage the floor is breakdown but elsewhere it is clay with a stream flowing on it. Four large pools are found along the passage. Formations in the form of massive flowstone (Dutch Ovens), columns, and stalactites are scattered along the passage.

Two thousand feet from the junction a large room 125 feet in diameter, 30 feet high, is developed on the east side of the passage. The east end of the room is blocked by breakdown. The passage continues south above the pool at the entrance to the room. It is a tortuous stream channel with a waterfall, pools, squeezeways, crawlways as well as a large room that extends 600 feet to the south. For the last 200 feet it enlarges to 6 to 20 feet high but is very narrow. The passage ends in a small exit that opens into the face of a low limestone ledge, 200 yards west of Timber Ridge road, ½ mile south of the north entrance to the cave. A small stream flows in. Several small side leads are developed along this passage.

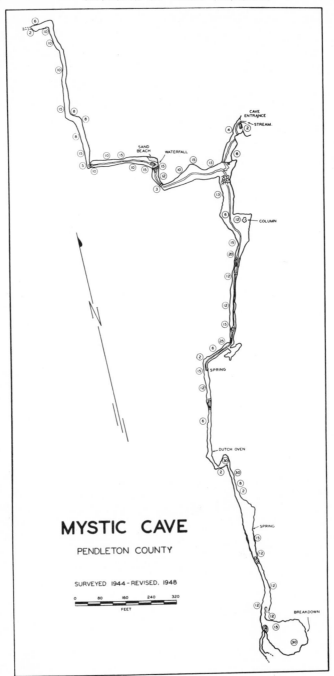

Figure 55.—Map of Mystic Cave.

The passage leading due west from the junction near the entrance averages 20 feet in width and 10 to 15 feet in height for 270 feet. A room is developed 100 feet from the junction where the passage widens to 60 feet. The passage heads alternately north and N. 70° W. for 1050 feet averaging 8 to 15 feet high and wide. The last 300 feet are narrower and require traversing a stream two feet deep. At the end of the passage, where it emerges to the surface, the passage is very low and narrow requiring considerable squeezing to effect an exit. The stream from the passage is resurgent in a large spring 100 feet below the exit. The floor of the passage is fallen rock near the junction but the remainder is sand or clay with a stream flowing along it. A waterfall, 8 feet high, is 350 feet from the junction. The stream enters the cave at the south end of the south passage (elevation, 2310 feet) and flows north to join a stream from the north entrance (elevation, 2260 feet) at the junction. The streams unite and flow west through the West Passage and exit in a spring on the west side of Timber Ridge (elevation, 2140 feet). Mystic Cave is in the Greenbrier Limestone and is developed along joints at S. 20° W., S 60° W., N. 80° W. in the south portion and along joints at N. 80° W., and N. 10° E. in the north portion.

NEW TROUT CAVE 38°36'09" N.; 79°22'08" W. Circleville Quadrangle.

New Trout Cave is in a low limestone escarpment 300 feet east of Trout Cave and 60 feet above U. S. Highway 220 (elevation, 1870 feet). The cave trends N. 40° E. and the first 600 feet is a straight passage 4 to 15 feet wide and 5 to 20 feet high. The ceiling is along bedding-planes which dip 35° to the southeast. Two rooms, 150 feet long, 50 feet wide, 15 feet high and 300 feet long, 50 feet wide, 10 to 25 feet high, are 600 and 800 feet from the entrance. Beyond these rooms are two parallel passages 225 feet long, 4 to 25 feet wide, and 3 to 15 feet high. The passages join near the end of the cave. The ceilings and walls of the cave are sooty. The cave is developed along two systems of joints (N. 40° E. vertical to bedding; N. 40° W. vertical) in the Coeymans-New Scotland Limestones. Saltpeter was mined in the cave during the War Between the States.

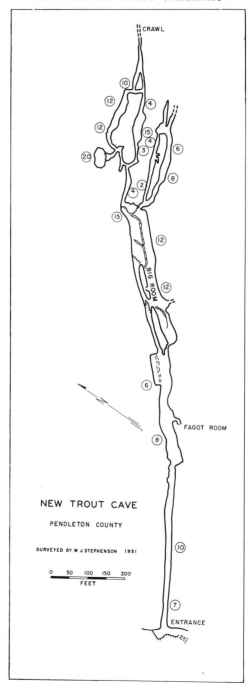

Figure 56.—Map of New Trout Cave.

ONEGO MILL STREAM CAVE 38°52'04" N.; 79°24'45" W. Onego Quadrangle.

One and one-half miles north of Onego, Roaring Creek sinks in a narrow crevice to flow in a subterranean passage (elevation, 2000 feet) for ¾ mile. Resurgence is at the mill, ¾ mile north of Onego. The fissure opening in the stream bed drops 28 feet to a passage 25 feet high and wide that continues south for over 1000 feet as a series of squeeze passages and rooms. It is dangerous to traverse because of loose rock in the walls and ceiling. It is open only in the severest droughts. The cave is in the Greenbrier Limestone.

PROPST CAVE 38°37'13" N.; 79°16'34" W. Circleville Quadrangle.

Propst Cave is on the north side of Brandywine Run, Dickinson Mountain, 2 miles WSW of Brandywine (elevation, 2600 feet). The entrance gallery, a passage 2 to 8 feet high, 4 to 10 feet wide, trends N. 35° E. and N. 50° E. for 200 feet. A narrow crawlway slopes southeast 150 feet from the entrance and connects through complex small chambers, to a series of galleries extending northeast parallel to the entrance chambers. The first gallery is 120 feet long, 6 to 20 feet wide, 4 to 10 feet high, with gypsum crystals incrusted in the clay floor and walls. The gallery opens through a narrow slot into the Main Room which is 200 feet long and 60 to 75 feet wide. The ceiling, 40 to 50 feet high, is gently arched and contains a number of stalactites. The floor is breakdown covered with flowstone. Several wide pits are developed along the east side of the room with a short crawlway leading east from one of them. On the west side a small passage below the level of the floor leads behind a pile of breakdown and joins the room again. At the north end of the Main Room is a large barrier of rock covered by flowstone sloping upwards at 60° for 50 feet. On the north side of this divide is an overhang drop to the floor of the last room (Far Room) of the cave. It is 100 feet long, 40 feet wide, and 40 to 50 feet high. The floor is covered with breakdown overlain by flowstone and other formations. At the end of the room is a pit 20 feet deep with a large white flowstone cascade descending into it. A small passage on the west side of the room leads to the pit. Propst Cave is in the Coeymans-New Scotland Limestones. Several small caves of little consequence are reported in the area of Propst Cave.

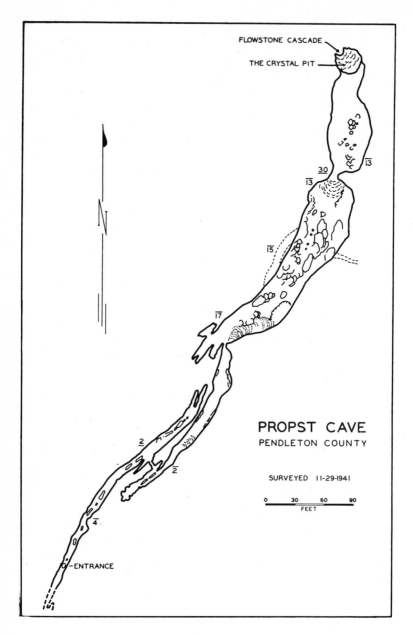

Figure 57.—Map of Propst Cave.

QUARRY CAVE 38°35′32″ N.; 79°23′54″ W. Circleville Quadrangle.

On the west wall of the State Road Commission's quarry, 5 miles southwest of Franklin, is a small but prominent opening, 20 feet above the quarry floor (elevation, 1900 feet). The cave is 400 feet long and trends S. 40° W. curving to S. 55° W. at the rear. The passage is a sewer 3 to 8 feet high and 5 to 10 feet wide with a dry clay floor. At the end of the passage are several pits, 20 to 25 feet deep and 5 to 10 feet in diameter. The base of the pit opens into a short passage with a pond at the level of the Potomac River (which lies 200 feet to the south). A short passage leads for 40 feet to the north at the end of the cave. The cave is in the Keyser Limestone.

REEDS CREEK CAVE 38°46′08″ N.; 79°19′27″ W. Onego Quadrangle.

This cave is on the north side of a tributary of Reeds Creek, 2.7 miles southwest of Upper Tract (elevation, 1800 feet). The entrance, in a low ledge, is a crawlway with a gentle slope downwards that opens into a room 50 feet long, 20 feet wide, and 15 feet high. Beyond the room it is again a crawlway with several branches. The cave has a few scattered formations and is in the Tonoloway Limestone.

REXRODE CAVE 38°34′22″ N.; 79°25′28″ W. Circleville Quadrangle.

Rexrode Cave is on the north side of Moyer Run, 1000 feet west of U. S. 220 (elevation, 2100 feet). The entrance is in a vertical sink, 15 feet deep, 10 feet square, in a ledge of limestone 40 feet above the stream. It opens to the north in a high fissure-like passage, 20 feet wide and 60 feet high. The floor, of hard clay and leaves, slopes 50° downward at the entrance and ends in a pit 20 feet deep. The passage extends N. 30° E. with vertical walls 60 feet high and a ceiling of jagged rock and stalactites. The floor is broken by several pits which are connected by a small passage at the base. One hundred and forty feet from the entrance a large mound of clay, fallen stalactites, and rocks rises 25 feet and then slopes down to a pit. At this point, 200 feet from the entrance, the cave divides into two levels. The upper level is at the top of a

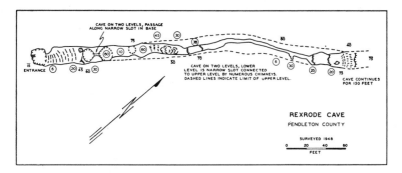

Figure 58.—Map of Rexrode Cave.

cliff 45 feet up. The lower level is a steeply inclined, slippery crawlway over a series of ledges of breakdown, flowstone, and stalagmites which connects with the upper level. On the north side of the pile the cave drops 50 feet and continues for about 150 feet (450 feet from the entrance).

Rexrode Cave is in the Keyser Limestone with a vertical dip and is developed along the bedding-planes.

A second cave exists on the north branch of Moyer Run, ½ mile northwest of Rexrode Cave. The entrance, in a sink at the base of a high ledge of limestone on the north side of the stream, is now plugged by leaves and clay. It is reported to be a large cave.

REXRODE DROP CAVE 38°35′03″ N.; 79°23′48″ W. Circleville Quadrangle.

This cave is on the north side of Sandy Ridge 5½ miles southwest of Franklin (elevation, 2850 feet). The entrance is a 25-foot pit at the base of which is a short passage sloping 30° down to another 15-foot pit. Offset from this is a 20-foot pit which connects with a fissure that is too narrow to traverse. This cave is in the Keyser (?) Limestone.

ROARING CREEK MILL CAVE 38°51′30″ N.; 79°24′59″ W. Onego Quadrangle.

Roaring Creek resurges 0.8 mile north of Onego (elevation, 1900 feet). The stream issues from a large opening and was carried by a flume, part of which collapsed in 1945, to a mill. The opening, rectangular in outline, 6 feet high, 15 feet wide, is in a cleft 20 feet above the valley floor. Just inside is a waterfall 10 feet high beyond which the passage heads northwest and is 3 feet high and 6 feet wide with a deep stream flowing through it. It is reported that the cave can be traversed its entire length (1500 feet) in dry seasons although much crawling is required. The cave is in the base of the Greenbrier Series.

RUDDLE CAVE 38°44'11" N.; 79°25'00" W. Circleville Quadrangle.

Ruddle Cave is 1.1 miles east of Riverton in a small ravine at an elevation of 2150 feet. The entrance is through a small hole, formerly covered by trap door, on the east side of the ravine. At the base of the entrance a sinuous passage trends east and southeast for 100 feet. It is 2 to 4 feet high and 1 to 4 feet wide descending gradually to 30 feet below the entrance. At the end of the passage is a drop of 22 feet to the floor of a room 25 feet high, 45 feet long and 35 feet wide. At the east end of the room is another room 100 feet long, 30 feet wide, 10 to 15 feet high, with a large pile of fallen rock in the center. At the southwest corner of the first room another room leads southwest for 70 feet with a width of 25 feet and a height of 20 feet. At the southwest end is a chimney, 35 feet in diameter, 65 feet high, with a pit 15 feet deep at its base. A large white flowstone column covers the west wall of the chimney. A room trending northwest is separated from the pit by a partition of rock 15 feet high. This room, 110 feet long, 25 feet wide, and 40 feet high, ending in a slope of broken rock, has a floor of wet clay. A number of formations including bacon rind and stalactites with a deep-red hue are found in this room. Formations are scattered along the walls of the other rooms as well. Ruddle Cave is in the upper part of the Lowville Limestone and is developed along sets of joints at N. 50° W. and N. 30° E.

RUDDLE CAVE NO. 2. 38°41'58" N.; 79°16'52" W. Circleville Quadrangle.

The entrance to this cave is on the west side of Dry Run, 4.8 miles northeast of Franklin (elevation, 2200 feet). The opening is a crawlway which becomes large enough for walking a short ways in. It extends south for 400 feet. The floor is of clay. Ruddle Cave No. 2 is in the Keyser Limestone.

SALTPETER CAVE 38°47'11" N.; 79°07'24" W. Petersburg Quadrangle.

This cave is on the west side of Sweedlin Hill one mile southwest of the Pendleton-Hardy county line (elevation, 1600 feet.) The cave trends south and is a crawlway for the first 50 feet. The cave, about 500 feet long, has a number of narrow fissure openings barely large enough to permit traverse, with pits opening in the floor.

A narrow crevice extends north from the entrance and opens into the face of a high cliff. A few stalactites decorate the cave. Saltpeter is reported to have been dug from the cave but no evidence exists to support such a report. Saltpeter Cave is in the Keyser Limestone.

SCHOOLHOUSE CAVE 38°47'06" N.; 79°22'30" W. Onego Quadrangle.

Probably no cave in West Virginia has received the attention and investigation that Schoolhouse has. It has been

Plate XL.—Schoolhouse Cave, Entrance. (Photo by Wm. E. Davies).

vividly described and pictured by Tom Culverwell in a number of publications.[25] Schoolhouse Cave is 100 yards north of the site of Cave School on the Harper Gap road (elevation, 2205 feet). The entrance is in a sink 50 feet east of the road and opens into a large gallery 30 to 40 feet wide, 70 feet high, and 150 feet long. The clay floor slopes steeply downwards at the entrance for 75 feet. The ceiling of the entrance gallery is flat with a large channel scar cut into it. The gallery ends in a vertical wall except on the southeast side where a clay bank gives access to three passages 75 feet above the floor. The center passage leads south into the main part of the cave while the one on the east is little more than a side room. The west passage is blocked by clay fill 100 feet in. The center passage trends south for 500 feet as a narrow passage, sometimes a trench cut by saltpeter workers, about 6 feet high. At the end of this passage the character of the cave changes abruptly. The Big Room, with a number of deep wells and overhangs, is developed here. It is 200 feet long, 30 feet wide and the bases of the pits are 200 feet below the entrance to the room. On the south side the cave continues as a small passage, similar to that leading off the entrance room, across a small room with a deep pit to another room (Thunderbolt Room) of the same character as the Big Room but less than half in size. On the south side of the room is a gallery 300 feet long, 20 to 30 feet wide, with several pits in the floor. The cave ends in a clay and rock fill 1600 feet from the entrance. The ceiling from the Entrance Room to the end of the cave remains at practically the same level.

At the bottom of the Big Room two passages lead off. One heads north parallel to the main upper passage for 500 feet to a room and then curves west and ends by pinching out at a point almost beneath the east end of the Entrance Room. The second passage is 50 feet below and apparently is the bottom of the cave. It is well named the Grind Canyon, for it is a crevice-like passage 2 feet wide, 25 feet deep and quite sinuous. The walls are covered by nodules of cave coral. A small stream flows south along the passage. Five hundred feet to the south of the pit giving access to it, the ceiling height of the passage reduces to the point where it is no longer passable.

[25] See listings in Bibliography for complete references.

Plate XLI.—Schoolhouse Cave, Entrance Room. (Photo by Wm. E. Davies).

The passage can also be followed 100 feet to the north. The passage is not directly beneath any of the other passages of the cave. Along the west wall of the Big Room are the entrances to several short side passages.

Formations are found in most of the rooms. The Big Room contains flowstone and travertine curtains. Clumps of stalactites hang from the ceiling at various places along the rooms and passages. One of the passages leading west of the Big Room has numerous small stalactites lining the ceiling as well as scattered groups of helictites. Gypsum flowers are found in the clay floors and walls in the lower passage north from the Big Room. The passage connecting the Entrance Room and the Big Room is dug in laminated clay 4 to 8 feet deep. The individual laminae are in the order of a fortieth of an inch in thickness and are distinct in any cross-section. The clay is now dry and peels along certain of the laminae, breaking into blocks an inch thick.

Plate XLII.—Laminated clay fill exposed in the saltpeter trench, upper level of Schoolhouse Cave.

Schoolhouse Cave, in the Lenoir and upper Mosheim Limestones near the crest of Wills Mountain Anticline, is developed along vertical joints at N. 30° E. with joints at N. 10° W. and N. 80° W. which modify the major trend.

SENECA CAVERNS 38°45′48″ N.; 79°23′23″ W. Onego Quadrangle.

Seneca Caverns, one of the three commercial caves in West Virginia, is 3 miles northeast of Riverton on the Riverton-Harper Gap road (elevation, 2200 feet). The entrance to the cave is in a shallow sink and opens into a broad passage for 50 feet. A large flowstone mound (Dutch Oven) on the west side restricts the passage near the end. The ceiling has a small

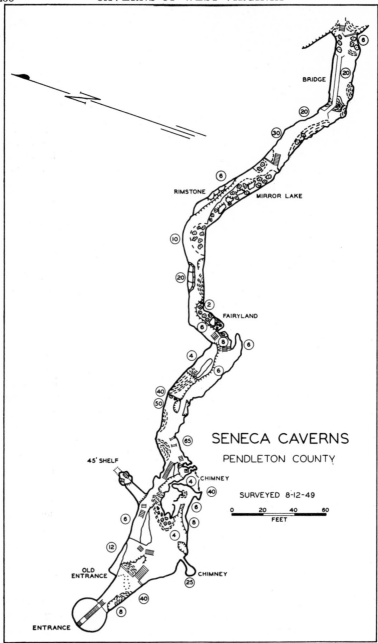

Figure 59.—Map of Seneca Caverns.

channel and pits scoured in it. A room, known as the Ballroom, lies at the end of the passage and is roughly triangular in shape, 60 feet long, 30 feet wide. A cluster of stalactites, columns, and flowstone is along the south wall. The only side passage in the cave leads off to the southeast from the Ballroom and is a low, clay-filled tunnel 60 feet long.

The pathway descends to a lower level on the northeast side of the Ballroom. The lower level is developed along the base of dome pits, some of which open into the Ballroom. Massive flowstone, most of it dazzling white, lines the passage. Two hundred feet from the entrance the cave heads S. 80° E. for 400 feet as a passage 10 to 60 feet high, and 20 to 30 feet wide. Formations are found throughout and consist of massive flowstones, columns, and stalactites. A flowstone mound, known as Niagara Falls, fills the passage at one point making necessary a detour through a man-made tunnel for 80 feet. The cave, after 400 feet, heads S. 40° E. for 200 feet, the first half of it through a low passage choked with stalactites, columns, and rimstone pools. The last half is an open passage 15 feet wide, 20 feet high, with a bank of clay on the south side. Columns rest on the clay bank and clusters of stalactites follow joint lines in the ceiling. The rear part of the cave heads due east 100 feet and opens in a low ledge on the west side of a narrow ravine. This section is 20 feet wide and high with large flowstone formations and columns along the walls and clusters of stalactites hanging from the ceiling along the joint lines. This section is quite wet and the pathway is on a long wooden bridge over a series of ponds.

The commercial aspect of the cave is quite pleasing. The pathways and lighting are ample and in keeping with the natural beauty of the passages. The formations are beautiful and well distributed. In addition to the formations mentioned above, attention should be directed to the Princess Snow Bird, a flowstone that forms in bas relief a perfect likeness to a head of a young girl. It is located near the entrance to the cave. The caverns were developed for commercial use in 1930.

Seneca Caverns is in the Lowville Limestone at the peak of the Wills Mountain Anticline. It is developed along joints at N. 50° W., and due west. Minor joints at N. 60° E. have little influence.

Plate XLIII.—Seneca Caverns. Flowstone and Stalactites along Joints. (Photo by Wm. E. Davies).

Several smaller caves lie near Seneca Caverns. In a shallow sink 300 feet south of the entrance to the caverns is a small cave. The entrance, a narrow slit at the base of the sink, opens into a room 200 feet long which heads N. 30° W. curving to S. 30° W. It averages 15 feet wide and has a ceiling height of 20 to 40 feet. The clay floor slopes towards a series of shallow pits near the center of the cave. A dome pit, 40 feet high and 2 feet in diameter, is in the west wall at the center of the room. Along the south side of the room is a shelf, 20 feet above the floor, which has a number of short, stubby stalagmites on it. The cave is in the Lowville Limestone.

Stratosphere Balloon Cave, also on the Seneca Caverns property, is described separately.

SENECA ROCK (CAVE HOLE) CAVE 38°50′38″ N.; 79°22′05″ W. Onego Quadrangle.

The entrance to Seneca Rock Cave is in a cliff on the east side of North Fork, 0.7 mile north of Mouth of Seneca (elevation, 1620 feet). The cave entrance, a fissure-like opening on the south end of the cliff 100 feet above the river, develops into a passage 3 to 4 feet wide, 10 to 15 feet high, that slopes downwards for 200 feet at 30° A number of small passages junction off here but are of little consequence as they are at river level and blocked by clay and water. The cave is in the Tonoloway Limestone with a vertical dip.

SINKHOLE HOLLOW CAVE 38°38′40″ N.; 79°15′05″ W. Circleville Quadrangle.

One mile northwest of Brandywine, on the southeast side of Dickinson Mountain, west of Heavener Run, is a 10-foot diameter sinkhole (elevation, 2200 feet) with a 31-foot drop to the top of a pile of debris. At the base of the drop a 15-foot slope extends to a passage floored by large boulders. Several short crawlways lead from the base of the entrance. The cave is in the New Scotland-Coeymans Limestones.

SINNIT CAVE 38°31′08″ N.; 79°22′08″ W. Circleville Quadrangle.

Sinnit Cave is 0.4 mile northwest of Moyers P. O., on the south side of Whitethorn Creek (elevation, 2250 feet). The entrance is in a low ledge at the top of a pile of fern- and moss-covered talus, 60 feet above the creek. It opens into a passage, 10 to 14 feet wide, 8 feet high, 400 feet long, which connects with a crawlway 450 feet long, having a fissure 1 to 2 feet wide, 10 to 15 feet deep, in the floor. Near the beginning of the keyhole-shaped passage is a junction with a narrow, twisting crevice passage that connects directly with the large room 100 feet to the west. A number of narrow side passages branch from this connecting fissure. The keyhole passage is paralleled

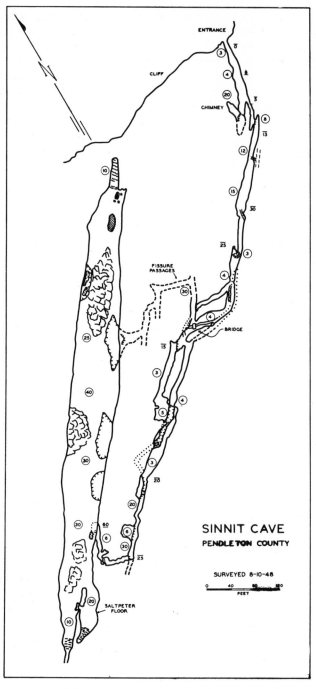

Figure 60.—Map of Sinnit Cave.

by a connecting crawlway for 75 feet from the junction. At the end of the keyhole passage is a vertical shaft resembling a silo, with three sets of shelves, 10 feet apart, that connects with a steeply sloping crawlway leading to the Long Room. The Long Room trending N. 50° E. is 90 feet above and parallel to the lower entrance passage. It is 800 feet long, averaging 70 to 80 feet wide, and is triangular in cross-section with ceiling height of 40 feet at the apex. The floor is covered with large blocks of breakdown encrusted with clay. Three large pits along the east wall slope down to lower crevice passages. The north end of the room is close to the face of the cliff above the entrance to the cave and is blocked by a mound of rock and clay with flowstone and formations on top. The south end pinches out by narrowing and the rise of clay banks. The east wall is formed by the bedding-plane of the limestone which dips 40° E. while the west wall is along a joint perpendicular to the beds.

Saltpeter was mined in the cave during the War Between the States. Apparently the earth dug in the large room was dumped down the northernmost pits on the east side of the room and hauled from there out of the cave. The walls of the cave are coated by a black sooty film of manganese dioxide, similar to that in Trout Cave. Gypsum flowers incrust the walls and floors of the Long Room and the rear portions of the entrance passages.

Sinnit Cave is in the Coeymans-New Scotland Limestones and is developed along joints at N. 50° E. and N. 50° W.

SITES CAVE 38°36'00" N.; 79°19'23" W. Circleville Quadrangle.

This cave is a quarter of a mile east of Dry Run, 2 miles north of Dahmer (elevation, 2250 feet). The entrance shaft is 298 feet deep and is vertical except for the lower 90 feet which is inclined to the west. At the base is a passage to the southwest which is 300 feet long. A similar passage extends to the northwest. The passages are 5 to 15 feet high and 10 to 40 feet wide. At the end of the southwest passage is a room 35 feet long and 45 feet high. Several shafts open in the ceiling near the entrance shaft. Sites Cave is in the Tonoloway Limestone.

SMOKEHOLE CAVE 38°50'36" N.; 79°17'30" W. Onego Quadrangle.

The entrance to this cave is at the base of a limestone cliff, 1.1 miles south of Branch, on the north side of the South Branch in the Smokehole (elevation, 1730 feet). A well-marked trail leads from the road at the camp ground south of Branch to the cave. The cave is a complex series of parallel and side passages trending east and west for 225 feet. An entrance passage heads N. 40° E. for 75 feet, connecting the entrance and the east-west passages. It is 4 to 10 feet high and 4 to 8 feet wide. The east-west passages are 2 to 6 feet and 40 feet below the base of the entrance. A large flowstone walls are undercut by broad openings about one foot high. Twenty feet from the entrance a narrow crevice passage extends S. 80° E. for 20 feet to a circular room, 15 feet in diameter, 20 feet high, with a gently arched roof. Several small windows open from the room to the face of the cliff. The floor of the cave is damp clay with some fallen rock.

Smokehole Cave, in the Coeymans Limestone, is developed along major joints at N. 30° E. and due west, with subordinate ones at N. 50° W., due north, and N. 60° E. The limestone strikes due north with a dip of 10° W.

STRATOSPHERE BALLOON (ASBURY) CAVE 38°45'48" N.; 79°23'30" W. Onego Quadrangle.

This cave, formerly a commercial one, is 200 yards south of Seneca Caverns (elevation, 2170 feet). The entrance is in a vertical sink, 20 feet deep. Wooden steps lead down to the main passage. This passage, 15 to 20 feet high, 20 feet wide, trends N. 40° E. for 50 feet, then east for 75 feet, and N. 50° W. for 50 feet to a room. The middle part of the passage has several beautiful flowstone formations and stalagmites along the north wall. The room is 30 feet in diameter, 20 feet high, wide, 4 to 15 feet high, with vertical walls. At the base the mound is on the east side of the room. Two passages lead off the room. One is a small crawlway on the west wall, 10 feet above the floor. The main passage leads off from a shallow pit on the north side and is 10 feet high and wide. The first part trends N. 40° E. for 70 feet and then N. 65° W. for 30 feet to a small room. The room is 50 feet long, 25 feet wide, with a

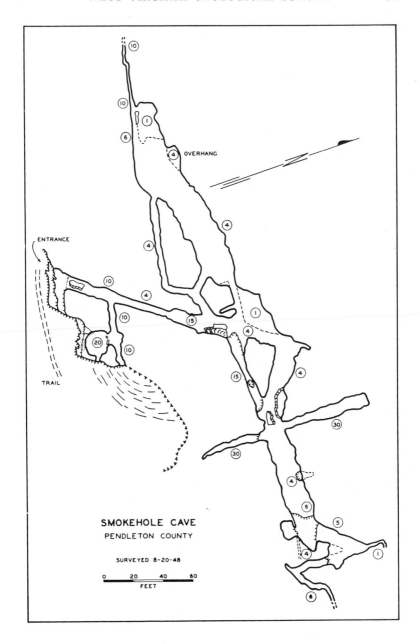

Figure 61.—Map of Smokehole Cave.

large ribbed flowstone mound, 18 feet in diameter and reaching 25 feet to the ceiling, at the end. The cave is named from this formation—the Stratosphere Balloon. The room is 80 feet below the base of the entrance.

Plate XLIV.—Stratosphere Balloon Cave. Speleothems near Entrance. (Photo by Wm. E. Davies).

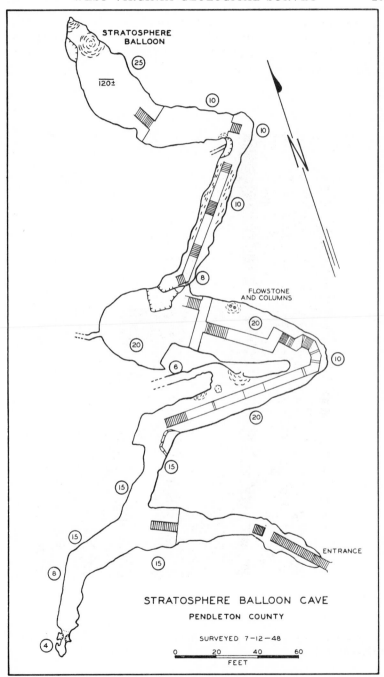

Figure 62.—Map of Stratosphere Balloon Cave.

Plate XLV.—Stratosphere Balloon Cave. Slime Fungus. (Photo by Wm. E. Davies).

While the formations in the cave are well worth the visit, of equal interest is the fungus action on the wooden stairs and walk. Large sheets of white slime fungus hang from the railings and steps which are now so weakened that they are dangerous to traverse. The wood attacked by the fungus is as light in weight as balsam.

Stratosphere Balloon Cave is in the Lowville and Lenoir Limestones at the crest of the Wills Mountain Anticline. It is developed along joints at N. 40° E., due east, and N. 60° W.

This cave is among the oldest known caves in the State. Bishop Francis Asbury described it in his journal[26] for June 21, 1781.

---

[26] Published in Pendleton Times, volume 23, no. 30, Franklin, W. Va., September 5, 1946.

Also in Clark, Elmer T., Ed., Journals and Letters of Bishop Asbury: Abingdon Press, 1958, Vol. 1, pg. 407.

Plate XLVI.—Stratosphere Balloon Cave. Stratosphere Balloon Formation. (Photo by Wm. E. Davies).

THORN MOUNTAIN CAVE 38°31'07" N.; 79°22'17" W.
Circleville Quadrangle.

Thorn Mountain Cave is 800 feet west of Sinnit Cave, on a spur of Thorn Mountain (elevation, 2500 feet). A description of the cave is most difficult and the map offers the simplest explanation. The entrance is a vertical shaft, 10 feet wide, 14 feet long, and 40 feet deep which opens into a passage 12 to 18 feet high, 10 to 30 feet wide, 200 feet long, which rises 50 feet and then drops to the level of the base of the entrance. At the end of this passage the cave opens into a series of interconnected rooms and passages at three levels. The main room trends S. 50° W. and is 400 feet long, 6 to 30 feet high with a width of 20 to 45 feet. The floor slopes steeply to the south and three small pits are developed along the west wall. At the south end the room ends in a pit 10 feet in diameter and 135 feet deep. The subordinate passages, including the entrance, are to the west and above this room.

Columnar flowstone cascades as well as spikes of calcite are found at various points in the cave. The floors are of breakdown or clay. Some gypsum occurs in the clay of the floor. Thorn Mountain Cave is in the Coeymans Limestone.

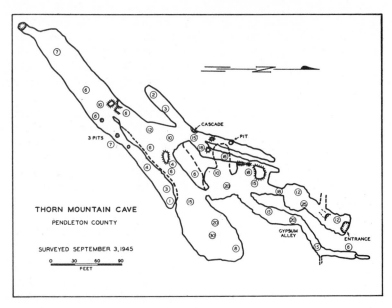

Figure 63.—Map of Thorn Mountain Cave.

THORN MOUNTAIN PIT 30°31'08" N.; 79°22'17" W. Circleville Quadrangle.

This pit is in the middle of a pasture halfway up the hill to Thorn Mountain Cave (elevation, 2400 feet). The entrance pit is two feet in diameter with a 5-foot drop to a steep slope leading 20 feet down to a dome-shaped room 6 feet high and 12 feet in diameter. Two passages 40 to 50 feet long lead from the base of the pit. The pit is in the Keyser Limestone.

TORYS (DONA) CAVE 38°34'38" N.; 79°21'45" W. Circleville Quadrangle.

This cave is at the base of a limestone cliff directly above the site of Hoffman School, on Thorn Creek, 2.4 miles south of McCoys Mill (elevation, 2100 feet). The cave is blocked by fallen rock but the entrance is indicated by a large indentation in the face of the cliff. A small opening in the northwest corner of this niche has a trickle of water flowing out. It is too small to traverse. The cave opening is supposed to exist beneath the pile of rock but removal of the rock to a depth of 10 feet has not revealed it. The cave is rumored to be quite large. Several stories relate to the collapse of the entrance. One relates the cave was a station on the Underground Railroad and that a number of negroes were trapped by the rock fall. Another states that the cave was being worked for saltpeter when it collapsed, trapping the workers. A third story relates that renegade soldiers of the Revolutionary War used the cave and that the collapse buried their equipment but did not trap anyone. Regardless of the veracity of the stories they have stimulated considerable effort to open the cave. Operations designed to open the cave are dangerous as the rock is shattered along the cliff and a large block is perilously suspended over the entrance. The cave is in the New Scotland Limestone.

TROUT CAVE 38°36'14" N.; 79°22'10" W. Circleville Quadrangle.

Trout Cave is in a prominent escarpment on the north side of South Branch, 3.5 miles southwest of Franklin, on U. S. 220 (elevation, 1975 feet). The entrance is 20 feet wide, 15 feet high, opening into a room of similar dimensions, 350 feet long. The floor is of fallen rock. The cave is offset to the west and continues as a passage 10 to 15 feet wide, 12 to 20 feet high, with a floor of huge boulders of fallen rock. This passage is 400 feet long where it develops into a maze of crevice passages to the northwest. A small hole leads to a lower level which continues northeast as a series of small, irregular rooms connected by passages 2 to 4 feet high and 10 to 15 feet wide. Three hundred feet from the junction it changes to a series of complex crawlways at least 400 feet long to a point where the passages are too low for further crawling. It is reported that a few persons have traversed this section and emerged at the surface through a small opening. A strong current of air at the rear of the cave indicates there is such an opening.

The floor throughout most of the cave is composed of fallen rock. In some sections deep beds of saltpeter earth occur that were mined extensively during the War Between the States. Gypsum crystals are imbedded in this earth near the rear part

Plate XLVII.—Trout Cave. Entrance. (Photo by Wm. E. Davies).

of the cave. The walls and ceiling have a soot-like deposit of manganese dioxide through all parts of the cave. The deposit is on a crust of crumbly travertine about a half inch thick. Fossils from the limestone lie on the floor of the cave free of the parent rock. Excellent specimens can be obtained in the rear part of the cave.

Trout Cave is in the Coeymans-New Scotland Limestones and closely follows the boundary between the two. The dip is 12° E. The cave is developed along joints at N. 70° E., N. 40° E., and N. 40° W.

A small fissure cave lies 100 feet west of Trout Cave. The passage, which opens 25 feet above the base of the cliff, is 75 feet long, 2 to 4 feet wide, and 10 feet high. It trends northeast for 50 feet and then heads east toward Trout Cave but is reduced to a low, narrow crawlway. It apparently connects with one of the passages on the west side of the entrance room of Trout Cave.

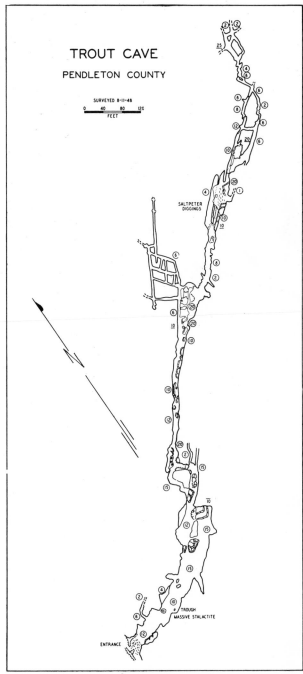

Figure 64.—Map of Trout Cave.

Plate XLVIII.—Trout Cave. Trough near Entrance. (Photo by Wm. E. Davies).

VANCE CAVE 38°51′43″ N.; 79°24′52″ W. Onego Quadrangle.

Vance Cave is 100 yards east of Roaring Creek, 1.1 miles north of Onego (elevation, 1980 feet). The entrance, a very low crawlway heading east along a stream that issues from the cave, is in a ledge of limestone. The cave turns north a short way in and extends 500 feet as a crawlway. It is lined with beautiful formations so dense that they all but fill the passage. Vance Cave is in the lower part of the Greenbrier Limestone.

WARNERS (BROKEN DOME) CAVE 38°46′45″ N.; 79°23′12″ W. Onego Quadrange.

Warners Cave is 600 yards west of the Harper Gap road, 2 miles south of Harper Gap (elevation, 2150 feet). The entrance a vertical shaft, 3 feet in diameter, 30 feet deep, is in a clump of trees in a meadow. The main passage extends north for 400 feet and curves slightly. It is 12 to 15 feet wide and 30 feet high and ends in a crawlway and mud slope which reach to the ceiling. The cave has a number of formations including a large flowstone dome, 30 feet in diameter, the bottom part of which has broken and slumped. A balcony, 15 feet above the floor, extends along part of the main passage and has a large number of formations on it. Warners Cave is in the Lenoir Limestone.

WARNERS CAVE NO. 2 38°40'10" N.; 79°33'57" W. Spruce Knob Quadrangle.

A large spring issues on the north side of the road, 500 feet north of Back Ridge School, 4 miles west of Circleville (elevation, 3550 feet). A low crawlway leads back along the underground channel for an unknown distance. The cave is in the base of the Greenbrier Limestone.

WARREN HARPER DROP CAVES 38°47'34" N.; 79°22'02" W. Onego Quadrangle.

On the north side of the entrance drive to the farm of Warren Harper, three miles south of Seneca Rock, one mile northeast of Schoolhouse Cave, are five pits (elevation, 2200 feet). Pit number one is 143 feet deep with no passage at the base. It is 5 by 8 feet in cross-section. The second pit has an entrance 2 feet in diameter opening to a shaft 20 feet in diameter and 166 feet deep. There is no passage at the base. Pit number three is a shaft 25 feet deep with a narrow crevice at the base. The fourth pit is 14 feet deep with no passage at the base. The fifth pit is 25 feet deep with a horizontal passage at the base trending south into a dome pit. The entrance to this pit is 1½ by 3 feet. The pits are in the Lowville-Lenoir Limestones.

Twenty other caves have been reported in Pendleton County as follows:

Bobs Mountain Cave—This is on the summit of Bobs Mountain. It is a cave in the shape of an inverted Y and is 3 feet in diameter with a 1-foot stem and 12-foot forks.

Coverts Crevice—In Thorn Valley; two pits, one 15 feet deep; the other a fissure 90 feet deep; may be the same as Bruce Rectors Drop Cave.

Don Down Cave—In Thorn Valley near Hoffman School; 40-foot pit.

Eye Pit—65-foot pit, breakdown to second pit 35 feet deep. On Sharps Ridge, one mile south of Dahmer.

Marshall Propst Pit—Near George Eye Cave, steeply sloping pit, 100 feet deep.

Moyers Twin Wells—These pits are 1½ miles southwest of Sinnit School on an old logging road along Long Run. Entrance is a slit 2½ feet wide, 6 feet long enclosed by a board fence opening to two pits about 78 feet and connected by a window halfway down.

Mullinax Cave—This cave is reported to be five miles northwest of Cave P. O. It is a 45° slope entrance, 15 feet long to a passage 100 feet long, 6 to 25 feet wide, and 10 feet high.

Nut Cave—1¼ miles south of Hoffman School Cave; entrance at road level on west side of Thorn Creek; cave is crawlway extending 400 feet SW to a stream passage 20 feet high and wide, 300 feet long; breakdown blocks passage on west and east ends; rimstone near entrance.

Propst Drop—Thirty-foot pit on the property of Oliver Propst above Thorn Creek Valley.

Simpsons Crawl Cave—A 40-foot crawl cave with the entrance at the base of a 10-foot cliff is on the east side of Dickinson Mountain, three miles south of U. S. Highway 33.

Simpsons Drop Cave—A 25-foot pit with a steeply sloping passage 30 feet long is ¼ mile southwest of Simpsons Crawl Cave.

Siples Caves—1.8 miles northeast of Deer Run Community is a pit 25 feet deep; 80 feet from this is a crawl hole 20 feet long.

Germany Valley Pits—Several pits have been reported in Germany Valley. The following are of significant size:

A 27-foot pit is 0.8 mile northeast of Judy Spring.

A 55-foot pit with an offset pit of 30 feet at its base is on the ridge south of Stringtown Run, 1½ miles southeast of Riverton. It is known as **Walnut Tree Pit.**

A pit, 1000 feet southeast of the junction of the road to Judy Spring and the road to Seneca Caverns, is 35 feet deep with an offset 10 feet from the bottom. It is known as **Bennetts Garbage Pit.**

A 6-foot deep fissure opens into a dome pit 19 feet deep 0.4 mile northeast of Seneca Caverns.

A 30-foot narrow pit is 0.4 mile N.N.E. of Seneca Caverns.

A pit opening into a dome room 15 feet high is 400 feet east of the junction of the Judy Spring and Seneca Caverns roads. A passage 100 feet long leads to the north from the room; a south passage is 300 feet long with domes. Several small passages lead from the domes. This is known as **Lawrence Dome Pit.**

A pit 30 feet deep, 3½ miles south of Seneca Rock is known as **Kindergarten Cave;** it is ¼ mile west of Cave School.

A 25-foot pit **(Russell Lawrence Cave)** with three passages is reported near Riverton School. This may be the same as Lawrence Dome Pit Cave.

One hundred fifty feet northwest of Cowhole Well there is reported to be a shaft 165 feet deep with a passage 15 feet long at the base; 100 feet north of this is another pit 100 feet deep.

A nameless cave is 100 yards north of Stratosphere Balloon Cave. It is a steep passage leading to a gallery 200 feet long, 15 feet wide and 30 feet high.

Two small caves are in the limestone bluffs along the South Branch a mile north of Franklin. The one at Bluehole has a large entrance but 30 feet in is a crawlway about 50 feet long. One thousand feet north of this is a short fissure opening 40 feet above the river.

POCAHONTAS COUNTY

There are 96 caves recorded in Pocahontas County. Of these, all but one are in the Greenbrier Series which outcrops as a broad band of limestone 2 miles wide from the county line north through Hillsboro and Marlinton. North of Marlinton the band is narrow and lies on the flank of the upland to the west of the Greenbrier River and passes near Cass and Durbin into Randolph County.

The Greenbrier Series outcrops on the valley floor of Elk River and its headwaters in the northern part of the county

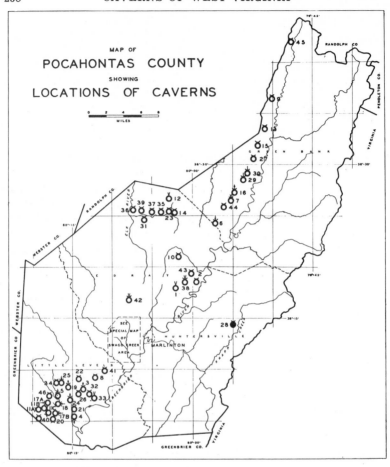

Figure 65.—Pocahontas County Caves

1. Barlow Pit.	14. Gatewood.
2. Barnett.	15. Greathouse.
3. Beards.	16. Grimes.
4. Bolling.	17. a, b, Herbert Hill.
5. Bruffey Creek.	18. Hills Creek.
6. Cass.	19. Hughes Creek.
7. Cassell.	20. Ice Cave.
8. Cemetery.	21. Jacksons.
9. Cherry Run.	22. Kinnison.
10. Cloverlick.	23. Linwood.
11. a, b, c, Clyde Cochrane.	24. Locust Creek.
12. Devils Dining Room.	25. Martens.
13. Durbin.	26. Marthas.

27.	Moore.	37.	Sharps Store.
28.	Moore No. 2.	38.	Shinaberry.
29.	Moores.	39.	Slaty Fork.
30.	Overhang.	40.	Snedegars.
31.	Pine Tree.	41.	Stephens Hole.
32.	Poor Farm.	42.	Tyler Hole.
33.	Poor Farm Pit.	43.	Walt Allen.
34.	Saltpeter.	44.	Wanless.
35.	Sharps.	45.	Wildell.
36.	Sharps Mill.	46.	Williams.

and in the valley on the west side of Droop Mountain in the southern part of the county. In the southern part of the county the series is 600 feet thick but it thins to the northeast and is reduced to 300 feet near Durbin. Because of poor exposures and the thinness of individual members of the series it has not been possible to identify the limestone member in which each cave is developed. Throughout most of the county the series has a gentle dip to the northwest. In the broad outcrops near Hillsboro broad, open folds are developed.

The limestones of the Silurian-Devonian System outcrop along the sides and top of Brushy Mountain and its continuation to the north as far as Green Bank. Only one cave in Pocahontas County is reported from these limestones. There are probably more but the remote position of the outcrops and the heavy vegetation cover have caused them to go unobserved.

BARLOW PIT 38°17'50" N.; 80°02'56" W. Mingo Quadrangle.

Barlow Pit is 1.4 miles northeast of Warwick at an elevation of 3000 feet. The pit is about 50 feet deep but is now filled with stone and trash. A short passage existed at the base. The pit is in the middle part of the Greenbrier Series.

BARNES PIT 38°12'43" N.; 80°09'10" W. Marlinton Quadrangle.

Barnes Pit is two miles northwest of Buckeye on the ridge between Overholt Run and Swago Creek (elevation, 2500 feet). It is a 20-foot pit with a waterfall. A dry passage at the base trends towards Swago Pit. The main passage is a crawlway downstream towards Overholt Blowing Cave. Barnes Pit is in the Greenbrier Limestone.

BARNETT CAVES 38°17′44″ N.; 80°00′45″ W. Mingo Quadrangle.

In a shallow sink, one mile south of Poages Chapel (elevation, 2900 feet), two cave openings exist with passages leading east. The passages, about 100 yards long, are large enough to permit walking. The caves are in the base of the Greenbrier Series.

BEARDS (BLUE HOLE) CAVE 38°07′45″ N.; 80°14′00″ W. Marlinton Quadrangle.

A large, vertical-sided sink lies one mile southwest of Hillsboro, ¼ mile west of U. S. 219 (elevation, 2200 feet). On the west side is a broad opening 40 feet wide, 8 feet high, which extends back 60 feet. Towards the rear the room broadens out to the south and is 70 feet wide. At the rear a low stream passage, 2 to 4 feet high and 6 feet wide, leads S. 60° W. for 150 feet. A stream flows out of the cave and forms a large pool in the entrance sink. Water also enters the sink from the north side under a pile of rocks. The water exits at the south side. Local residents believe the water entering the sink comes from Hills and Bruffey Creeks. During wet weather the sink fills with water and a decade ago a boy drowned in the flooded sink while retrieving stray sheep. A cave entrance, 250 feet to the south in an adjacent sink, is now blocked by trash.

Beards Cave is in the Patton (?) Limestone, Greenbrier Series.

BLUE SPRINGS 38°09′42″ N.; 80°11′13″ W. Marlinton Quadrangle.

Blue Springs is the resurgence of Stamping Creek, ½ mile northwest of Mill Point (elevation, 2220 feet). A low opening in a ledge of limestone on the south side of the valley has a large stream of water and blast of cold air coming out. It is not known if the passage can be traversed. The springs are in the base of the Greenbrier Series.

BOLLING CAVE 38°05'53" N.; 80°15'00" W. Lobelia Quadrangle.

Bolling Cave is on the east side of Locust Creek, one mile south of its head (elevation, 2200 feet). A rough wooden bridge across the creek and a trail lead to the cave. The entrance, 30 feet wide and 4 feet high, is enclosed now in glass to serve as a wintering place for sheep. This room is 20 feet long and the cave continues to the east as a low passage for 1500 feet. A large stream flows out of the cave. Many but small formations line the small stream passage. The cave is in the Hillsdale Limestone, Greenbrier Series.

BRUFFEY CREEK CAVE 38°07'25" N.; 80°16'45" W. Lobelia Quadrangle.

Bruffey Creek sinks under Droop Mountain in a cave 1.1 miles southeast of Lobelia (elevation, 2450 feet). The entrance is 10 feet square and opens into a passage heading S. 60° E. The passage is 10 to 20 feet high and averages 15 feet wide for about 500 feet where it joins a similar passage from Hills Creek and heads east. The east passage can be traversed for 100 feet where it fills with water and is too narrow for further progress. The floor of the cave has a small stream but logs jammed in crevices 30 feet above the floor indicate the fury of flood waters that invade the cave in wet weather. Bruffey Creek Cave is in the Union Limestone, Greenbrier Series.

CARPENTERS PIT-SWAGO PIT 38°13'01" N.; 80°09'10" W. 38°13'02" N.; 80°08'51" W. Marlinton Quadrangle.

These pits and cave are 2.5 miles northwest of Buckeye. The entrance to Swago Pit (elevation, 2900 feet) is 54 feet deep with a waterfall. At the base is a passage 100 feet long, 2 to 5 feet high and wide to a series of 5 pits and domes. The pits connect with a second level 50 feet below the first. This level is a slot passage 550 feet long, 2 to 3 feet high, and 2 to 10 feet wide. The stream is at the base of the slot and is 2 to 5 feet deep. At the end of this level are two waterfalls each about 30 feet high. At the base of the second waterfall the passage connects with Carpenters Pit.

The second level, 100 and 300 feet from its terminus, connects via crawlways to the north with the passage from the base of Carpenters Pit. Carpenters Pit is a shaft 75 feet deep, 70 feet west of the Swago Creek road (elevation, 2750 feet).

The initial drop is through the Union member of the Greenbrier Limestone. A second 15 foot pit slightly offset from the first continues through the Pickaway member. Most of the cave is developed in the shaly Taggard member.

The passages at the base of the pit are essentially two parallel galleries developed on several levels along parallel N. 60° E. joints; the galleries are about 200 feet apart. The western gallery is a little over 5000 feet long. It terminates in

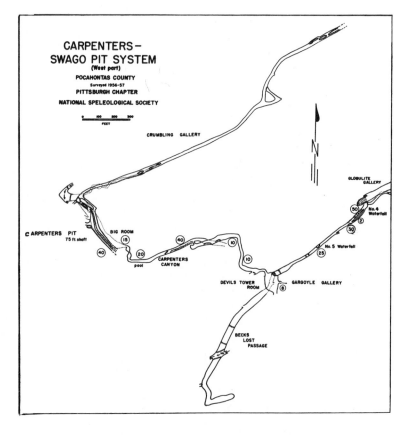

Figure 66.—Carpenters-Swago Pit System, west part.

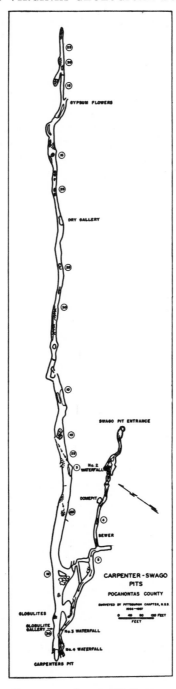

Figure 67.—Carpenters-Swago Pit System, east part.

a dome complex which is apparently on the opposite side of a large ridge from the entrance. Under the ridge the central parts of the gallery are perhaps 650 feet below the surface. The passage is broken in the middle by 500 feet of breakdown which is traversable in a small crawlway. The gallery has a small stream which drains into the large room at the foot of the entrance shaft. At the foot of the entrance shaft, an additional drop of 40 feet connects with the floor of the Big Room. This room is developed on a cross joint connecting the two parallel galleries. It is 200 feet long, 35 feet wide and roughly 40 feet high. At its eastern end, it is a canyon passage 40 feet high and 10 feet wide trending N. 60° E. After 600 feet, this canyon is broken into several superimposed levels. One thousand feet from the entrance room is the foot of the fourth waterfall of the Swago Pit cave system. The eastern gallery is less complicated and consists primarily of one long passage. To the northeast of the connection with the Swago Pit cave system it is 5 to 20 feet wide and 10 to 20 feet high for 2000 feet. The floor in this section is dry earth and breakdown. This part of the cave is known as the Dry Gallery. The Swago Pit stream joins the Big Room stream and drains to the south. The downstream passages are low water crawls and have not been explored. One and one-half miles of passage have been mapped in Carpenters-Swago system with at least an additional mile to be mapped.

CASS (SHEETS) CAVE 38°23'59" N.; 79°56'49" W. Cass Quadrangle.

Cass Cave is 1000 feet west of Cold Run School (elevation 2975 feet). The entrance is a stoopway trending northeast for 700 feet to the Big Room, 180 feet high, 900 feet long, and 20 to 40 feet wide. The entrance passage intersects the Big Room in a sheer cliff about 150 feet above the floor. A stream flows along the entrance passage and drops into the Big Room in a waterfall 130 feet high. At the end of the Big Room are walkways and crawlways extending 2500 feet to the east. A lower stream passage reverses direction and trends 2500 feet to the west. Just before the waterfall is reached a passage connects with the entrance passage on the west side and extends N.N.E. for 2,000 feet. Cass Cave is in the Greenbrier Limestone.

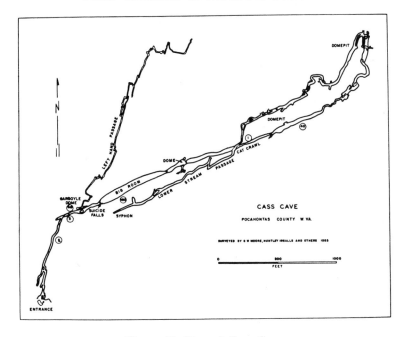

Figure 68. Map of Cass Cave.

CASSELL CAVE 38°27′24″ N.; 79°53′48″ W. Cass Quadrangle.

On the south fork of Trout Run, 1000 feet west of the road along the flank of Back Allegheny Mountain is a pit 96 feet deep (elevation, 3060 feet). At the base are two parallel fissure passages 1100 feet long trending S. 65° W. Three rooms, each about 200 feet long, 30 feet wide, and 70 feet high, are along the passages. Two pits, 60 and 80 feet deep, also are in the passages. There is a small stream in the cave. Cassell Cave is in the Greenbrier Limestone.

CAVE CREEK CAVE 38°12′12″ N.; 80°08′40″ W. Marlinton Quadrangle.

Cave Creek, a short but important tributary to Swago Creek, ¼ mile north of McClintock Run, rises in a cave ½ mile due west of Dry Creek School (elevation, 2300 feet). The entrance is one of the most beautiful of any cave. It is a broad, fern-covered opening, 50 feet wide and 10 feet high, with a

Plate XLIX.—Cave Creek Cave. Entrance. (Photo by Wm. E. Davies).

picturesque waterfall 6 feet high just inside. The cave extends west in two passages. The north passage is dry with a ceiling height of 2 to 4 feet and a width of 15 feet. The south passage is a stream passage of similar dimensions. One hundred and eighty feet from the entrance the passages join and continue for 1500 feet to the west as a low stream passage of similar dimensions. In 1957 it was reported that breakdown blocked the stream passage about 100 feet beyond the point where the passages joined. The stream flowing in the cave is a foot deep with a swift current and the floors of the cave are made of gravel. Cave Creek Cave is in the Hillsdale Limestone, Greenbrier Series.

CEMETERY CAVE 38°09′24″ N.; 80°11′43″ W. Marlinton Quadrangle.

Cemetery Cave, at the north side of the cemetery (elevation, 2400 feet), ¾ mile west of Mill Point, is a vertical shaft 25 feet deep with a small room at the base. It is in the Patton (?) Limestone, Greenbrier Series.

CHERRY RUN CAVE 38°35'46" N.; 79°50'17" W. Durbin Quadrangle.

A tributary to the West Fork of Greenbrier River rises in a cave 0.9 mile west of Brocker Station. The cave is a crawlway of unknown length at the base of the Greenbrier Series.

CLOVERLICK CAVE 38°21'11" N.; 80°01'17" W. Mingo Quadrangle.

In a low escarpment on the south side of Cloverlick Creek, 3.2 miles northwest of Clover Lick Station, is a small cave (elevation, 2600 feet). It consists of a single passage, 7 to 8 feet high, 8 to 10 feet wide, and 300 feet long, which heads southwest. At the end of the passage is a small crawlway sloping steeply upwards. A spring issues 100 feet below the cave's entrance but no stream is in the cave. Clover Lick Cave is in the base of the Greenbrier Series.

CLYDE COCHRANE SINKS 38°05'48" N.; 80°17'30" W. Lobelia Quadrangle.

In a low sink, ½ mile east of Oak Grove School, are three small caves (elevation, 2500 feet). The largest one is 500 feet north of the county road and in wet weather receives the drainage from a small run that heads on Jacox Knob. The entrance is in a steep-sided sink and opens into a low crawlway. The crawlway, a typical sewer, heads west and north for 400 feet with the ceiling height becoming progressively greater. At 400 feet a small room develops. East of the room the cave continues as a low passage, 4 to 6 feet high and 4 feet wide, for 200 feet where a room 50 feet long and 60 feet wide is encountered. The room is occupied by a deep pool which receives water from a stream passage to the east that is 300 feet long. The pool has a "whirlpool" current in it. The outlet to the pool is probably a narrow hole at the base that leads to lower channels. This cave is called Lost River Cave by local residents.

The second cave is in a large sink 150 feet southeast of the one described above. It is an opening, 40 feet wide and 20 feet high, which extends 35 feet to the east. Small fissure openings leading off from the entrance are blocked by debris washed into the cave.

The third cave is in an elongated sink 200 feet west of the second one. It is a room trending N. 10° W., 60 feet high, 30 feet wide, and 100 feet long, that has a waterfall on the west side. The floor, of clay and rock, drops steeply to the west. No passages lead off the room.

The caves are in the Union Limestone, Greenbrier Series, and are developed along joints at N. 30° E., N. 40° W. with subordinate joints at N. 70° E., and N. 10° W.

COOK CAVE 38°10′15″ N.; 80°08′52″ W. Marlinton Quadrangle.

A cave is reported at the east end of Rodgers Mountain at an elevation of 2750 feet, ¼ mile northwest of U. S. 219. No data are available concerning its details.

DEVILS DINING ROOM 38°26′00″ N.; 80°02′45″ W. Mingo Quadrangle.

Devils Dining Room is one mile north of Linwood, 1000 feet west of U. S. 219 (elevation, 3100 feet). It is a shaft 3 feet in diameter which is over 50 feet deep. No passage is reported to exist at the base. The pit is in the upper part of the Greenbrier Series.

DURBIN CAVE 38°33′02″ N.; 79°51′00″ W. Durbin Quadrangle.

This cave is on Back Allegheny Mountain, one mile west of Durbin at an elevation of 3200 feet. The entrance is 1000 feet west of the Durbin-Cass road and opens into a narrow fissure over 100 yards long where it develops into a large room, occupied by a lake. A stream flows out of the cave and is used as a source of water supply for Durbin. Durbin Cave is in the base of the Greenbrier Series.

FRIELS CAVE 38°12′28″ N.; 80°09′10″ W. Marlinton Quadrangle.

The entrance to Friels Cave is in a small sink 1.2 miles west of Dry Creek School on the south side of Overholt Run road (elevation, 2500 feet). It is a sewer passage 30 feet long that opens into a room and three short passages. The main stream passage is a slot with a 15-foot canyon. Crawlways and small rooms extend 150 feet to a room with a waterfall 35 feet high. The cave is in the Greenbrier Limestone.

GATEWOOD CAVE 38°25'20" N.; 80°02'40" W. Mingo Quadrangle.

The entrance to Gatewood Cave is 500 feet southeast of Linwood at the rear of the cattle scales (elevation, 3000 feet). It opens into a crawlway sloping gently downwards. A short distance from the entrance the passage is large enough to permit walking. One hundred feet in is a small low room, 20 feet square. The cave is decorated by a number of formations. It is in the middle part of the Greenbrier Series.

GAY CAVE 38°12'30" N.; 80°07'40" W. Marlinton Quad-Quadrangle.

This cave is on Buck Run ¾ mile northeast of Dry Creek School (elevation, 2550 feet). From the entrance a dry passage extends east for 15 feet and a stream passage is 120 feet long to the west. The cave is in the Greenbrier Limestone. Eighteen hundred feet to the east of the cave are two pits each about 40 feet deep.

GREATHOUSE CAVE 38°31'34" N.; 79°51'49" W. Durbin Quadrangle.

Greathouse Cave is 200 feet west of the Durbin-Cass road, 2.5 miles from Durbin (elevation, 3100 feet). The cave is a rough rocky opening which develops into a low passage extending 100 yards to the east. A creek, which descends from the mountain, falls into the cave and comes out as a spring 300 feet east of the road. A pit, 600 feet west of the cave, is 40 feet in diameter, 50 feet deep, and has a small stream passage at the base. The cave is in the base of the Greenbrier Series.

GRIMES CAVE 38°27'32" N.; 79°54'01" W. Cass Quadrangle.

Grimes Cave is 2000 feet west of the road along the east flank of Back Allegheny Mountain (elevation, 2975 feet). It is on the middle fork of Trout Run and the entrance is 40 feet above the stream in a cliff 20 feet high. The main passage ex-

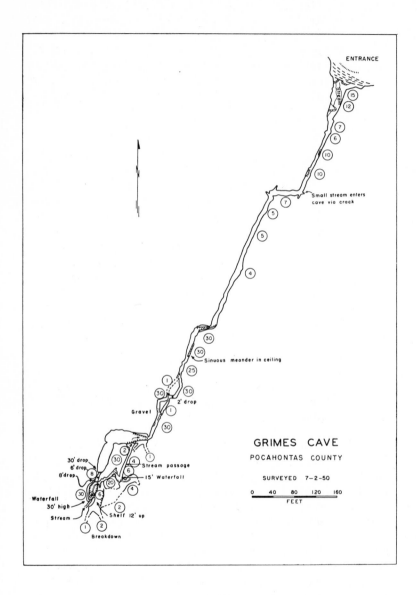

Figure 69.—Map of Grimes Cave.

tends southwest for 800 feet. It is 4 to 10 feet high, 2 to 8 feet wide. A small stream flows along the floor. At the end of this passage is a room 160 feet long, 20 feet wide, and 30 to 40 feet high. Two waterfalls, each 30 feet high, drop into the room. Beyond the waterfalls the cave continues as a small sewer passage for several hundred feet. The cave is developed along vertical joints at N. 25° E. and due east in the Greenbrier Limestone.

HAUSE NO. 1 CAVE 38°13′40″ N.; 80°08′06″ W. Marlinton Quadrangle.

Hause Cave is on the west side of Dry Creek, two miles north of U. S. Highway 219 (elevation, 2750 feet). The entrance is a 15-foot drop to a passage 70 feet long, 15 feet wide, and 25 feet high. A 14-foot drop is along the passage. A side passage 50 feet long leads off near the end of this main passage. The cave is in the Greenbrier Limestone. A pit 85 feet deep with three interconnected domes is 500 feet north of Hause Cave. On the west fork of Dry Creek 1000 feet west of Hause Cave is a narrow fissure with walkway passages 30 feet long. Another pit 35 feet deep **(Ruckers Jug Pit)** is across the stream from the fissure cave.

HAUSE WATERFALL CAVE 38°13′38″ N.; 80°08′18″ W. Marlinton Quadrangle.

Hause Waterfall Cave is located on a small tributary of Dry Creek on the Kyle Hause farm 3 miles north of Buckeye (elevation, 2750 feet). A creek plunges over a 15 foot waterfall and drains into the entrance of the cave in a limestone ledge. It is possible to enter through a small fissure for 30 feet. At this point a fissure in the floor requires the use of a rope for a drop of 25 feet to a small passage. One can descend an additional 20 feet through a waterfall to the floor of the main chamber. The water flows southeast and disappears in a fill. The passage continues to the southwest, mainly as a ledge 40 feet above the floor of a high canyon passage. The extent of the cave is not known. The cave is in the Greenbrier Limestone.

HERBERT HILL CAVE NO. 1 38°06′00″ N.; 80°17′17″ W. Lobelia Quadrangle.

Rush Run sinks in a cave ¾ mile northeast of Oak Grove School (elevation, 2500 feet). The cave, at the south end of a long sink, is in a low cliff with an opening heading east. The opening is filled with logs, rocks, and other debris. A channel 8 feet high is clear for 50 feet to a point where it is blocked by the debris. A small fissure opening, that is clogged 20 feet in, is located 100 feet to the west of the cave. It is reported that the entrance occasionally clears and the cave opening from it is large in size and can be traversed for considerable distance. The cave is in the Union Limestone, Greenbrier Series.

A series of terraces are developed along the sides of the valley sink to the west of the cave. Near the cave the terraces are 30 feet above the stream but 500 feet upstream they merge with the valley floor. The material in the terraces is red, loamy sand with masses of red sandstone pebbles and cobbles up to 6 inches in size, all well rounded by stream action. The terraces were formed during a period when the cave could not accept the drainage of Rush Run and a lake formed. The stream has subsequently cut through the deposits leaving the terraces on the flanks of the valley.

During low water Rush Run sinks in gravel 1000 feet north of the cave. The creek enters the cave in wet weather.

HERBERT HILL CAVE NO. 2 38°05′34″ N.; 80°17′12″ W. Lobelia Quadrangle.

At the southeast corner of Herbert Hill's farm is a second cave. The entrance is in a low cliff directly beneath the county road at an elbow turn, 0.7 mile east of Oak Grove School (elevation, 2600 feet). It is 15 feet wide, 10 feet high, and can be traversed for 70 feet where it is plugged by rock debris. A stream flows into the cave. It is in the Union Limestone, Greenbrier Series.

HILLS CREEK CAVE 38°07′10″ N.; 80°16′38″ W. Lobelia Quadrangle.

Hills Creek goes underground in a cave 1.4 miles southeast of Lobelia (elevation, 2430 feet). The entrance is at the base of a cliff 50 feet high and is an opening 8 to 10 feet high and

70 feet wide. The entrance is blocked by logs, rocks, and similar debris. A 60-foot shaft, 100 yards east of the cave entrance, leads to the underground passage of Hills Creek. The passage, 8 to 20 feet high and 15 feet wide, trends north for 200 feet, where it joins the subterranean course of Bruffey Creek and heads east. In low water Hills Creek sinks in gravel 1000 feet northwest of the cave. In high water it enters the cave and at times is dammed into a lake 20 feet deep covering the meadow in front of the cave entrance. Hills Creek Cave is in the middle part of the Greenbrier Series.

HUGHES CREEK CAVE 38°07′47″ N.; 80°15′19″ W. Lobelia Quadrangle.

At the east base of Droop Mountain, 2¼ miles west of Hillsboro, are two long caves (elevation, 2250 feet). The southern cave is a large room and stream passage, 3 to 8 feet high and 20 feet wide, that extends for 600 feet. Breakdown partially blocks the passage in places. The cave is in the middle part of the Greenbrier Series. The stream that flows through the cave is a part of the underground drainage of Millstone Creek.

HUGHES CREEK LOWER CAVE 38°07′50″ N.; 80°15′16″ W. Lobelia Quadrange.

This cave is 600 feet north of Hughes Creek Cave. It is a low stream passage about 1000 feet long. The cave is in the middle of the Greenbrier Series.

ICE CAVE 38°05′35″ N.; 80°17′10″ W. Lobelia Quadrangle.

On the north side of Droop Mountain, 1.2 miles north of West Droop School (elevation, 2800 feet), is a high cliff with considerable talus at the base. Ice Cave is a small shelter 50 feet wide at the base of the cliff and is named from the ice that accumulates and remains into the summer in the talus below the cave. Ice Cave is in the Droop Sandstone.

JACKSONS CAVE 38°06′21″ N.; 80°15′04″ W. Lobelia Quadrangle.

Jacksons Cave is on the east side of Locust Creek Valley, ½ mile from the head of the creek (elevation, 2200 feet). The entrance to the cave is in a low cliff 100 feet above the creek and opens into a low crawlway that is reported to enlarge enough for walking. The cave is 100 yards long and is in the base of the Greenbrier Series.

KEE CAVE NO. 1 38°13′23″ N.; 80°06′05″ W. Marlinton Quadrangle.

Two vertical pits opening into small caves are in Kee Hollow, one mile west of Marlinton. The north pit is on the nose of a spur of Stony Creek Mountain at an elevation of 2700 feet. The pit is 30 feet deep and opens into a small passage at the base. The cave is in the middle of the Greenbrier Series.

KEE CAVE NO. 2 38°13′10″ N.; 80°06′39″ W. Marlinton Quadrangle.

The second vertical pit in Kee Hollow is at an elevation of 2400 feet, ½ mile up the hollow from U. S. 219. It is a vertical pit 87 feet deep and no opening is reported to exist at its base. It is in the base of the Greenbrier Series.

KINNISON CAVE 38°09′24″ N.; 80°14′15″ W. Marlinton Quadrangle.

Kinnison Cave is 2 miles northwest of Hillsboro, at the base of Little Mountain (elevation, 2580 feet), and 500 feet north of the Hillsboro-Lobelia road. The entrance is 20 feet wide, 8 feet high, but after 20 feet reduces to a fissure passage 2 to 3 feet wide with a high ceiling, 300 or more feet long. The cave is in the top of the Greenbrier Series.

LINWOOD CAVE 38°25′20″ N.; 80°02′41″ W. Mingo Quadrangle.

This cave is on the west side of U. S. 219, 600 feet north of Linwood (elevation, 3000 feet). The entrance, in a low ledge of rock, is 6 feet high and 8 feet wide. The cave is a passage of similar size, 500 feet long, that leads steeply down at the front. The floor is of hard clay and a small stream crosses the passage a short distance from the entrance. The cave is in the middle part of the Greenbrier Series.

LOCUST CREEK CAVE 38°06'43" N.; 80°15'13" W. Lobelia Quadrangle.

Locust Creek rises as a large stream flowing from a low opening, 0.8 mile east of Spice (elevation, 2090 feet). The ceiling is 1 to 2 feet high and 20 feet wide in a low bluff of limestone. The creek is 6 to 10 feet deep inside the passage which extends due west. The passage becomes a narrow water-filled fissure 300 feet from the entrance. Locust Creek Cave is in the base of the Greenbrier Series.

MARTENS (PECK) CAVE   38°08'00" N.; 80°16'26" W.
Lobelia Quadrangle.   38°08'05" N.; 80°16'35" W.

Near the head of Cave Run, 1.2 miles east of Lobelia, Martens Cave pierces a flanking ridge of Droop Mountain. The cave, at an elevation of 2600 feet, is 600 feet south of the Lobelia-Hillsboro road. The south entrance, in a large sink, opens into a cliff 50 feet high. The entrance room is 30 feet wide, 50 feet long, and 20 feet high, at a direction N. 40°W. The passage heads N. 40°E. at the end of the room and is 30 to 40 feet wide and 10 to 20 feet high with the floor covered by large slabs of breakdown. After 100 feet the passage heads north over more breakdown for 225 feet to a room 110 feet long, 60 feet wide, 10 feet high, with a floor of damp silt. Two dome pits, over 40 feet high, are developed on the east side of the room. A narrow passage heads S. 20°W. for 60 feet to a large room, 50 feet wide and long, that opens on the face of a low cliff, 100 yards northwest of the south entrance. The drop from the south to north entrance is 10 feet. A small stream enters and flows through the length of the cave. A strong draft of air flows from south to north in the cave. Martens Cave is in the top of the Greenbrier Series.

MARTHAS (MARTHA CLARKS; LONGS) CAVE 38°07'39" N.; 80°14'45" W. Marlinton Quadrangle.

This cave, 1.9 miles southwest of Hillsboro and ¾ mile west of U. S. 219, is in a low hill on the south side of Millstone Creek (elevation, 2250 feet). The entrance passage, in a cliff 50 feet high, is 30 feet wide and 2 feet high for a distance of 40 feet, after which it opens to 8 or 10 feet high. It trends N. 70°W. Considerable driftwood blocks the south

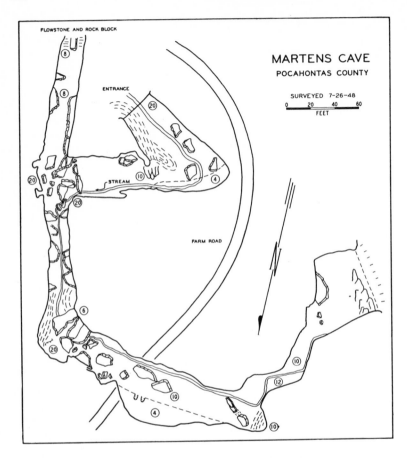

Figure 70.—Map of Martens Cave.

side of the entrance. 50 feet from the entrance is a section
of breakdown that all but blocks the passage. Beyond the
breakdown the main passage is 20 to 30 feet high and wide.
It trends S. 60°W. for 3200 feet to a point where a pool of
water blocks it. A small stream flows along the main passage.
The cave is commonly flooded and large logs are wedged in the
ceiling of the main passage. The floor of the main passage
is bare limestone with a few deposits of silt. Another long
passage on an upper level is reported to exist. Thomas C.
Barr, Jr., traversed this upper passage in 1958 while studying
cavern fauna in the Appalachians. He reports that the en-

trance to the upper passage is a short distance to the southwest and above the lower one. A passage 10 to 15 feet wide and 10 feet high trends southwest for about 750 feet where it intersects a stream passage. The stream flows northeast between high silt banks for 1450 feet where the passage is blocked by a silt fill. This passage is 15 to 20 feet high and midway along it is a large dome 50 feet high. Southwest of the point where the stream passage intersects the entrance passage is a passage about 20 feet high and wide. Three domes are along the passage; the third, 600 feet along the passage, is 60 feet high and has a large waterfall, the source of the cave stream. At the junction of the passages is a third stream passage of unknown size trending south. Marthas Cave is in the lower part of the Greenbrier Series.

MOORE CAVE 38°30′06″ N.; 79°52′24″ W. Durbin Quadrangle.

Moore Cave is a small crawlway with a stream flowing out, 4 miles southwest of Durbin on the Durbin-Cass road (elevation, 3050 feet). The cave is in the middle part of the Greenbrier Series.

MOORE CAVE NO. 2 38°14′14″ N.; 79°55′15″ W. Warm Springs Quadrangle.

This is the only cave recorded in Pocahontas County that is not in the Greenbrier Series. It is a short crawlway in Valley Draft (elevation, 2700 feet), 3.25 miles southwest of Frost and ½ mile west of W. Va. Highway 28. It is in the upper part of the Tonoloway Limestone.

MOORES CAVE 38°28′57″ N.; 79°53′08″ W. Cass Quadrangle.

Moores Cave is a mile southwest of Hevener Church, ¼ mile west of the Cass-Durbin road (elevation, 3100 feet). The entrance is a crawl leading to a room about 15 feet square and long. A crawlway to the left of the entrance, 20 feet long, leads to a passage 10 feet high and 12 feet wide. The passage is 25 feet long and ends at a low stream passage. The cave is in the Greenbrier Limestone.

OVERHANG CAVE 38°29'07" N.; 79°53'09" W. Cass Quadrangle.

This cave is ¾ of a mile southwest of Hevener Church (elevation, 3200 feet). The entrance is in breakdown and opens to a passage 25 feet high and 15 feet wide. Breakdown is extensive along this passage. A fissure with a stream lies below and to the left of the main passage. A crawlway 30 feet long is below and to the right of the main passage. The cave is in the upper part of the Greenbrier Limestone.

OVERHOLT BLOWING CAVE 38°12'12" N.; 80°08'40" W. Marlinton Quadrangle.

Several large caves are located along Swago Creek northwest of Buckeye. Overholt Blowing Cave is ¾ mile northwest of U. S. 219 and opens into a ledge of limestone 50 feet high (elevation, 2300 feet). The eastern opening is a stream passage, 8 to 10 feet wide and 4 feet high, which can be traversed for 100 feet where the passage and stream continue north as a crawlway. A small opening at this point gives access to the upper room. The western opening is 150 feet west of the water entrance and 30 feet above it. It is a small hole with an old door that opens into a room 35 feet long, 30 feet wide, and 4 to 6 feet high, with a steeply sloping floor of rock debris. It connects with the water channel by a small hole at the southeast corner of the room.

The main part of the cave trends N. 20° E. to N. 30° E. The crawlway 100 feet from the eastern opening is 18 inches high and 8 feet wide. One hundred feet farther is a room 40 feet wide by 15 feet high by 20 feet long. The stream emerges from a syphon at one end of this room and forks. One fork flows into the entrance crawlway, the other to the west into a mud choke to emerge as a spring at the base of the quarry some 200 feet northwest of the entrance. A dry passage 15 feet wide and 8 feet high leads from the east side of the room for 400 feet where it joins the main stream passage beyond the syphon.

The main stream passage continues for 3000 feet with only minor side passages. The width is 6 to 10 feet and the height 5 to 20 feet. The water on the floor pools in places to depths of 4 feet. The floor is level and mostly gravel covered. Pools are formed by shallow gravel bar dams.

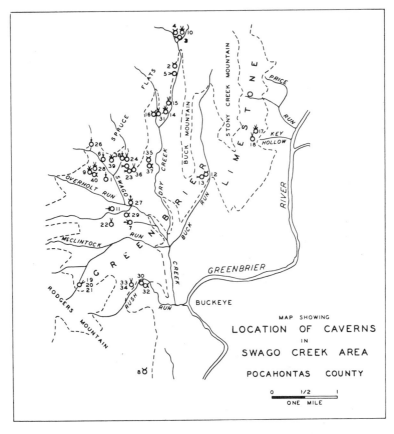

MAP SHOWING
LOCATION OF CAVERNS
IN
SWAGO CREEK AREA
POCAHONTAS COUNTY

0   1/2   1
ONE MILE

Figure 71.—Caves in the Swago Creek Area.

1. Barnes Pit.
2. Beveridge Cave.
3. Beveridge Dome Pit.
4. Beveridge Hole.
5. Beveridge Pit.
6. Carpenters Pit.
7. Cave Creek Cave.
8. Cook Cave.
9. Crossed Fingers Well.
10. Dry Creek Indian Cave.
11. Friels Cave.
12. Gay Cave.
13. Gay Pit.
14. Hause No. 1 Cave.
15. Hause Pit.

16. Hause Waterfall Cave.
17. Kee No. 1 Cave
18. Kee No. 2 Cave.
19. McClintocks Grapevine Pit.
20. McClintocks No. 1 Pit.
21. McClintocks No. 2 Pit.
22. McClintocks Wormsway Cave.
23. McKeevers Chimney Pit.
24. McKeevers No. 1 Pit.
25. McKeevers No. 2 Pit.
26. McKeevers Waterfall Cave.
27. Overholts Blowing Cave.
28. Overholts Dome Cave.
29. Overholts Saltpeter Cave.
30. Rockhouse.

At the end of this passage, a large room 100 feet long, 40 feet wide and 10 to 20 feet high opens on the east side of the passage. The floor of the room is 15 feet above the level of the stream. The end of the room is blocked by massive ceiling breakdown. Two passages open from this room. To the south, a low wide passage continues at least 300 feet. At the end of the room a small hole in the breakdown leads to an extensive series of passages on an upper level.

The upper passage (Anne's Avenue) is 1500 feet long and runs south paralleling the stream passage over much of its length. The ceiling height varies from 3 to 15 feet, and the width from 5 to 6 feet. The cross-section is for the most part rectangular and is usually wider than it is high. The passage is dry. There is one section in the middle where speleothems consist of a group of rimstone pools and some stalactites covered with globulite. A little gypsum is in the soil. The passage ends at the edge of a 15 foot wide, 25 foot deep dome pit with 5 feet of water in the bottom. On the other side of the pit, the passage continues at least 200 feet into a large breakdown room. This is the limit of exploration. Two hundred feet from the terminal pit, a low crawlway to the south leads into an unmapped complex of small passages and domes. Some surface fill and debris is visible here. Lower levels are developed at several points along the passage.

At the end of the main stream passage, one can continue upstream by crawling in the water for 500 feet underneath an extensive rockfall that blocks the passage. Beyond this the passage is 20 feet high and 25 feet wide continuing for 1500 feet to a complete choke in breakdown. This passage has a stream on the floor and is littered with large breakdown blocks.

At the breakdown choke, a small hole opens into the Mountain Room, a breakdown floored, roughly circular room, about 150 feet in diameter. A small waterfall pours from the ceiling of this room, and falls about 40 feet into a pit in the floor. The room is decorated with several massive stalagmites.

Two passages lead from the Mountain Room. One of them leads an estimated 500 feet through a series of small rooms decorated with pure white speleothems. The second is a 25 foot wide and 15 foot high gallery 1000 feet long. The floor is dry and covered with breakdown.

At the end of this dry gallery, a 20 foot crevice in the floor goes down to stream level. Six hundred feet of low stream crawlway connects with a large passage which has been explored an estimated 4000 feet in a north to northeasterly direction.

In all, one mile of passage has been mapped and an estimated 1½ miles additional explored in Overholt Blowing Cave. There are still many passages that have never been entered. The cave is in the Sinks Grove member of the Greenbrier Limestone and the floor at the entrance is at or near the contact between the Sinks Grove and Hillsdale members.

OVERHOLTS DOME CAVE 38°12′56″ N.; 80°09′20″ W. Marlinton Quadrangle.

Four hundred and fifty feet N.N.E. of the sink of Tub Cave is a 15-foot pit (elevation, 2800 feet). This pit opens to a 45° talus slope 12 feet long. The slope connects with two interconnected domes 30 feet high. A small fissure leads to two other domes. This cave is directly above part of Tub Cave and is in the upper part of the Greenbrier Limestone.

OVERHOLTS SALTPETER CAVE 38°12′20″ N.; 80°08′45″ W. Marlinton Quadrangle.

This cave is in a low, tree-covered hill, 500 feet west of Overholts Blowing Cave (elevation, 2400 feet). The entrance was formerly an opening 6 feet square but is now a narrow crawl due to slumping of the overburden. The entrance room is 25 feet long, 20 feet wide, 10 feet high, and is blocked by a clay bank at the rear. A small sinuous passage, intersected by many short side passages, leads off the east side of the room and is large enough for walking for 40 feet after which it is a crawlway to a crevice passage and room 100 feet from the entrance. This room is 100 feet long and trends N.20°E. with a large bank of clay along the east side. The cave was used extensively for saltpeter earth in the War Between the

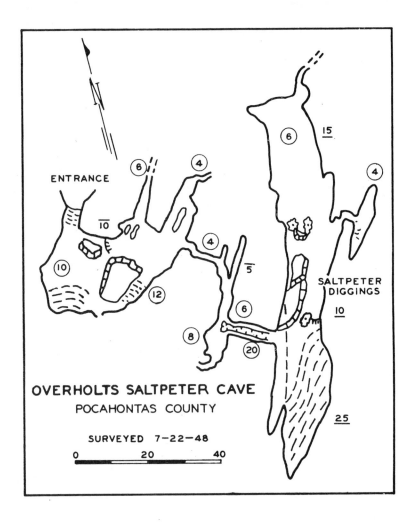

Figure 72.—Map of Overholts Saltpeter Cave.

States and remains of troughs and a puddler were located in the cave. A broad flat area outside the entrance is an old refuse pile. The cave, in the Sinks Grove (?) Limestone Greenbrier Series, is developed along joints at N. 30° E. and N. 50° W.

PINE TREE CAVE 38°24'56" N.; 80°06'42" W. Mingo Quadrangle.

This cave is south of Sharp's store, one mile east of Slaty Fork. The entrance (elevation, 2800 feet) is in a road cut on the old road up Big Spring Fork and opens into a crawl passage extending south for 100 feet. The cave is in the top of the Greenbrier Series.

POOR FARM CAVE 38°07'23" N.; 80°13'17" W. Marlinton Quadrangle.

Poor Farm Cave is one mile southwest of Hillsboro on the northeast side of a low hill at an elevation of 2360 feet. The entrance is an obscure sink in an open woodland, 500 feet at S. 30° W. from an isolated barn in the middle of a meadow and 100 feet south of a fence line separating the meadow and woodland. The entrance room is 15 feet square and drops 12 feet over slabs of fallen rock. A broad straight passage, 15 to 20 feet wide, 10 feet high, heads due south for 300 feet. The clay floor is smooth and level. A side passage leads off to the east for 160 feet and is 15 feet wide, 10 feet high for 80 feet. The last 30 feet are at the top of a clay bank, 10 feet deep, which fills to the ceiling at the end. The main passage continues for 300 feet, similar in size to the front part of the cave, but with rock fall and formations interrupting it. 600 feet from the entrance the cave divides into three passages. To the west is a broad passage, 30 feet wide, 6 to 10 feet high, 800 feet long which is an alternation of smooth floors and areas of heavy breakdown. The last 200 feet is an intricate maze of dangerous, fallen rock. The center passage trends S. 50° W., 30 feet above the general level of the cave. It is 40 feet wide, 20 feet high, and 550 feet long. The last 150 feet is over large slabs of breakdown, the remaining being on smooth clay floors. After 550 feet the passage changes to S. 20° W. as a chasm 50 feet deep with walls of dry clay and rock debris that is dangerous to traverse. The passage continues for 1000 feet and has a number of formations mainly stalactites, near the end. The passage ends in a clay-filled room containing two deep pits. The east passage is sinuous and extends for 200 feet with a width of 20 feet and height of 10 feet. Beyond this the passage continues as a narrow fissure, 2 feet wide at the base, 10 feet wide at the

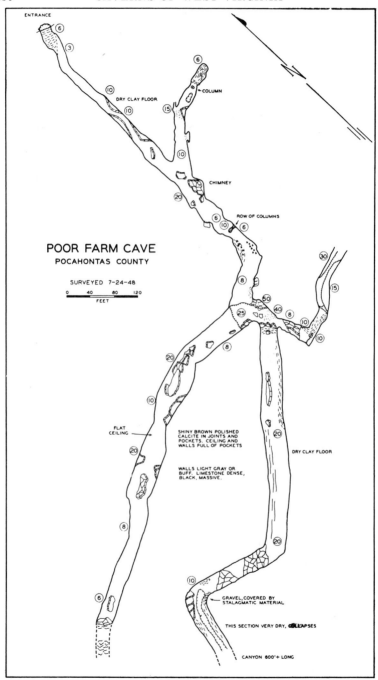

Figure 73.—Map of Poor Farm Cave.

Plate L.—Poor Farm (Pocahontas County) Cave. "Subway" Passage. (Photo by Wm. E. Davies).

Plate LI.—The Curtains, Poor Farm (Pocahontas County) Cave. (Photo by Wm. E. Davies).

Plate LII.—Poor Farm (Pocahontas County) Cave. Breakdown. (Photo by Wm. E. Davies).

top, and 20 feet high for over 200 feet. This section has numerous columns and stalactites. A large Dutch Oven formation is located at the junction of the east and central passage.

In the west passage a peculiar mineral growth is found in a number of small pockets in the ceiling. It consists of a layer of material $\frac{1}{8}$ to $\frac{1}{4}$ inch thick that is brown in color and has a high surface polish. It was observed in other caves but in Poor Farm Cave it is abundant enough for easy study. Gypsum crystals are found in pockets in the clay deposits of the cave. Clusters of fine, hair-like fibers of gypsum hang from the ceiling in the rear portion of the cave. The breakdown in the cave is from anastomosis along bedding-planes in areas of broad flat ceilings with the collapse resulting from weakening of bonds between beds. The fallen rock is in the form of large flat slabs weighing up to 5 tons. The network of solution channels is clearly displayed on the ceiling above the rock fall. Poor Farm Cave is in the Hillsdale Limestone, Greenbrier Series.

A cave 75 feet below and 300 feet north of the entrance to Poor Farm Cave receives a small stream. The cave is 2 to 3 feet high and 10 to 30 feet wide. It extends for 140 feet where the stream sinks below gravel. It flows in a low level beneath Poor Farm Cave and is seen in a clay-lined passage 100 yards long at the base of a pit in the canyon of the center passage.

POOR FARM PIT 38°07′23″ N.; 80°13′17″ W. Marlinton Quadrangle.

A vertical shaft 65 feet deep is 100 yards southeast of Poor Farm Cave (elevation, 2350 feet). The base of the shaft is blocked by fallen rock. It is in the Hillsdale Limestone Greenbrier Series.

ROCKHOUSE 38°11′26″ N.; 80°08′38″ W. Marlinton Quadrangle.

At the head of Rush Run, 0.8 mile northwest of Buckeye, is a large shelter cave (elevation, 2275 feet). The entrance, in a cliff 40 feet high, is 20 feet wide, 15 feet high, and extends S. 30° W. for 50 feet. At the rear two small fissure passages lead off on each side of the cave at right angles to the shelter. A large stream rises from a low siphon at the rear of the cave and covers the floor of the shelter. The cave is in the Hillsdale Limestone, Greenbrier Series.

Another small cave with a 25-foot walkway passage leading to a small room is reported to be near Rockhouse.

SALTPETER CAVE 38°08′05″ N.; 80°16′49″ W. Lobelia Quadrangle.

Saltpeter Cave is on the south side of Cave Run, 0.8 mile east of Lobelia, at an elevation of 2550 feet. The entrance is 200 feet south of the Lobelia-Hillsboro road and opens into a passage heading S. 40°E. At the entrance, it is 4 feet high and 10 feet wide enlarging to 6 feet high and 30 feet wide, 150 feet from the entrance. At this point the ceiling, to a depth of 10 feet, has collapsed *en masse* making it necessary to climb 10 feet up to the top of the rock debris. The passage continues for 25 feet as a broad opening, 30 feet wide, and 2 feet high, which ends at a fissure 20 feet deep that cuts across the cave. The fissure is 60 feet long, 10 feet wide and opens on the west into a small room 15 feet in diameter, 15 feet high, and 15 feet above the floor of the fissure. Saltpeter operations were carried on in this portion of the cave during the War Between the States. Remains of a hopper and trough as well as numerous mattock marks are relics of this project. The cave, in the upper part of the Greenbrier Series, is developed along joints at N. 40°W. and due east.

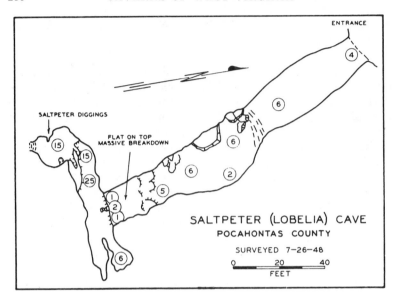

Figure 74.—Map of Saltpeter (Lobelia) Cave.

Plate LIII.—Saltpeter (Lobelia) Cave. Mattock Marks in Saltpeter Earth. (Photo by Wm. E. Davies).

SCHOOLBERRY CAVE 38°12′58″ N.; 80°08′24″ W. Marlinton Quadrangle.

Schoolberry Cave is on the west side of Dry Creek, 1.2 miles north of Dry Creek School (elevation, 2750 feet). The entrance is a 20-foot walkway at the end of which is a 20-foot pit. Another 20-foot pit is offset from this and connects with a fissure passage 35 feet long to a dome and pit 51 feet high. A second pit is adjacent. Beyond this is a crawlway for 165 feet to a complex of pits and domes. The total length of the cave is 630 feet and it trends southwest. The cave is in four levels and has 18 dome pits. A small stream is in parts of the cave. The cave is in the Greenbrier Limestone. 200 feet south of Schoolberry Cave is a small walkway 40 feet long **(Swago Horse Cave)**.

SHARPS CAVE 38°25′02″ N.; 80°05′08″ W. Mingo Quadrangle.

Sharps Cave is 2.5 miles east of Slaty Fork, on the north side of Big Spring Fork (elevation, 2,900 feet). The entrance, a vertical drop of 15 feet, is in a low sink below the Western Maryland Railroad grade, directly opposite the concrete water-tank on U. S. 219. The passage at the base trends east-west and is 2 to 3 feet wide, 5 to 10 feet high. The east passage ends in a pit 15 feet deep, after 100 feet. The west passage goes 12 feet to a 20-foot pit connecting with a lower level. The west passage continues beyond the pit and joins the lower level via a clay slope. Two rooms, 25 feet in diameter are developed here. The passage trends north for at least 3600 feet to a waterfall. There is a large amount of breakdown and a few rooms up to a 100 feet long and 30 feet high along the main passage. The last 200 to 300 feet of this passage is a crawl through breakdown. A stream flows along the lower passage and is reported to exit near Sharp's store. Local residents report blind fish in the stream but this has not been verified. Similar comments can be made concerning a pot of gold reputed to be buried in the cave. The cave is in the top of the Greenbrier Series.

SHARPS MILL CAVE 38°25′03″ N.; 80°08′45″ W. Mingo Quadrangle.

This cave is along the Western Maryland Railroad opposite the mill at Slaty Fork (elevation, 2680 feet). It is a small fissure passage leading northeast for about 100 feet and is in the upper part of the Greenbrier Series.

SHARPS STORE CAVE 38°25′10″ N.; 80°05′50″ W. Mingo Quadrangle.

Sharps Store Cave is 1.9 miles east of Slaty Fork, 150 yards north of U. S. 219 (elevation, 2750 feet). Two adjacent entrances lead to a short but roomy passage that is floored by a large amount of breakdown. As far as is known the cave is less than 100 feet long. It is at the top of the Greenbrier Series.

SHINABERRY CAVE 38°19′04″ N.; 80°01′15″ W. Mingo Quadrangle.

The entrance to Shinaberry Cave is in a sink 0.8 mile northwest of Poages Chapel (elevation, 2800 feet). A vertical shaft descends 30 feet to a single large room at the base. A stream falls into the shaft. The cave is in the lower part of the Greenbrier Series.

SLATY FORK CAVE 38°25′00″ N.; 80°07′15″ W. Mingo Quadrangle.

A small short crawlway with a low room 10 feet square, opens in the bank behind the schoolhouse, ½ mile east of Slaty Fork (elevation, 2730 feet). It is in the upper part of the Greenbrier Series.

SNEDEGARS CAVE 38°04′50″ N.; 80°18′23″ W. Lobelia Quadrangle. 38°04′40″ N.; 80°18′18″ W.

Snedegars Cave is located on the road through Friars Hole, ¾ mile south of Jacox (elevation, 2450 feet). The cave has two entrances about 1000 feet apart. The southern entrance is in a low escarpment and opens into a passage 20 to 50 feet wide, 20 to 25 feet high, that extends west for 500 feet. The

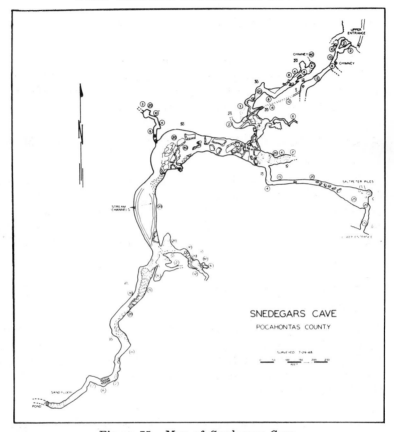

Figure 75.—Map of Snedegars Cave.

passage expands into a long room 40 to 100 feet wide, 15 to 40 feet high, and 600 feet long. The floor is covered with large boulders of breakdown. At the west end of the room the passage trends south for 1200 feet as a channel 20 to 50 feet wide, 15 to 20 feet high, which gradually reduces to a crawlway and is finally blocked by a small pool that reaches to the ceiling. Throughout its length this passage has large banks of clay along it as well as rock from breakdown. Three hundred feet south of the Big Room a passage extends 200 feet to the east and consists of series of travertine terraces, with a pool of water lying in each step of the terrace. At the summit of the terraces a dome pit, 8 feet in diameter, is cut into the ceiling for 80 feet.

Plate LIV.—Snedegars Cave. Sewer Passage off Big Room. (Photo by Wm. E. Davies).

Plate LV.—Snedegars Cave. Rimstone Pools at base of Dome Pit. (Photo by Wm. E. Davies.)

Plate LVI.—Snedegars Cave. Dome Pit. (Photo by Wm. E. Davies).

On the north side of the Big Room several openings lead to an intricate maze of intersecting fissures and crawlways. From this maze two small passages extend to the north entrance and are very difficult to traverse. Another opens into an intricate passage extending several hundred feet to the north. Other channels, that are sewers in wet weather, can be followed for some distance before they are too small for crawling.

The northern entrance has two openings that connect a short distance in. Several unmapped side passages develop from the crevice that connects with the main room. A stream enters the passages in wet weather and driftwood and other debris are strewn along these passages. Care should be taken in traversing the sewers in this section as they flood quickly when it rains.

Saltpeter was dug from the small passages north of the Big Room and in a small side passage at the east end of the Big Room. Troughs and mattock marks as well as pathways remain from the work.

Snedegars Cave is in the Alderson Limestone, Greenbrier Series. Its intricate pattern is difficult to relate to specific structural features and more study is necessary to ascertain the origin of its pattern. From the south entrance to the lower end of the cave the floor descends 140 feet. Much of this drop is in the Big Room.

STEPHENS HOLE CAVE 38°09′48″ N.; 80°10′26″ W. Marlinton Quadrangle.

On the cliffs at the center of the amphitheater that forms the head of Stephens Hole Run is a small cave opening (elevation, 2300 feet). It is 75 feet above the floor of the meadow, on a low limestone cliff, and opens into a sinuous crawlway which extends for more than 100 yards trending N. 20° E. The entrance is a small shelter and a hermit is reported to have lived in it many years ago. The cave is in the base of the Greenbrier Series.

ROADSIDE PIT 38°12′57″ N.; 80°09′03″ W. Marlinton Quadrangle.

Two miles northeast of Buckeye is a small opening in the ditch along Swago Creek road (elevation, 2800 feet). A 60-

foot shaft 5 x 20 feet in size connects with a passage at the base. The first 20 feet of the shaft is a narrow fissure. The passage at the base is 5 to 40 feet high, 10 to 20 feet wide, and 500 feet long, trending N. 65° E. Three hundred feet from the entrance is a dome pit complex. A room on the north side of the passage 300 feet from the entrance is 120 feet long and 40 feet wide and 15 feet high. Speleothems are numerous along the main passage and in the room. The cave is in the middle part of the Greenbrier Limestone.

TUB CAVE 38°12′50″ N.; 80°09′20″ W. Marlinton Quadrangle.

The largest room in any West Virginia Cave is found in Tub Cave. This cave is near the head of Swago Creek, 1.7 miles northwest of Dry Creek Church. The entrance is in a sink in a saddle between Overholt Run and Swago Creek (elevation, 2700 feet). The entrance opens into a large oval-shaped room 625 feet long, 200 feet wide, 25 to 60 feet high, with an axis N. 20° E. No passage leads off the room. The

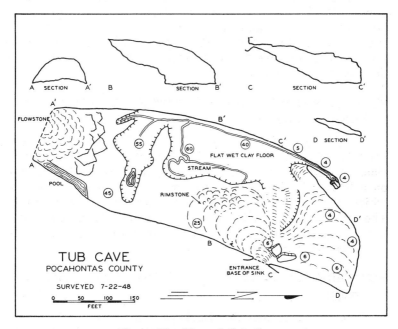

Figure 76.—Map of Tub Cave.

floor is of clay that is banked to the ceiling on the east side. In the center of the room is an intermittent lake bed 15 feet below the floor level. A stream flows into the cave from the northwest corner, meanders across the lake bed, and disappears under the clay bank. A large flowstone, on breakdown, blocks the south end of the room. It is 40 feet in diameter and 50 feet high. A small drip hole in the ceiling is building travertine terraces on the clay bank near the entrance. The cave is in the middle part of the Greenbrier Series.

TYLER HOLE 38°15'10" N.; 80°08'26" W. Mingo Quadrangle.

At the south end of the hollow, ¾ mile south of West Union School, four miles northwest of Marlinton (elevation, 3000 feet) is a shaft 15 feet wide dropping 15 feet to a 45° mud slope. A second drop of 25 feet with a talus slope at the base opens into a chamber 25 feet long, 10 feet wide, and 40 feet high. A small well 10 feet deep opens from the room. It is plugged at the base by fill. This cave is in the Greenbrier Limestone.

WALT ALLEN CAVE 38°19'22" N.; 80°00'52" W. Mingo Quadrangle.

This cave is 0.9 mile north of Poages Chapel at an elevation of 2800 feet. The entrance is a crawlway for 20 feet opening into a passage 12 to 15 feet wide and 25 to 100 feet high. Seventy feet from the entrance is a pit 25 feet deep at the base of which the passage continues 200 feet to another pit, 53 feet deep. Beyond this pit the cave continues for 500 feet as a sloping passage similar in size to those on the upper levels. Several rooms are developed along the passage on the second level. The cave trends northeast and a stream flows in it. The floor is of fallen rock except at the second pit where wet clay predominates. Formations are numerous but small. The cave is in the base of the Greenbrier Series.

WANLESS CAVES 38°26'22" N.; 79°54'49" W. Cass Quadrangle.

This cave is 2050 feet west of the Durbin-Cass road, 3.0 miles north of Cass, near the settlement of Wanless (elevation,

3250 feet). The entrance, near an old sawmill site, is in a sink 40 feet deep, 100 feet long, and 35 feet wide. A narrow passage trends S. 35° W. for 500 feet. It is 2 to 5 feet wide and 3 to 6 feet high. A shaft 150 feet high is at the end. Rimstone pools are at the base of the shaft. A triangular-shaped room 20 x 20 feet is near the entrance. A dome pit 40 feet high opens on the west side of the main passage near the entrance. Another cave is 1000 feet E.N.E. of Wanless Cave. It is a 30-foot pit connecting to a crescent-shaped fissure. Two passages lead from the fissure. One is a sinuous stream passage 3 feet square trending west. A second passage has pits and domes with a stream. It is 500 feet long and ends in a pinchdown. The caves are in the top of the Greenbrier Limestone.

WILDELL CAVE 38°43' N.; 79°47' W. Durbin Quadrangle.

A small cave is reported near Wildell Station on the Western Maryland Railroad. No data are available on the cave.

WILLIAMS CAVE 38°07'24" N.; 80°17'34" W. Lobelia Quadrangle.

Williams Cave is 0.65 mile south of Lobelia, 100 yards east of the Lobelia-Jacox road (elevation, 2550 feet). The entrance, in a shallow sink, opens into a short passage that ends in a pit 10 feet deep. To the southeast a sinuous crevice passage extends 20 feet to a pit 35 feet deep with a chimney extending 40 feet above the pit. The cave continues as an inaccessible crevice beyond the pit. Ice is reported obtainable from the cave in late spring and summer. The cave is in the top of the Greenbrier Series.

Recent exploration in Pocahontas County has resulted in data on a number of pits and small caves. The major ones are summarized below:

Allen Cave—A cave is reported seven miles up Cloverlick Creek from the town of Clover Lick. This may be the same as Cloverlick Cave.

Beveridge Cave—A 40-foot long passage with two small rooms is reported on the west side of Dry Creek, 2½ miles north of U. S. Highway 219.

Beveridge Dome Pit—A crevice opening into a dome 25 feet in diameter is at the fork in Dry Creek, three miles north of U. S. Highway 219.

Beveridge Hole—This cave is 200 yards W.N.W. of Beveridge Dome Pit. The entrance is 30 feet from the road in a shallow sink. The cave is a 20-foot passage to a small room seven feet high. A small stream is in the back part of the cave.

Beveridge Pit—This pit is 700 feet S.S.W. of Beveridge Cave. It is 50 feet deep with a waterfall. Several passages less than 50 feet long are at the base.

Crossed Fingers Well—250 feet N.N.E. of sink of Tub Cave is a 15-foot pit, 2½ feet in diameter. At the base is a small offset to a 4-foot pit.

Dry Creek Indian Cave—100 yards north of Beveridge Dome Pit is a 37-foot pit at the base of which is a steeply sloping passage 60 feet long.

McClintocks Pits—On the north fork of McClintocks Run 2.2 miles W.N.W. of Buckeye are three pits 30 to 40 feet deep; one pit is double domed.

McClintocks Wormsway Cave—This is a crawlway 65 feet long at the base of a pit 0.9 mile west of Dry Creek School, 0.3 mile north of McClintocks Run.

McKeevers Pits—On the southeast end of Spruce Flats at the head of Swago Creek Valley are three pits 40 to 80 feet deep; no cave passages open at their bases. A fourth pit has a waterfall in it. Another pit **(Swago False Bottom Cave)** on the southeast projection of Spruce Flats 1.2 miles northwest of Dry Creek School is 58 feet deep. A stream at the base drops into a narrow fissure.

Ramp Hole—A fissure cave is reported on the middle fork of Trout Run, ¼ mile west of Grimes Cave.

Rush Run Pits—Four pits, 8 to 60 feet deep, are in the vicinity of Rush Run, 2½ miles south of Lobelia.

An unnamed cave is reported 4.3 miles north of Cass on the south branch of Trout Run (⅜ mile west of Cassell Cave). No data are available on it.

PRESTON COUNTY

The Greenbrier Limestone outcrops in Preston County on the flanks of two broad anticlines trending northeast-southwest across the county. The limestones are about 100 feet thick and have gentle dips. Five caves are recorded in the county, four of which are in the Greenbrier Limestone. The fifth is in a soft sandstone in the Pottsville Group.

AURORA CAVE 39°19'42" N.; 79°34'10" W. Kingwood Quadrangle.

One-half mile north of Aurora a collapsed sink opens to a steep slope of breakdown partially filling a fissure (elevation, 2560 feet). At the base of the slope are two holes 20 feet in diameter, 35 feet deep, which connect with a room 20 feet in diameter. Beyond the room is a 30- to 40-foot deep pit with water at the bottom. The cave is in the Greenbrier Limestone.

BEAVERHOLE UPPER CAVE 39°36'36" N.; 79°46'53" W. Morgantown Quadrangle.

This cave is on the north side of the Cheat River, 0.85 mile east of the Preston-Monongalia county line (elevation, 1100 feet). The entrance, a narrow, wet, crawlway, opens into a very narrow fissure passage heading east for over 300 yards. The passage, 8 to 15 feet high, enlarges in several places to small rooms at the base of chimneys. A stream flows through the cave and cascades down the talus slope at the entrance. The cave is in the Greenbrier Limestone.

BROOK STEMPLE CAVE 39°20'16" N.; 79°33'40" W. Kingwood Quadrangle.

Brook Stemple Cave it 1.1 miles N.N.W. of Aurora, on the southwest end of Brushy Knobs (elevation, 2650 feet). The entrance, a crawlway 10 feet long, opens into a long, dry passage that extends for 300 yards. The passage, large enough to permit walking, is in the Greenbrier Limestone.

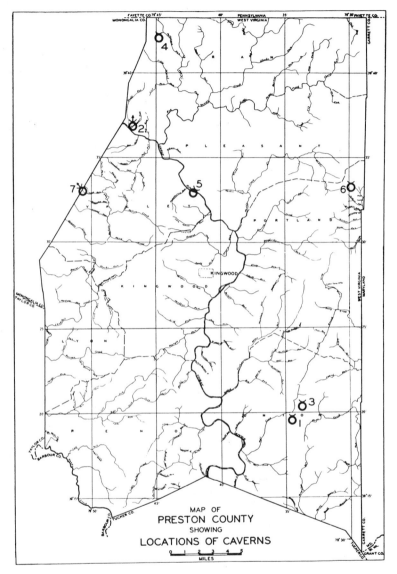

Figure 77.—Preston County Caves

1. Aurora Cave.
2. Beaverhole, Upper.
3. Brook Stemple.
4. Collins.

5. Cornwell.
6. Cranesville.
7. McKinney.

COLLINS CAVE 39°42'15" N.; 79°45'00" W. Bruceton Quadrangle.

Collins Cave is on the east flank of Chestnut Ridge one mile south of the Pennsylvania-West Virginia boundary (elevation, 1950 feet). It is near the west shore of Lake-of-the-Woods.

The cave trends west as a passage 3 to 6 feet high and 3 to 8 feet wide for about 50 feet. A sand fill blocks the passage. At the end is a side passage to the north. It is 30 feet long, 4 feet high, and 3 to 8 feet wide. It is blocked by a sand fill. The cave is in the Loyalhanna Limestone. Another cave consisting of a crawlway and a small room is located a quarter of a mile south on the opposite side of the ridge.

CORNWELL CAVE 39°32'56" N.; 79°42'12" W. Bruceton Quadrangle.

Cornwell Cave, the largest in Preston County, is on the south side of the gorge of Cheat River, 2 miles E.N.E. of Herring, at an elevation of 1300 feet. The entrance, a small opening in a low limestone cliff 200 feet above the river, opens to a maze of interlacing passages heading west for 400 feet. The passages near the front are 2 to 4 feet wide and 4 to 8 feet high. At the rear and on the south side they are narrow crevices, 1 to 3 feet wide and 10 to 60 feet high. The floor is wet clay and in one passage on the west side it is occupied by a small stream. The stream develops in the rear part of the cave from a series of dome pits with considerable water dripping from them. The formations are mainly flowstone and isolated columns.

Cornwell Cave, in the Greenbrier Limestone, which is cross-bedded, is developed along joints at N. 80° W.; N. 10° E., and N. 60° E.

Cave rats nest in great numbers in the front part of the cave. Their nests are scattered along the passages and the rats can be heard but are seldom seen.

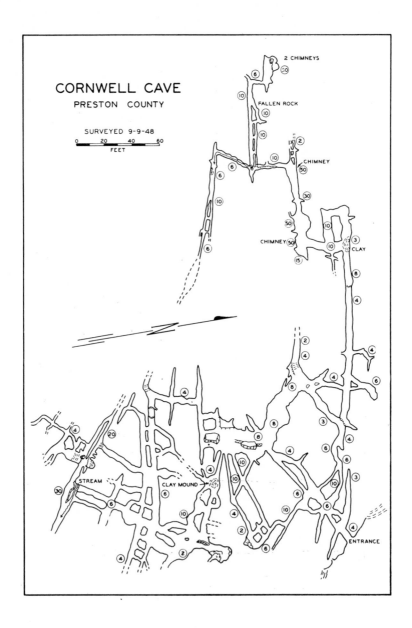

Figure 78.—Map of Cornwell Cave.

CRANESVILLE CAVE 39°33′06″ N.; 79°29′45″ W. Accident Quadrangle.

A small cave is located on the western outskirts of the town of Cranesville (elevation, 2650 feet). The cave, a passage 75 feet long, is large enough to permit walking. A large number of small stalactites and flowstone decorate the front part of the passage. The cave is in the Greenbrier Limestone.

McKINNEY CAVE 39°33′02″ N.; 79°50′41″ W. Morgantown Quadrangle.

McKinney Cave is at the head of Back Run on the Monongalia-Preston county line (elevation, 1920 feet). The cave is a large room, 15 to 20 feet high, 50 to 125 feet wide, and 250 feet long trending west. At the rear the ceiling height is reduced rapidly to a pinch out. S. T. Wiley [27] reports a passage on the south side of the room which leads to a smaller room, 10 feet high and 80 feet long, on a lower level. A stream rises in the middle of the cave and flows out to form Back Run. The cave is in the sandstones of the Pottsville Series.

RANDOLPH COUNTY

Forty-five caves are known in Randolph County. All of the caves are in the Greenbrier Limestone which is brought to the surface on the flanks of three major anticlines. The western outcrop is along the west side of the Tygart Valley and on the west flank of Cheat Mountain. The limestone is found along the east side of Shavers Mountain and the western flank of Rich Mountain on the Blackwater Anticline. The eastern outcrop is on the west flank of Allegheny Mountain along the Horton Anticline. Dry Fork and its tributaries and the headwaters of Elk River have cut into the Greenbrier Series and limestone is exposed along the valley floor and on the adjacent hillsides. The Greenbrier Series is 400 feet thick in the southern part of the county, thinning northwards to 100 feet. The reduction results from the disappearance of the basal members of the series below the Union Limestone.

---

[27] Wiley, S. T. History of Preston County: Journal Printing House, Kingwood, Pt. I, p. 21; 1882.

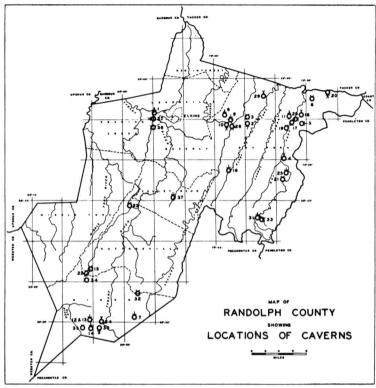

Figure 79.—Randolph County Caves

1. Aggregates.
2. Alpena No. 1.
3. Alpena No. 2.
4. Armentrout Pit.
5. Bazzle.
6. Bickle Run (Bear Heaven) Caves.
7. Big Run.
8. Bonner Mountain.
9. Bowden No. 1.
10. Bowden No. 2.
11. Cooper.
12. Crawford (Wymers) No. 1.
13. Crawford No. 2.
14. Falling Spring Cavern.
15. Fortlick.
16. Glady.
17. Harman.
18. Harman Pits.
19. Hazelwood.
20. Jordan Drop.
21. Keyhole (Chalk).
22. Limekiln Run.
23. Mill Creek.
24. Mingo Pit.
25. Nelson.
26. Railroad Caves.
27. Rich Mountain.
28. Rouse.
29. Schmidlen Shafts.
30. Simmons-Mingo.
31. Sinks of Gandy Creek.
32. Stewart Run.
33. Stillhouse (Hermit, Dead Mans).
34. Stony Run.
35. Swacker School.
36. Tyre School.
37. Ward.

AGGREGATES CAVE 38°56'02" N.; 79°54'33" W. Elkins Quadrangle.

Aggregates Cave is on the south side of Tygart River, at Aggregates, 3.5 miles west of Elkins (elevation, 1910 feet). The entrance is in a large quarry at the east end of the gap through Rich Mountain. The cave is large enough to permit walking but in less than 50 feet reduces to a crawl. A small stream flows out. The cave was used for "moonshine" operations at one time. It is in the lower part of the Union (Greenbrier) Limestone with a dip of 15° N.W.

ALPENA CAVE NO. 1 38°54'22" N.; 79°39'26" W. Horton Quadrangle.

This cave is 150 feet west of the cross-roads at Alpena and 100 feet south of U. S. 33 (elevation, 2700 feet). The entrance, at the base of a limestone ledge, leads south as a low crawlway 25 feet long, opening into a passage about 1000 feet long, 12 to 14 feet wide, 10 feet high, with three dome pits 35 to 40 feet in diameter developed along it. The floor is wet clay except in limited areas of breakdown. Formations are scarce and are mainly soda straw stalactites scattered along the passage. A stream flows through the cave and issues beneath a ledge, 10 feet west of the entrance. The cave is in the base of the Greenbrier Limestone which dips 10° to the northwest.

ALPENA CAVE NO. 2 38°54'45" N.; 79°39'23" W. Horton Quadrangle.

At the level of the old road, 1000 feet due north of the postoffice at Alpena (elevation, 2850 feet), is an entrance to a cave that is reported to be of considerable size. The entrance is blocked now by a rock fill. The cave is in the Greenbrier Limestone.

ARMENTROUT PIT 38°50'02" N.; 79°34'15" W. Horton Quadrangle.

A deep vertical shaft, with a passage at the base, formerly was open 2.3 miles south of Job and 200 feet east of the Whitmer road (elevation, 2680 feet). The pit is filled now with stone. It is in the Greenbrier Limestone.

BAZZLE CAVE 38°54′44″ N.; 79°30′53″ W. Horton Quadrangle.

One mile southeast of Harman, 600 feet south of U. S. 33, at an elevation of 2700 feet, is a small crawlway that leads south. It opens into a passage that extends for 500 feet as an alternation of crawlways and rooms. A stream flows through the cave. Bazzle Cave is in the Greenbrier Limestone.

BICKLE RUN (BEAR HEAVEN) CAVES 38°55′15″ N.; 79°42′45″ W. Horton Quadrangle.

Two caves are located along Bickle Run north of Bowden. The largest is on the east branch, 100 feet south of a small waterfall (elevation, 2600 feet). The entrance, an obscure hole in a pile of rock, opens into a passage large enough to permit walking. The passage is 100 yards long with two circular branches. A stream flows into the cave. The second cave, on the west branch, at an elevation of 2550 feet, is a short crawlway. The caves are in the Greenbrier Limestone.

BIG RUN CAVE 38°30′ N.; 80°00′ W. Pickens Quadrangle.

A large cave is near the head of Big Run 3½ miles south of Valley Head. The main passage is arcuate in plan and is a walkway about 1000 feet long with a stream. The passage decreases gradually in size upstream and ends in breakdown. Big Run Cave is in the Greenbrier Limestone.

BONNER MOUNTAIN CAVE 38°57′20″ N.; 79°29′05″ W. Onego Quadrangle.

This cave, on Bonner Mountain, is 1.3 miles southeast of Dry Fork (town), and 0.6 mile west of Bonner Mountain School (elevation, 2750 feet). The cave is a muddy crawlway heading west for 300 feet in the Greenbrier Limestone.

BOWDEN CAVE NO. 1 38°54′47″ N.; 79°42′27″ W. Horton Quadrangle.

On the north side of U. S. 33 at Bowden is a large quarry. At the west end of the quarry are several fissure openings, one of which leads to a large cave (elevation, 2225 feet). The fissure opens into the second room of the cave, the first room being blocked by the highway fill and now full of water. The cave is an alternation of rooms and passages extending about 1000 feet to the north. Several branches develop towards the rear of the cave. Formations are plentiful and include several large stalactites and stalagmites. A stream flows south through the cave. The source of the stream is reported near Mylius School. A quarry blast in 1945 left piles of rock debris that block the entrance fissure but little digging would be required to open it. The cave is in the base of the Greenbrier Limestone.

BOWDEN CAVE NO. 2 38°54'20" N.; 79°42'56" W. Horton Quadrangle.

This cave is in a small hollow above the quarry, 0.5 mile southwest of Bowden (elevation, 2450 feet). The entrance is a shaft 25 feet deep that opens into a crawlway extending south for 300 feet. The cave is in the top of the Greenbrier Limestone.

COOPER CAVE 38°55'12" N.; 79°32'23" W. Horton Quadrangle.

Cooper Cave is 0.7 mile west of Harman in a hollow at an elevation of 2500 feet. The entrance, 4 feet wide, 7 feet high, opens into a long passage with several branches. Some sections are narrow squeezes and crawls. A large stream flows out the entrance. The cave is in the Greenbrier Limestone.

CRAWFORD (WYMERS) CAVE NO. 1 38°30'40" N.; 80°04'45" W. Pickens Quadrangle.

Crawford Cave is on the south side of Ralston Run, 1000 feet west of Trough Spring School (new location), 1.7 miles northwest of Mingo (elevation, 2950 feet). The entrance, an opening 3 feet wide, 6 feet high, is 25 feet above the base of a low cliff, 500 feet south of the road. It opens into a passage, 8 to 10 feet wide and 10 to 15 feet high, that extends south for 800 feet. Several rooms, 15 to 20 feet wide, 30 to 40 feet high, 20 to 25 feet long, as well as a number of short crawlways occur along the passage. Three short side leads branch from the passage. At the rear the passages are reduced to crawlways and pinch out. A stream flows along the clay floor and emerges at the base of the entrance cliff. Crawford Cave is in the Greenbrier Limestone.

CRAWFORD CAVE NO. 2 38°30′30″ N.; 80°04′26″ W. Pickens Quadrangle.

This cave is 400 yards southeast of Crawford Cave No. 1 (elevation, 2950 feet). It consists of a room, 30 feet wide, 20 feet high, 100 feet long, with no passages leading off. A spring emerges below the entrance. The cave is in the Greenbrier Limestone.

FALLING SPRING CAVERN 38°29′08″ N.; 80°06′30″ W. Mingo Quadrangle.

Hu Maxwell [28] described this large cavern in his history of Randolph County. The cave is on Falling Spring Run, ¾ mile east of Elk River, at an elevation of 2650 feet. The entrance, in a broad, deep sink, opens into a single passage, 4 to 20 feet high and 5 to 20 feet wide, which drops at the rate of 1 foot in 5 to the west. The passage is 500 feet long and has large logs jammed in crevices in the ceiling for much of its length. At the end it opens into a wide, low room. A cleft in the floor opens into a maze of tunnels, one of which continues 100 yards to a large, low room banked with sand. The cave pinches out just beyond the room. Falling Spring Run flows into the cave which is in the upper part of the Greenbrier Limestone.

FORTLICK CAVE 38°36′03″ N.; 80°04′58″ W. Pickens Quadrangle.

This cave is at the head of the south branch of Fortlick Run, a tributary of Elkwater Fork, 4.8 miles northwest of Valley Head (elevation, 2750 feet). The entrance is a crawlway which opens into a passage 1000 feet long with five rooms developed along it. The cave has a number of formations and a stream flows through it. It is reported to have been used for saltpeter previous to the War Between the States. Fortlick Cave is in the base of the Greenbrier Limestone.

---

[28] Maxwell, Hu. History of Randolph County: Acme Publishing Co., Morgantown, pp. 281-285; 1898.

GLADY CAVE 38°48′31″ N.; 79°43′00″ W. Horton Quadrangle.

Glady Cave is 0.9 mile north of Glady, 50 feet west of the Glady-Alpine road (elevation, 2850 feet). The entrance, a small crawl hole at the top of a bank, 20 feet above the road, slopes steeply downwards for 30 feet to a room, 15 feet wide, 20 feet high, 30 feet long, trending N. 20° W. At the rear of the room a clay bank reaches nearly to the ceiling where a crawlway extends west for 100 feet. A stream enters the room from a small sewer passage on the west side and disappears in a pool at the south end of the room. It emerges as a spring along the road 100 yards to the south. The cave is in the base of the Greenbrier Limestone.

HARMAN CAVE 38°55′04″ N.; 79°31′45″ W. Horton Quadrangle.

This cave is directly beneath the grade of U. S. 33, ¼ mile south of Harman (elevation, 2360 feet). The entrance, in a low ledge of limestone on the west side of the road, opens to a twisting channel, 2 to 4 feet wide and 4 to 6 feet high, which extends east for 150 feet. The cave is a stream channel in wet weather. It is in the base of the Greenbrier Limestone.

HARMAN PITS 38°55′40″ N.; 79°31′00″ W.
               38°55′28″ N.; 79°30′53″ W.
Horton Quadrangle.

Two large vertical shafts, 50 feet deep, lie on the flank of Allegheny Mountain, ¾ mile northeast of Harman (elevation, 2650 feet). Small rooms are reported to open at their bases. The shafts are in the middle part of the Greenbrier Limestone.

HAZELWOOD CAVE 38°54′06″ N.; 79°32′59″ W. Horton Quadrangle.

Hazelwood Cave is 300 feet west of the Harman-Job road, 0.5 mile north of Hazelwood (elevation, 2500 feet). This cave is a crawlway, 100 yards long, in the lower part of the Greenbrier Limestone. Directly across the valley to the east is a deep vertical shaft.

JORDANS DROP CAVE 38°58'17" N.; 79°26'19" W. Onego Quadrangle.

Jordans Drop Cave is 2.8 miles northeast of Bonner Mountain School, one mile west of Laneville (elevation, 2525 feet). It is a pit 15 feet in diameter and 60 feet deep. No passages lead from the pit. The pit is in the Greenbrier Limestone.

KEYHOLE (CHALK) CAVE 38°47'32" N.; 79°34'03" W. Horton Quadrangle.

Keyhole Cave is in a hollow that heads at the south end of Little Low Place, 1.7 miles southwest of Whitmer (elevation, 3050 feet). The cave is a crawlway about 100 yards long in the base of the Greenbrier Limestone.

LIMEKILN RUN CAVE 38°35'42" N.; 80°05'14" W. Pickens Quadrangle.

This cave is at the head of Limekiln Run, 4.6 miles northwest of Valley Head, at an elevation of 2750 feet. The cave is a short, muddy crawlway in the upper part of the Greenbrier Limestone.

MILL CREEK CAVE 38°44'16" N.; 79°59'45" W. Durbin Quadrangle.

Mill Creek Cave is 1.7 miles west of Mill Creek P. O. at an elevation of 2280 feet. The cave, a passage 6 feet wide and 6 to 7 feet high, extends 100 feet to a pinch down. A spring issues below the cave and is used as a water supply for the town of Mill Creek. The cave is dry and is in the base of the Greenbrier Limestone.

MINGO PIT 38°29'40" N.; 80°03'56" W. Mingo Quadrangle.

This deep vertical shaft opens in the base of the Greenbrier Limestone, ½ mile northwest of Upper Mingo (elevation, 2900 feet). No passage or room is reported at the base.

NELSON CAVE 38°48'17" N.; 79°33'16" W. Horton Quadrangle.

This cave is 1030 feet up the farm lane to Little Low Place, 1.6 miles west of Whitmer (elevation, 3155 feet). The entrance, 15 feet high and 4 feet wide, opens into a passage 4 to 10 feet wide and 30 feet high which trends S. 25° W. There is a small room on the west side of the passage 50 feet from the entrance. The main passage is 500 feet long after which it is a small fissure for another 1000 feet where it connects to the surface by a small hole in a sink. A small stream flows through the cave and out the entrance. Nelson Cave is in the lower part of the Greenbrier Limestone.

RAILROAD CAVES 38°54'33" N.; 79°42'15" W. Horton Quadrangle.

Three small cave openings are in a cut on the Western Maryland Railway, 0.4 mile east of Bowden Station (elevation, 2260 feet). The caves are crawlways about 50 feet long. The largest one ends in a pit at the rear. The caves are in the upper part of the Greenbrier Limestone.

RICH MOUNTAIN CAVE 38°55'30" N.; 79°54'52" W. Elkins Quadrangle.

Near the top of Rich Mountain, on the east side, 3.5 miles due west of Elkins (elevation, 2300 feet), is a steeply sloping shaft, 30 feet deep. A passage trends north from its base and is rather difficult to traverse, involving much climbing and crawling. The passage is dry and is reported to connect with the cave at Aggregates. A quarry blast is reported to have blocked the north end of the passage. The cave is in the upper part of the Greenbrier Limestone.

ROUSE CAVE 38°55'10" N.; 79°31'41" W. Horton Quadrangle.

Rouse Cave is in a low ledge of limestone on the south side of Horsecamp Run, 100 feet east of U. S. 33 at Harman (elevation, 2350 feet). The front part of the cave is a crawlway 100 feet long that enlarges enough to allow walking in the last 100 feet. The cave heads south and is in the base of the Greenbrier Limestone.

SCHMIDLEN SHAFTS 38°57'14" N.; 79°37'18" W. Horton Quadrangle.

Three vertical shafts are located ½ mile north of Mylius School at an elevation of 2800 feet. Two of the shafts are pits over 50 feet deep, one of which has a stream at the base. The third is a deep fissure opening that is about 50 feet deep. It is reported that the stream beneath the shafts ultimately flows to Bowden Cave. The shafts are in the Greenbrier Limestone.

SIMMONS-MINGO CAVE 38°29'00" N.; 80°04'30" W. Mingo Quadrangle.

This cave is on the south side of Mingo Run, 1¼ miles southwest of Upper Mingo, at an elevation of 3000 feet. The entrance shaft is 35 feet deep and opens into a debris laden passage trending southwest to a large room (The Big Room). This room is 100 feet high, 192 feet long, and 132 feet wide. The floor is covered to a considerable depth by massive slabs of breakdown. The cave continues as an irregular crawlway beneath the breakdown to a pit 38 feet deep which leads to a series of crawlways, high fissures, pits, and breakdown extending to the southwest. The beginning of these lower level passages is 372 feet below the entrance while 500 feet farther on (the end of present exploration) it is about 600 feet down. A stream flows along the lower level. A branch of the cave opens to the northeast just below the entrance pit and is only partially explored. It extends for over 1000 feet with extensive chambers and passages. The cave apparently extends through the entire thickness of the Greenbrier Limestone, with the entrance at the top and the lower passages along the base of the limestone.

SINKS OF GANDY CREEK 38°42'55" N.; 79°38'34" W.
Spruce Knob Quadrangle.   38°43'08" N.; 79°38'04" W.

Gandy Creek flows along a subterranean channel for about 3000 feet through a spur on the south side of Yokum Knob, ½ mile west of Osceola. The south entrance is in a low ledge of limestone at the north end of a large depressed meadow. It is 30 feet wide, 15 feet high, heading north for 100 feet and then turning northeast along a fairly straight channel for 2725 feet to its northern exit. The passage averages 36 to 60

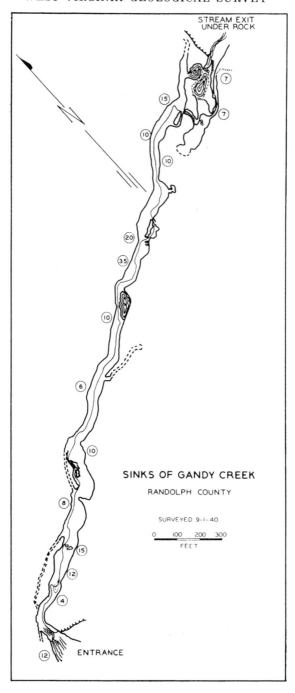

STREAM EXIT
UNDER ROCK

SINKS OF GANDY CREEK

RANDOLPH COUNTY

SURVEYED 9-1-40

0   100   200   300
FEET

ENTRANCE

Figure 80.—Sinks of Gandy Creek.

Plate LVII.—Sinks of Gandy Creek, South Entrance. (Photo by Wm. E. Davies).

feet wide with some sections up to 100 feet wide and the ceiling is 6 to 30 feet high. Side passages are small, short leads except at the north end where the exit passage is offset 100 feet to the east of the stream channel. Several narrow passages connect the two sections. In places the stream occupies the entire floor of the passage. In other sections it is restricted to narrow trenches while the remainder of the passage is on a ledge or gravel bank. About midway and at the northern end of the passage the stream flows in deep pools almost blocking the passage. The grade through the cave is 6 inches per hundred feet with the south entrance at 3500 feet and the exit at 3460 feet. The Sinks are in the base of the Greenbrier Limestone which is horizontal at this point.

STEWART RUN CAVE 38°33' N.; 79°58' W. Durbin Quadrangle.

A cave is reported near the head of Stewart Run, 3.9 miles northeast of Valley Head. It has a large entrance but no data are reported concerning its length or other characteristics. It is in the Greenbrier Limestone.

STILLHOUSE (HERMIT, DEAD MANS CAVE) 38°42'54" N.; 79°38'15" W. Spruce Knob Quadrangle.

Stillhouse Cave is ¼ mile west of Osceola. The entrance, in a low limestone ledge on the east side of the country road (elevation, 3500 feet), is an opening 5 feet high, 20 feet wide, that is partially filled with trash. For the first 20 feet the passage is 3 feet high but opens up to a room 10 to 15 feet high, 30 feet wide, extending west for 50 feet and then north for 100 feet. A broad crawlway leads north to two rooms. To the northeast the room is 100 feet long, 45 feet wide, and 10 to 15 feet high, ending in a pile of breakdown. The room to the west is 200 feet long, 65 feet wide, and 15 feet high. The cave continues as a large passage to the west for 190 feet where it turns south for 150 feet as a crawlway with breakdown at the end. A side passage opens at the top of a clay bank on the north side of the Big Room near its west end. It extends east, parallel to the Big Room, and is 100 feet long ending in a small room. A small stream is near the entrance of the cave and flows west in a small passage for 200 feet west of the end of the entrance passage. Small streams are encountered in several other parts of the cave. A few rimstone pools lie at the east end of the Big Room. The floor throughout most of the cave is wet clay. The cave is named Stillhouse after a still that was operated in it in 1881. It is in the base of the Greenbrier Limestone.

STONY RUN CAVE   38°34'52" N.; 80°05'19" W.
Pickens Quadrangle. 38°35'10" N.; 80°05'30" W.

Two small caves lie near the head of Stony Run. They are on the south side of the creek, one being one mile west of Elkwater Fork, the other ¾ mile west of Elkwater Fork. Both are at an elevation of 2750 feet. They are reported to be short crawlways in the Greenbrier Limestone.

A third cave is reported in a sink, at 2700 feet elevation, on a spur between Limekiln Run and Elkwater Fork, 1.1 miles southwest of the junction of the two streams. No data are available on it.

SWACKER SCHOOL CAVE 38°29′54″ N.; 80°08′04″ W. Mingo Quadrangle.

A small cave is developed in the top of the Greenbrier Limestone 100 yards northwest of Swacker School (elevation, 2435 feet).

TYRE SCHOOL CAVE 38°54′40″ N.; 79°54′37″ W. Elkins Quadrangle.

Tyre School Cave, at the head of the hollow on the north branch of Mathias Run, 0.65 mile due west of Tyre School (elevation, 2300 feet), is a muddy crawlway about 100 yards long. It is in the Greenbrier Limestone.

WARD CAVE 38°44′54″ N.; 79°51′21″ W. Durbin Quadrangle.

Ward Cave is on the west flank of Cheat Mountain, at the head of the Right Fork of Files Creek, 6 miles east of Mill Creek (elevation, 2900 feet). The entrance to the cave, a narrow fissure, 6 feet high on the south side of the valley, opens into a small passage that has considerable breakdown. The cave extends south along the strike for about 1000 feet as an alternation of passages and rooms. In a number of places it is reduced to a muddy crawlway. A stream flows through the cave and emerges as a spring below the entrance. The cave is in the base of the Greenbrier Limestone.

One other cave has been reported in Randolph County. **Massconny Cave** is near Star in the southeast part of the county. It is a 19-foot pit with a few small passages at the base.

TUCKER COUNTY

There are twenty caves known in Tucker County. All of them are in the Greenbrier Limestone which outcrops on the east flank of Laurel Ridge, the west flank of Backbone Mountain, and along the valley floor and sides of Dry Fork. An isolated outcrop encircles Limestone Mountain and another band

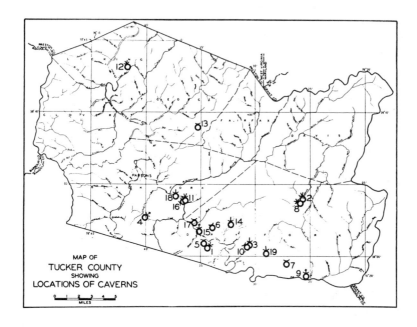

Figure 81.—Tucker County Caves

1. Arbegast.
2. Beall.
3. Bennett.
4. Big Springs (Blowing).
5. Cave Hollow.
6. Falling Spring.
7. Hadey.
8. Harmon Pits.
9. Harr.
10. Lambert.

11. Laurel Run.
12. Limestone Mountain.
13. Maxwell Run Caves.
14. Mill Run.
15. Moore (Red Run Quarry).
16. Otter Creek.
17. Red Run.
18. Stillhouse Hollow.
19. Wolford.

is brought to the surface by the Blackwater Anticline along the sides of Canaan Valley. The beds are nearly horizontal except on Limestone Mountain where they have a distinct dip to the west. The Greenbrier Limestone is 430 feet thick in the southeast corner of the county but is reduced to 165 feet in Limestone Mountain. With the reduction in thickness the ratio of impurities increases. Beds of shale and arenaceous limestone are prevalent, being scattered through the series but most numerous near the top.

ARBOGAST CAVE 39°00'31" N.; 79°34'30" W. Parsons Quadrangle.

This cave is in a hollow on Shavers Mountain, 0.7 mile due south of Richford (elevation, 2600 feet). The entrance, a pit 15 feet deep, opens into a small passage heading north for over 300 yards. This passage connects with Cave Hollow Cave to the north. Arbogast Cave is in the base of the Greenbrier Limestone.

BEALL CAVE 39°03'55" N.; 79°25'42" W. Davis Quadrangle.

A vertical pit formerly opened into a cave 600 feet south of Cortland in Canaan Valley (elevation, 3170 feet). The entrance is filled now with rock. It is in the middle part of the Greenbrier Limestone.

BENNETT CAVE 39°00'43" N.; 79°30'34" W. Parsons Quadrangle.

Bennett Cave is on Big Run, 100 yards north of Dry Fork road (elevation, 2450 feet. The cave is an easily traversed passage extending north for several hundred feet. A small stream flows through the passage. The cave is in the Greenbrier Limestone.

BIG SPRINGS (BLOWING) CAVE 39°02'42" N.; 79°40'02" W. Parsons Quadrangle.

Big Springs Cave is on the west side of Elklick Run, ¼ mile west of Big Springs Gap (elevation, 2450 feet). The entrance is 12 feet high and 10 feet wide and breakdown partially blocks the passage 40 feet in. Two hundred feet beyond the breakdown the passage divides. The left (north) passage follows a stream. The right passage is a walkway 1000 feet long to a long crawlway and squeeze beyond which is open passage for 1000 feet to a room. At this point are five leads above a stream passage one of which opens into a 45-foot crawlway and a 1000-foot walkway. The latter passage doubles back towards the entrance. The cave is in the base of the Greenbrier Limestone.

CAVE HOLLOW CAVE 39°00′50″ N.; 79°34′45″ W. Parsons Quadrangle.

This cave is on the south side of the hollow opposite Richford, 1.8 miles west of Gladwin (elevation, 2500 feet). The entrance is 8 feet high and 12 feet wide. A walkway stream passage trends southwest for 300 feet. It is 20 feet wide and 40 feet high with smooth walls and bedrock floor. A wet crawlway 30 feet long opens into a passage similar to the first large passage and is 200 feet long. A crawlway 20 feet long continues from this passage and connects with another large passage 2000 feet long. At the end of this large passage is a shaft in the ceiling 75 feet high and 15 feet in diameter. On the northeast side of the shaft is a crawlway 10 feet long opening into a passage trending southwest. This passage divides after 50 feet with one part trending south-southeast for 4000 feet to Arbegast Cave. The second part of the passage is a squeeze over breakdown for 500 feet to the south where it connects with a roof 50 feet wide, 8 feet high, and 200 feet long. From the south end of the room is a passage to the southeast 1000 feet long. On the east side of the room is a passage 200 feet long that connects with Arbegast Cave. The stream in the latter cave flows north along the east passage and then through Cave Hollow Cave. Sixteen hundred feet from the entrance to Cave Hollow Cave is a small crawlway to the northeast which opens up after 150 feet to a large passage trending north for 1700 feet to breakdown. A small stream follows along this passage. Several other passages also lead off the main passage. Cave Hollow Cave is in the Greenbrier Limestone.

Professor George Jordan published a pamphlet in 1855 describing a large cave located near the Blackwater River, 40 miles from Beverly.[29] His description began a controversy that is still far from settled. The cave described—"The Great Cave of Cheat River"—was reported to consist of a main passage over 30,000 feet long with huge dome pits, large rooms, and a lake over 1200 feet long. His description is in minute detail leaving little to the imagination. Many persons have searched in vain for a cave that meets the description

---

[29] Jordan, George. The Great Cave of Cheat River: Hanzsche and Company, Baltimore, 1855.

and Prof. Jordan's statements have been branded false. Hu Maxwell [30] in his history of Tucker County described Cave Hollow Cave and identified it as the one recorded by Jordan. Allowing for extreme exaggeration and overenthusiastic descriptions, Professor Jordan's cave is probably the same as Cave Hollow Cave.

FALLING SPRING CAVE 39°02′ N.; 79°34′ W. Parsons Quadrangle.

Hu Maxwell [31] reported a pit close to the Dry Fork road, which is 30 feet deep, receives a small stream and is believed to open into a cave. The location is approximately 6 miles south of Hendricks. The pit was not located during field work.

HADEY CAVE 38°59′20″ N.; 79°27′11″ W. Onego Quadrangle.

Hadey Cave is 100 yards east of the Laneville road, 2.0 miles south of Buena (elevation, 2850 feet). The cave is a single passage extending northwest for over 100 yards. A few short crawlways interrupt the passage. The cave is in the middle part of the Greenbrier Limestone.

HARMON PITS 39°03′36 N.; 79°25′52″ W. Davis Quadrangle.

Several pits in the Greenbrier Limestone open into small passages, ½ mile south of Cortland (elevation, 3190 feet). The pits are 30 to 50 feet deep.

HARR CAVE 38°58′30″ N.; 79°25′24″ W. Onego Quadrangle.

Harr Cave is on the north side of Laneville (elevation, 2550 feet). The entrance room is 10 feet high and wide extending north for 40 feet to a low crawlway over 100 feet long. A stream flows out of the cave. Harr Cave is in the top of the Greenbrier Limestone.

---

[30] Maxwell, Hu. History of Tucker County, West Virginia: Preston Publishing Co., Kingwood, W. Va., p. 137; 1884.

[31] Op. cit., p. 136.

LAMBERT CAVE   39°00′36″ N.; 79°30′45″ W.   Parsons Quadrangle.

Lambert Cave is 200 yards south of the Dry Fork road and 200 yards west of Big Run, 1.8 miles east of Gladwin (elevation, 2450 feet). The entrance is a crawlway opening in a low cliff that extends north for about 20 feet. A passage, large enough to permit walking, extends north for 100 yards from the crawlway. The cave is in the base of the Greenbrier Limestone.

LAUREL RUN CAVE 39°03′50″ N.; 79°36′30″ W. Parsons Quadrangle.

On the west side and directly below the Dry Fork road, ¼ mile north of Laurel Run (elevation, 1730 feet), is a vertical shaft 10 feet deep. A straight passage, 4 feet wide, 10 feet high, trends northeast for 200 feet. The cave is in the base of the Greenbrier Limestone.

LIMESTONE MOUNTAIN CAVE 39°13′03″ N.; 79°41′42″ W. Parsons Quadrangle.

This cave is on the east side of Limestone Mountain, 500 feet west of the St. George-Limestone Church road, 1.4 miles southwest of Limestone Church (elevation, 2550 feet). The entrance is a pit, 18 feet deep, at the base of a shallow trash-filled sink. The main passage, 2 to 5 feet wide and 4 to 10 feet high, extends southwest for 300 feet where it pinches out.

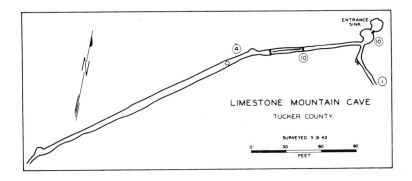

Figure 82.—Map Limestone Mountain Cave.

One hundred feet from the entrance is a dome pit 35 feet high and 6 feet in diameter. A similar but smaller dome pit is located near the end of the cave. A small passage, 3 feet wide, 5 feet high, extends 130 feet south from the base of the entrance. The cave is in the base of the Greenbrier Limestone.

MAXWELL RUN CAVES 39°08'52" N.; 79°35'19" W. Parsons Quadrangle.

Two small crawlways, each extending 500 feet to the east, are developed at the head of Maxwell Run, 5 miles west of Thomas (elevation, 2950 feet). The air is reported to be bad near the end of the passages. The caves are in the base of the Greenbrier Limestone.

MILL RUN CAVE 39°02'08" N.; 79°32'15" W. Parsons Quadrangle.

This cave is on the east side of Mill Run, 1/4 mile north of Mill Run Church (elevation, 2350 feet). The entrance, in a steep-sided sink 10 feet deep, opens into a passage, 5 to 8 feet high, 4 to 10 feet wide, extending S. 80° E. for 2000 feet. Several side passages as well as rooms are developed along the main passage. The floor is broken rock and formations are scattered along the walls of the cave. A stream flows through the main passage and drops down a narrow crevice 100 yards from the entrance. It emerges 100 yards southwest of the entrance to form Mill Creek. The cave is in the base of the Greenbrier Limestone.

MOORE (RED RUN QUARRY) CAVE 39°01'40" N.; 79°35'10" W. Parsons Quadrangle.

A small quarry, 0.8 mile south of Red Run along the road-bed of the abandoned Central West Virginia and Southern Railroad, has a small cave opening (elevation, 1850 feet). The quarry is just north of the site of Moore Siding. The cave extends southeast as a crawlway for 200 feet where it enlarges to a fissure opening up to 20 feet high and 1000 feet long. At the rear is a chimney, 10 feet by 15 feet in cross-section and 25 feet high. The cave continues a short distance beyond but is a small crawlway. A small passage leads up a mud slope and emerges at the surface at this point also. A stream falls into the cave at the chimney and flows through the cave emerging at the entrance. The cave is in the base of the Greenbrier Limestone.

OTTER CREEK CAVE 39°03'48" N.; 79°36'34" W. Parsons Quadrangle.

Otter Creek Cave is along the west side of Dry Fork directly opposite Laurel Run Cave (elevation, 1750 feet). It is a small crawlway, 50 feet long, that is in the base of the Greenbrier Limestone.

RED RUN CAVE 39°02'18" N.; 79°35'34" W. Parsons Quadrangle.

A fissure cave is developed on the north side of Red Run 200 yards east of Dry Fork road (elevation, 1900 feet). The fissure is 2 feet wide and 10 feet high extending 100 feet to the east. It is in the middle part of the Greenbrier Limestone.

STILLHOUSE HOLLOW CAVE 39°04'10" N.; 79°37'19" W. Parsons Quadrangle.

Stillhouse Hollow is directly south, across Dry Fork, from Hendricks. A cave is located near the mouth of the hollow at an elevation of 2000 feet. The cave, at the base of the Greenbrier Limestone, is less than 100 yards in length and consists of several passages large enough to permit walking. A stream flows through the cave.

WOLFORD CAVE 39°00'07" N.; 79°28'58" W. Davis Quadrangle.

This cave is in a hollow, 100 yards south of Big Run, 0.7 mile east of Red Creek P. O. (elevation, 2950 feet). The entrance, a pit 15 feet deep at the base of a shallow sink, trends southwest for 700 feet. It is large enough to permit walking except at the entrance where it is a crawlway. There is one main passage and two subordinate ones. Rooms up to 50 feet long and wide are reported along the passage. A stream flows through the cave towards the entrance. A rock fall now blocks the cave at the end of the crawlway, 100 feet from the entrance. Wolford Cave is in the lower part of the Greenbrier Limestone.

Three other caves are reported in Tucker County. They are:

Bonner Cave—Two miles southeast of Moore on the west side of West Virginia Highway 72; 8- by 10-foot sink with passage at base sloping 45° down for 50 feet to an 8-foot drop in a narrow fissure; fissure continues as a passage several hundred feet long. This cave may be the same as Arbegast Cave.

Fanchler Cave—Southwest end of Backbone Mountain, 1000 feet above stream; north of Hendricks; vertical shaft with passage at the base.

Groundhog Cave—Twelve miles southwest of Davis; entrance passage 4 feet in diameter sloping 8 feet to a room 13 by 20 feet; short crawlways lead from the room.

INDEX

Speleological Features

Cavern Descriptions

Page   *Page*

State of West Virginia

HULETT C. SMITH, *Governor*

Geological and Economic Survey

PAUL H. PRICE, *Director and State Geologist*

SUPPLEMENT TO VOLUME XIX(A)

Caverns of West Virginia

(Supplement)

Compiled By

William E. Davies, *Speleologist*

1965

PREFACE

In 1949 the West Virginia Geological and Economic Survey published Volume XIX, **Caverns of West Virginia,** by William E. Davies. This book was so popular that it was revised and reprinted in 1958 as Volume XIX(A). All stocks of these printings have been exhausted, so it was necessary to reprint the book this year to meet the continuing requests for information on the caverns of our State.

This Supplement to Volume XIX(A) contains data and maps on new caves as well as further information on caves described in the earlier volumes. It has been prepared as a separate publication for those hundreds of persons who purchased Volume XIX(A) in the past and wish to maintain up-to-date information on West Virginia caves.

PAUL H. PRICE, M.Sc., Ph.D.

*Director and State Geologist
and Professor of Geology*

Morgantown, W. Va.
May 20, 1965

CONTRIBUTORS

Hermine Zotter
Vic Schmidt
D. B. Williamson
John F. Fisher
West Virginia Association for Cave Studies

CONTENTS

FIGURES

CAVERNS OF WEST VIRGINIA
(Supplement)

by William E. Davies

INTRODUCTION

Since 1958, when the second edition of the Caverns of West Virginia was published, there has been a continued interest in West Virginia caves. Most of the interest has been in the Swago Creek area, Pocahontas County, and in the vicinity of Organ-Hedricks Cave in Greenbrier and Monroe Counties. One hundred and fourteen additional caves have been described in the literature and these descriptions form the basis for this revision. In addition to the cavern studies, detailed stream tracing has been done on subterranean drainage in several areas in Pocahontas County.

Citations for data obtained from published sources are given for each cave description where applicable. To the authors cited, as well as to the contributors, must go most of the credit for making this supplement possible. Conditions in the past few years have carried the author of the original edition of **Caverns of West Virginia** to the ends of the earth and greatly curtailed the time available for continuing studies in West Virginia.

As indicated in previous editions any cave study must be considered as a report on status of knowledge with the expectation that new caves will be described and additional parts of already described caves will be found. So it will be with this revision and so it should be as speleology is a progressive and developing field.

HYDROLOGY

Through the work of Miss Hermine Zotter and others considerable knowledge of subterranean drainage has been gained in the Swago Creek, Hills Creek and Little Levels areas. Dye tests carried on since 1960 indicate that Hills Creek drains under Droop Mountain directly to the Locust Creek resurgence. Martha Clarks Cave also drains underground to the same resurgence. Bruffey Creek flows east and northeast through Hughes Creek Cave, into Hughes Creek Lower Cave, apparently into Martha Clarks Cave, thence south to resurge at Locust Creek Cave also. During flood stage Hughes Creek Cave overflows forming Hughes **Creek** (rather than Millstone Creek), completely inundates the Lower Cave, then flows east into Beards Blue Hole. Poor Farm Water Cave in Little Levels drains southwest to McNeels Mill Run Cave resurgence. Stamping Creek submerges about 5 miles from its mouth and follows an underground course to near Mill Point. Steam Cave is one source of the subterranean drainage resurging at Blue Springs Cave, also at Mill Point, but south of the Stamping Creek resurgence. Water sinking on the southern side of Rodgers Mountain drains southwest under Gillilan Mountain resurging at Mill Point to form McNeel Run.

In the Swago Creek area Hause Waterfall Cave, Swago-Carpenters Pits, and Barnes Pit form a subterranean system resurging at Cave Creek Cave. Tub Cave and Friels Cave also resurge at Cave Creek Cave. The pits and caves along the west side of Dry Creek resurge at Overholt Blowing Cave. Dynamite Pit, near the head of Dry Creek, resurges at the Dry Creek resurgence near Swago Creek. Dry Creek Swallow Hole at the head of Dry Creek flows 1¼ miles east under Stony Creek Mountain resurging at the Sharp Farm resurgence, from which the Campbelltown water supply is piped. Water sinking on the east side of Stony Creek Mountain resurges at the head of Price Run and at Sharp Run.

CONSERVATION

Since 1959, when Volume XIX(A) was published, the interest in caves for both recreational and scientific use has increased greatly. With this increased use has come an alarming increase in the deterioration of the physical condition of caves and a corresponding deterioration of relations between cave owners and cavers. The changing times with regard to cave exploration have brought about a change in ethics. A decade ago it was considered proper to leave a record of a visit to a cave by inscribing the visitor's name on the wall. Such practices today are unethical and are now accepted as near-criminal acts which if continued would shortly destroy the beauty of every cave.

With continuing increases in urban population and wealth there will be an increased use of caves for recreation. If this increase is to be accomplished without totally destroying all caves and without greatly aggravating the already poor relations between owners and cavers, each person entering a cave will have to accept specific responsibilities and discipline. If not, it can be anticipated within a decade that entry into every significant cave will be barred by law or property right.

Every caver, whether a recreationist or a scientist, must recognize that most cavers are on private property and that entry is a privilege granted by the owner and not an inherent right of a caver. This is also true of caves on government property. Permission of the owner or caretaker of the property should always be obtained before entering a cave. If possible this should be done in advance or at least at a time convenient to the owner. Property must be respected and protected. Buildings should not be used by cavers without permission; fence gates should always be returned to their original position after passage.

Waste materials, especially carbide, should be buried in deep pits, or better, placed in plastic or other containers and disposed of at the caver's home. On an initial visit to a cave fit your schedule so that caving will be done during daylight hours.

If access to a cave is barred by a gate or by the owner's decree against entry accept the fact and do not circumvent the closure. It must be understood that owners have well-founded reasons for closing caves. In some cases acts of vandalism have been committed; in others the steady traffic to the cave is an extreme inconvenience to the owner; and some liability insurance companies prohibit access to the cave while the insurance policy is in effect.

It is the better-known caves that have suffered most from closure. To prevent additional closure cavers should limit their visits to caves. Parties should be kept small and visits coordinated with other cavers so that an individual cave owner is inconvenienced only by a few intrusions in a year.

Vandalism is destruction or removal of objects from a cave, either willfully or because of negligence. Vandalism is a crime and is punishable by law. Fortunately vandalism in West Virginia caves has been very limited. If, as a cave visitor, you are tempted to remove a speleothem—a stalactite, or piece of flowstone—think for a moment of the time necessary to create such a feature; think also that a speleothem, like most natural objects, is beautiful only in its natural setting and once removed its beauty, utility and stability are gone. In a home or office it becomes merely another rock facing eventual discard. So, for speleothems and all other cavern features, look, photograph, and admire, but don't touch.

Wastes of any kind left in a cave greatly upset the ecology and permanently mar the beauty. All wastes, from carbide to human wastes, should be removed in suitable containers from a cave. Plastic bags do well for this. As far as cave animals are concerned, serious disturbance and destruction can occur by deposition of waste in a cave.

The caver must understand the restorative action in most caves is so slow compared to similar conditions on the surface, that it can be considered nonexistent. A foot print in a cave, a defaced wall, or broken speleothems remain without change for centuries. Because of this cavers should stick to existing paths or the tracks of others and save as much of the cave as possible from wear and tear.

Safety is a part of conservation. Unfortunately, of late, cave accidents are increasing and death in a cave is no longer an unheard of rarity. West Virginia has had her share of such deaths. Most accidents are of three kinds: falls into pits, drowning, and entrapment. These can be traced to an increasing tendency to use caves for personal gratification by going the farthest, the deepest, or through the smallest of openings. While the desire to push back the horizons of exploration is a laudable human endeavor, it becomes foolhardy if it is done with improper equipment, undersized parties, poor planning that fails to provide for natural calamities such as flooding, or exceeding personal physical conditions.

Conservation means keeping West Virginia caves safe, hospitable, and preserved for the use of others. Do your part to help keep these unrestorable natural features available to everyone. Make your visits so that they will be recreation without destruction.

At present 12 caves in West Virginia are restricted for entry. Coffmans, Cricket, Hellems, Benders, Silers, Mystic, Stratosphere Balloon, Seneca Caverns (except for commerical tourist parts), Lawrence Dome, Hourglass, Piercys Mill, and Schoolhouse are closed to casual visitors. Egress across property is restricted in the vicinity of Ruddle Cave. McClung Cave has a locked gate within the cave. Organ-Hedricks and other entrances to the Greenbrier Cavern are restricted or barred by gates. Hoffman School Cave is restricted to entry on a voluntary basis because of the bat colony there. Permission to visit is specifically needed for Jones Quarry, Molers, and Whitings Neck caves.

Civil Defense installations are in Schoolhouse, Seneca, Stratosphere Balloon, Trout, New Trout, Kenny Simmons, and Sinnett. Unless otherwise restricted, these caves are open for visits on the condition that Civil Defense materials are not tampered with.

The list of restricted caves and those with Civil Defense installations will change and before entry all cavers should check on the status of the caves involved.

BIBLIOGRAPHY

Thirty-one major papers dealing specifically with West Virginia caves have been published since 1958.

Barr, Thomas C., Jr., 1960, Speciation and distribution of cavernicolous invertebrates in the eastern United States: American Philosophical Soc., Yearbook, 1959, p. 229-230.

Barr, Thomas C., Jr., 1965, The Pseudanophthalmus of the Appalachian Valley (Coleoptera, Carabidae): Amer. Midland Naturalist, v. 73, no. 1, Jan., p. 41-72.

Causey, Nell B., 1960, Speciation in North American cave millipeds: Amer. Midland Naturalist, v. 64, no. 1, July, p. 116.

Conrad, Lyle G., 1961, Distribution and speciation problems concerning the Long-eared Bat, **Plecotus townsendii virginianus:** D. C. Speleograph, v. 17, no. 8, Aug., p. 49-52.

Cooper, John E., 1960, Collective notes on cave-associated vertebrates: Baltimore Grotto News, v. 3, no. 10, Oct., p. 152-158.

Cooper, John E., 1961, Some accumulated biospeleological data: Baltimore Grotto News, v. 4, no. 5, May, p. 87-91.

Cooper, John E., 1962, Cave records for the salamander, **Plethodon r. richmondi** Pope: Herpetologica, v. 17, no. 4, p. 250-255.

Cooper, John E., 1962, Cave-associated salamanders of Virginia and West Virginia: Baltimore Grotto News, v. 5, no. 2, Feb. p. 43-45.

Copley, J. B., 1965, Influence of surface conditions on temperature in large cave systems: National Speleological Society, Bulletin, v. 27, no. 1, Jan., p. 1-10.

Davies, William E., 1960, Origin of caves in folded limestone: National Speleological Society, Bulletin, v. 22, pt. 1, Jan., p. 5-18.

Davies, William E., 1960, Meteorological observations in Martens

Cave, West Virginia: National Speleological Society, Bulletin, v. 22, pt. 2, July, p. 92-100.

Davis, Wayne H., 1959, Disproportionate sex rations in hibernating bats: Jour. Mammalogy, v. 40, no. 1, Feb., p. 16-19.

Edwards, Jay, 1959, Germany Valley speleological report: Netherworld News, v. 7, no. 3, March, p. 58-71.

Faust, Burton S., 1959, Observations and remarks relative to the production of saltpeter in Snedegars Cave: NSS News, v. 17, no. 3, March, p. 39-40.

Giles, Harry N., 1962, Black widow spiders in West Virginia caves: Cavalier Caver, v. 4, nos. 5-6, June—Oct., p. 19-20.

Handley, Charles O., Jr., et al, 1961, A West Virginia puma: Jour. Mammalogy, v. 42, no. 2, May, p. 277-278.

Hobbs, Horton, Jr., 1964, A new cave-dwelling crayfish from the Greenbrier drainage system, West Virginia (Decapoda, Astocidae): Biol. Soc. Washington, Proc., v. 77, 30 Oct., p. 189-194.

Ingalls, Huntley, 1959, The exploration of Cass Cave, West Virginia: National Speleological Society, Bulletin, v. 21, pt. 1, Jan., p. 21-32.

Janssen, Raymond E., 1964, Earth Science . . . . a handbook on the geology of West Virginia: W. Va. Dept. Education, p. 196-209.

Krekeler, C. H., 1959, Dispersal of cavernicolous beetles: Systematic Zoology, v. 8, no. 3, Sept., p. 119-130.

Krutzsch, Philip H., 1961, A summer colony of male Little Brown Bats: Jour. Mammalogy, v. 42, no. 4, Nov., p. 529-530.

Landis, Charles, 1961, Notes on growth rate of gypsum crystals: Nittany Grotto Newsletter, v. 9, no. 6, March, p. 102.

McCrady, Allen D., 1960, New Years expedition to Overholt Blowing Cave: Netherworld News, v. 8, no. 1, Jan., p. 6-10.

McCrady, Allen D., et al, 1963, The big push at Overholt Blowing: Netherworld News, v. 11, no. 1, Jan., p. 2-5.

Plummer, William, 1961, Meteorology of Martens Cave, West Virginia: Baltimore Grotto News, v. 4, no. 5, May, p. 66-68.

Ruhe, Benjamin, 1965, Underground adventure: Washington Star, Sunday Magazine, Jan. 24, p. 3-5.

Stafford, Roger, 1961, Bones in a cave: NSS News, v. 19, no. 7, July, p. 80.

Steeves, Harrison R. III, 1963, Two new troglobitic asellids from West Virginia: Amer. Midland Naturalist, v. 70, no. 2, April, p. 462-465.

Steeves, Harrison R. III, 1965, Two new species of troglobitic asellids from the United States: Amer. Midland Naturalist, v. 73, no. 1, Jan., p. 81-84.

White, W. B., 1960, Exploration and discovery at Swago Creek: Netherworld News, v. 8, no. 12, Dec., p. 198-206.

Zotter, Hermine, 1963, Stream tracing techniques and results: Pocahontas and Greenbrier Counties, West Virginia: NSS News, v. 21, no. 10, Oct., p. 136-142.

DESCRIPTIONS OF CAVERNS

BERKELEY COUNTY

NESTLE QÚARRY CAVE (p. 54)*.

Another cave, 400 to 500 feet long, opens into the face of Nestle Quarry. Dangerous, loose rocks occur near the entrance. This cave is in Beekmantown limestone.

(Rick Peterson: D. C. Speleograph, v. 20, no. 8, Aug., 1964, p. 60.)

GRANT COUNTY

ALONZO SITES CAVE 39°14′05″ N.; 78°59′30″ W. Moorefield Quadrangle.

The entrance to this cave is in a small sinkhole in a pasture on the east side of the ridge northeast of Twin Mountain (elevation 2350 feet). From the entrance a crawlway leads to a walkway pas-

* Page number of original description in Vol. XIX(A), **Caverns of West Virginia.**

sage sloping down 45°. A room, 35 feet long, 10 feet wide, and 15 feet high is at the base of the entrance passage.

Alonzo Sites Pit, 25 feet deep, is located on the west side of the same ridge in which Alonzo Sites Cave is developed. The cave and pit are in limestones of the Helderberg Group.

(Bob Dunn: Netherworld News, v. 10, no. 2, Feb., 1962, p. 30.)

GREENBRIER COUNTY

ACME MINE (p. 134).

The caves encountered in Mine No. 5 were on several levels and had over 10,000 feet of passages.

(John F. Fisher, personal communication.)

BOGGS CAVE White Sulphur Springs Quadrangle.

This cave is near Higginbothams No. 1 Cave. The entrance is in breakdown connecting with a long sewer passage and crawlway. Beyond the crawlway is a large passage with several side passages.

(Dal Vipond: Cleve-O-Grotto News, v. 8, no. 4, July-Aug., 1961, p. 40.)

BONE CAVE (p. 77).

The upper cave is 70 feet above the quarry floor. A low walkway extends for a short distance from the entrance but reduces to a short crawl connecting with a long narrow room. At the end of the room two low passages extend at right angles to the direction of the entrance passage for several hundred feet. The lower cave is a crawlway extending 200 feet to a small room with a floor of sand. From this room a small hole opens into a succession of crawlways and walkways 1,400 feet long.

(Vic Schmidt: Baltimore Grotto News, v. 4, no. 7, July, 1961, p. 106-107. Tom Tucker: D. C. Speleograph, v. 20, no. 10, Oct., 1964, p. 75. Gunther B. Schmidt, Jr.: Baltimore Grotto News, v. 5, no. 5, May, 1962, p. 134-135.)

BROWNS CAVE 38°02'14" N.; 80°19'47" W. Lobelia Quadrangle.

At 0.6 mile southwest of Bethel Church, the creek draining Renicks Valley enters a cave (elevation 2250 feet). The entrance, 15 feet wide and 4 feet high, is in a zone of large breakdown. Twenty feet from the entrance several small, decorated passages on the east side circle around and rejoin the main stream passage within a short distance. The main passage opens to a width of about 50 feet with clay ridges cutting across the floor. Beyond this is an extensive area of rimstone pools and flowstone. The wide passage grades into a stream channel 3 feet wide flanked by mud banks up to 10 feet high, with several 3-foot high rimstone dams across the stream. In this section, which extends for about 500 feet, the ceiling is 15 to 20 feet high. The main passage ends in fill and debris. The stream has cut a new channel into the left side and flows over a series of short drops into the Waterfall Room. A crawlway leads to a partially clogged crevice. Globulites and flowstone are common in the new section. This cave is in the Hillsdale Limestone, Greenbrier Group.

(Hermine Zotter: Netherworld News, v. 8, no. 11, Nov., 1960, p. 190.)

Figure 1.—Legend for all cave maps.

BUCKEYE CREEK CAVE (p. 79).

The entrance, triangular in shape, 15 feet high and 8 feet wide, is alongside the road and opens into a high ceiling room 100 feet long and 60 feet wide. A walkway extends east and southeast from the southeast corner of the room. At 50 feet a 6-foot drop connects with a stream passage several hundred feet long ending in a low crawlway. The stream flows south. Large, massive silt banks are along part of this passage. A small crawlway leads north from the passage, 115 feet from the entrance room. The passage extending west from the entrance room is a narrow, high fissure opening up to a large passage with a big stream. This passage is 4,880 feet long. In the front part of the passage are rust-colored speleothems and a rimstone pool. Opposite the pool are slopes leading up to well decorated galleries. High banks of silt occur along most of the passage. Two thousand feet from the entrance a passage on the north curves sharply and trends towards the entrance. It is a stoop-way, several hundred feet long, terminating at a flowstone mound.

The stream passage, 2,000 feet from the entrance, has water 3 feet deep and a near-siphon with 6-inch clearance above the water for 60 feet. Beyond this the ceiling is up to 60 feet high. A side passage to the left near the 60-foot low area leads to two pits, 25 and 30 feet deep. Near the end of the stream passage a gallery opens to the south that connects with a 60-foot pit. A 30-foot pit and breakdown intersect the main passage 30 feet beyond the gallery. A 20-foot passage leads down through the breakdown to a stream. The stream passage terminates in a siphon. The silt banks contain a rich fauna of earthworms.

(Chuck Thornton: Netherworld News, v. 12, no. 1, Jan., 1964, p. 8-9. John E. Cooper: Baltimore Grotto News, v. 3, no. 10, Oct., 1960, p. 147-149; v. 5, no. 7, July, 1962, p. 162-164.)

BURNS CAVE NO. 2 (p. 80).

At the end of the crawlway is a room with a stream that resurges from a small hole near the entrance to the cave. A stream passage extends 200 feet from the room to a very low crawlway.

(John F. Fisher, personal communication.)

CABBLE CAVE (p. 80).

There is no cave at the base of the pit.

(John F. Fisher, personal communication.)

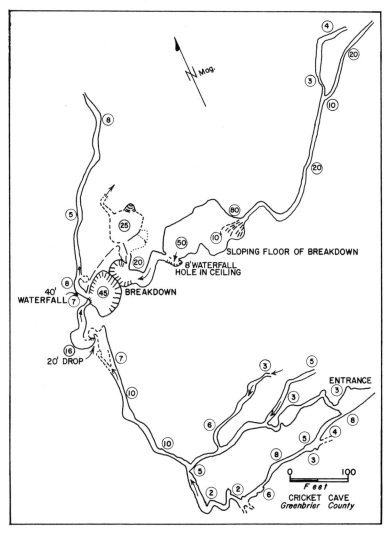

Figure 2.—Cricket Cave. (Guacharo, v. 4, no. 1, July, 1963).

CRICKET CAVE 37°42'15" N.; 80°25'25" W. Ronceverte Quadrangle.

Cricket Cave is ¾ of a mile ESE of Organ Cave (elevation 2400 feet). The entrance passage, 72 feet long, is in breakdown. Beyond the breakdown the passage is 4 to 5 feet high. A passage leading off to the right, 5 feet above the floor of the entrance passage, is 160 feet long to a winding stream passage, parts of which are walkways and crawlways. Several small passages lead off to the left and one stream passage, at 280 feet, trends towards the entrance.

The main passage from the breakdown area is a walkway after 300 feet. Another passage trending northwest from the entrance is a dry crawlway 3 to 8 feet wide for 70 feet, changing to a narrow fissure. The fissure trends northeast over rimstone pools for 170 feet and joins the main passage 400 feet from the entrance. Beyond this junction the main cave trends northeast 220 feet to a domepit. The stream leaves the passage at this point and the passage continues as a dry crawlway for 60 feet to the north, turning east to a 27-foot pit. A stream enters the pit over a flowstone slope and drops into a pool. From the pit a walkway extends 50 feet to the northwest connecting to the northeast with a high fissure passage for 70 feet to a waterfall 37 feet high. At the waterfall is a room 80 feet long, 70 feet wide, and 40 feet high. Breakdown slabs extend across this room as ridges piled almost to the ceiling. Cricket Cave is in the Hillsdale Limestone, Greenbrier Group.

(Phil Sollens: Guacharo, v. 4, no. 1, July, 1963, p. 14-15.)

CULVERSON CREEK CAVE (p. 84).

Four thousand feet from the entrance the stream turns north and leaves the main passage. Silt banks in the main passage are up to 30 feet high.

(Roger Stafford: Cavalier Caver, v. 2, no. 2-3, Dec., 1959, Feb., 1960, p. 20-21.)

CURRY PIT 38°02′42″ N.; 80°17′40″ W. Lobelia Quadrangle.

About 1½ miles northeast of Bethel Church, near the top of a hill, is a hole about four feet in diameter (elevation 2850 feet). The hole opens into a pit 100 feet deep, extending as a steep debris covered slope for 25 feet, and ending in another 25 foot pit. A waterfall drops into the first pit below the entrance and the stream flows into the second pit. Four hundred yards from Curry Pit is **Curry Cave** consisting of a 50 foot high domepit open to the steep hillside. The cave extends 30 to 50 feet into the hill and is well decorated with flowstone, curtains and coral. Both are in the Alderson Limestone, Greenbrier Group.

(Hermine Zotter: Netherworld News, v. 9, no. 1, Jan., 1961, p. 17.)

FOX CAVE (p. 86).

The lower stream passage is 6 to 15 feet high, 4 to 15 wide, and extends 1,000 feet to a low crawlway. The stream flows along a fill of cobbles and clay coated with a layer of manganese dioxide. Two hundred feet from the drop to the stream is a vadose slot with a passage 25 feet long to a waterfall, at the top of which is a walkway 20 feet wide and 8 feet high, extending 200 feet to where the passage divides. The left branch is 25 feet high, 15 feet wide, 800 feet long with breakdown, and ends in a mud choke.

(Tom Tucker: D. C. Speleograph, v. 20, no. 10, Oct., 1964, p. 73-74.)

FOXHOLE NO. 1 CAVE (p. 86).

Dye tests indicate the stream connects with Organ-Hedricks Cave in the Waterfall Room.

(John F. Fisher, personal communication.)

FRIARS HOLE CAVE 38°03′46″ N.; 80°20′13″ W. Lobelia Quadrangle.

This cave is in the lower part of Friars Hole (elevation 2340 feet). The entrance is a small crack that was dug out at the base of a shallow sinkhole. The entrance passage leads steeply down to the north, curving to the west with drops of 30 and 20 feet. The main passage of the cave trends northeast and southwest from the entrance passage. To the southwest it is a large stream passage several hundred feet long to a Junction Room where the present stream passage is offset to the west. This stream passage is about 1,500 feet long ending in a drop of 15 feet in an area of breakdown. To the east at the Junction Room is a passage about 1,500 feet long ending in breakdown and crawlways. A stream flows west along this passage. Southwest from the Junction Room is a large lower level passage with breakdown for 1,000 feet. Beyond this is a low, sand floored room. At the end of the breakdown is a side passage to the east with a drop to a room. A circular passage leads off to the east from the room and curves back toward the drop. Northeast of the entrance passage the large stream passage extends for 2,500 feet to an area of domepits. Beyond this the passage is floored with porous mud for about 1,000 feet. This mud is so soft that it acts like quicksand and crossing it requires some buoyant support. At the end of the mud the passage forks into two walkways extending north and northwest. The north passage is 600 feet long ending in breakdown. The northeast fork is about 1,000 feet long and is multiple level.

At the north end of the mud area 3 side passages, up to 500 feet long, open from the main passage. One, a crawlway, leads to breakdown beyond which is a large, dry room with breakdown.

Friars Hole Cave is in the upper part of the Greenbrier Group. The entrance and possibly much of the cave is subject to flooding from surface water draining to the entrance sink.

(Lew Bicking: Baltimore Grotto News, v. 7, no. 11, Nov., 1964, p. 314-327; v. 8, no. 1, Jan., 1965, p. 8-9.)

GENERAL DAVIS CAVE (p. 88).

The stream passage is 1,600 feet long to the north and east where breakdown and a near-siphon occur. Beyond the siphon the passage is smaller and extends 800 feet to a T intersection where the stream forms a deep pool under flowstone. The left fork of the passage is on a higher level and is 5 feet wide and 6 feet high for 300 feet to a dead end; the right passage leads to a deep pool.

(Dave Strope: Tech Troglodyte, v. 3, no. 2, Winter, 1965, p. 57.)

HELLEMS CAVE (p. 94).

The entrance to Hellems Cave is a 4-foot square shaft, 10 feet deep, opening to a 10- to 20-foot high breakdown room. The cave consists of two main stream passages flowing northwest and joining about 400 feet from the entrance room. Two other streams are in short passages in the breakdown area near the entrance to the cave. A walkway with flowstone and dripstone extends 200 feet from the left side of the breakdown area to a semicircular room. Two short passages lead off this room. A third passage from the breakdown area is about 200 feet long with the last half floored with breakdown. Total length of all passages is about 1200 feet.

(Guacharo, v. 4, no. 1, July, 1963, p. 20-22.)

HIGGINBOTHAMS CAVE NO. 1 (p. 95).

Seventy-five feet from the end of the east passage is a small opening connecting with Higginbothams Cave No. 4 near its entrance. The east passage on No. 1 Cave ends in a siphon. The siphon, 400 feet east of the entrance, can be passed in dry weather and the cave continues south and east as a large stream passage to a junction with a side passage. The side passage is a dry crawlway for 200 feet to a series of rimstone pools. The main stream passage trends south as a walkway reducing to a low stoopway. At the end of the stoopway is a near siphon beyond which is 200 feet of crawl-way with stream. At the end of the crawlway is an opening that connects with the bottom of a sinkhole, 100 feet south of Higgin-botham's house. South of this entrance is a downstream crawlway to a couple of rooms, beyond which is a siphon. The siphon is 50 feet from the entrance to Higginbothams Cave No. 4. Plummer designated the part of the cave south of the intermittent siphon Higginbothams No. 5, but Vipond preempted this name for a pit nearby in 1959.

(Dal Vipond: Cleve-O-Grotto News, v. 8, no. 4, July-Aug., 1961, p. 40. Bill Plummer: Baltimore Grotto News, v. 4, no. 4, April, 1961, p. 53-54.)

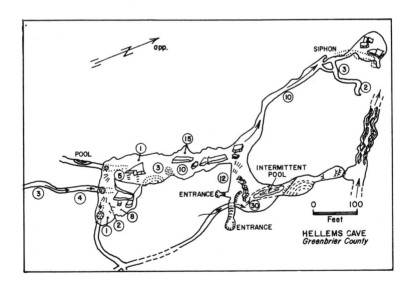

Figure 3.—Hellems Cave. Sketch map by Paul Ramer and Phil Sollins (Guacharo, v. 5, no. 1, Feb., 1964).

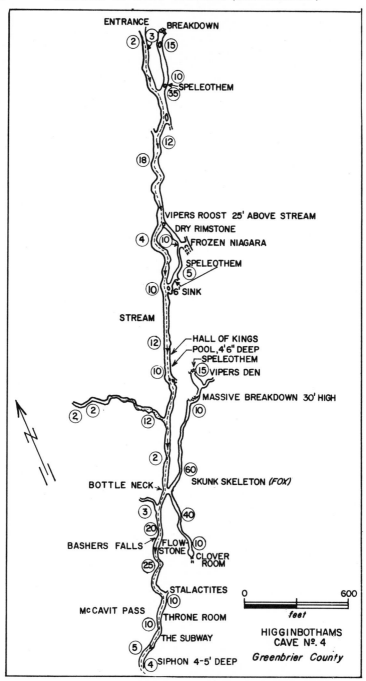

Figure 4.—Higginbothams Cave No. 4. Surveyed by Dal Vipond and W. Mc-Cavit (Cleve-O-Grotto News, v. 6, no. 1, Jan.-Feb., 1959).

HIGGINBOTHAMS CAVE NO. 4 (p. 98).

The entrance is at the south end of the pond 100 feet south of Higginbotham's house. Near the waterfall, on the east side of the passage at a higher level, is a room with a low passage trending east to another room 55 feet long and 8 to 10 feet high. A 35-foot crawlway leads out of the lower end of the room. Beyond the waterfall, the main passage continues 600 feet to a siphon. This part of the passage is 5 to 10 feet high. A pit, 60 feet deep, known as Higginbothams Cave No. 5, is near Cave No. 4. A very narrow fissure at the base of the pit connects with a small room. In 1959 the skeleton of a puma was found on the higher level passage near the waterfall.

(Dal Vipond: Cleve-O-Grotto News, v. 6, no. 5, Sept.-Oct., 1959, p. 2-3.)

HOYT CAVE (p. 100).

This cave is now better known as **Whites Cave.**

(John F. Fisher, personal communication.)

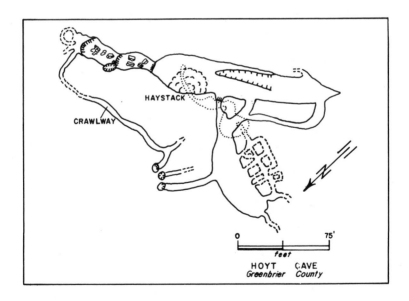

Figure 5.—Hoyt Cave. Sketch map (Guacharo, v. 5, no. 1, Feb., 1964).

LEGGS CAVE (p. 104).

A cave with a small pit-like entrance opening to a low room is reported at or near the site of Leggs Cave. From the room a 50-foot crawlway extends to another room, 20 feet in diameter and 7 feet high. Beyond this is a small sloping passage.

(John O. Davis: Baltimore Grotto News, v. 7, no. 11, Nov., 1964, p. 331-333.)

LIPPS CAVE NO. 2 (p. 105).

A walkway passage extends for over 1,000 feet southeast from the entrance room. Beyond 1,000 feet it is a narrow fissure passage with a stream for several hundred feet. A 30-foot drop connects with a room beyond which is a second room 40 feet in diameter and 70 feet high. A wide fissure passage leads from the room for 300 feet to breakdown and another room. A large stream passage intersects the room; the upstream part of the passage is 30 to 40 feet high and 70 to 80 feet wide for over 5,000 feet to breakdown; downstream the passage is similar in size for 7,500 feet to a massive block breakdown and a siphon beyond. Near the end of the downstream passage on the west side is a side passage (crawlway and walkway) several hundred feet long to pit with a 50-foot waterfall.

Lipps Cave No. 2 connects with the Handley Room in the Organ-Hedricks system through small side passages, many of which are crawlways opening into large passages to the east.

(Roger Stafford: Cavalier Caver, v. 1, no. 1, May, 1959, p. 8; v. 2, no. 1, Oct., 1959 p. 5.)

LUDINGTON CAVE (p. 106).

Ludington Cave is one of the large caves of West Virginia, having over 10,000 feet of passages. The entrance is in a small karst valley. The stream in this valley flows towards the cave but drops into a subterranean course several hundred feet from the cave. The cave entrance is an archway 15 feet wide and 6 feet high. The cave trends northeast from the entrance in two narrow and sinuous passages for 600 to 800 feet to drops of 35 to 40 feet which connect with a lower cave. Several small streams drain to the north in the front part of the cave. The lower cave continues 600 feet to the north connecting with a large passage, the Thunderbolt Passage. This passage is up to 50 feet wide, 10 to 30 feet high, and about

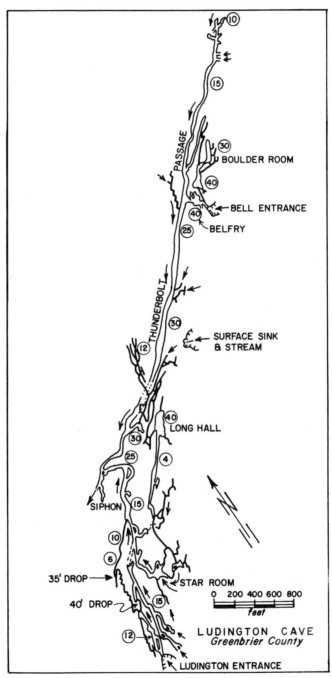

Figure 6.—Ludington Cave. Surveyed by West Virginia Association for Cave Studies, 1963.

4,000 feet long. A stream flows southwest along it and the other cavern streams are tributaries to it. To the southwest the passage ends in a siphon 300 feet from the junction with the lower cave.

A series of narrow passages and crawlways roughly parallel and at a higher level lie to the southeast of the lower cave and the southwestern part of the Thunderbolt Passage. A complex of fissure passages and large rooms is on the southeast side of the Thunderbolt Passage, 2,000 feet northeast of its connection with the lower cave. A second entrance in this part of the cave was excavated to connect with a sinkhole, but the tunnel is now blocked by collapsed soil.

(West Virginia Association for Cave Studies.)

MADISON KNOB, NORTH CAVE (p. 111).

The passage at the base of the entrance pit extends southwest for 30 feet and is 20 feet high and 3 to 5 feet wide. To the northeast the passage is of similar size and 40 feet long, dropping about 10 feet over debris to the base of a domepit about 80 feet high and 20 feet in diameter. A small pool is on the floor of the domepit.

(West Virginia Association for Cave Studies.)

MARY McFERRIN CAVE 37°58'07" N.; 80°22'45" W. White Sulphur Springs Quadrangle.

75 feet southwest of McFerrin Water Cave is a small dry fissure in a limestone outcrop 25 feet above the streambed (elevation 1925 feet). The entrance, 3 feet wide and 4 feet high, opens into a steeply sloping floor of a small room. Beyond the room a fissure 1½ feet wide continues for 20 feet. The cave is in the Union Limestone, Greenbrier Group.

(Hermine Zotter: Netherworld News, v. 10, no. 7, July, 1962, p. 121.)

MATTS BLACK CAVE 37°58'07" N.; 80°22'45" W. White Sulphur Springs Quadrangle.

Several caves are located along Spring Creek 2 miles SSE of Renick. The largest, Matts Black Cave, is on the west bank at the bend in the stream (elevation 1900 feet). The entrance, at the base of the cliff, gives access to a sloping crawlway 20 feet long. Beyond this the cave continues as a large passage, averaging 25 feet wide and 7 feet high for about 500 feet. The floor is irregular with numerous mounds and depressions. A stream, waist deep, crosses the cave just inside the entrance and occurs alongside the passage at several points. The floor of the cave is covered by a film of black manganese minerals. The cave is in the Union Limestone, Greenbrier Group.

(Hermine Zotter: Netherworld News, v. 10, no. 7, July, 1962, p. 119.)

McCLUNG CAVE (p. 107).

The cave is over 10,000 feet long with 6,500 feet of surveyed passages.

McFERRIN BREAKDOWN CAVE 37°58'07" N.; 80°22'45" W. White Sulphur Springs Quadrangle.

This cave is 100 feet downstream from Matts Black Cave on the southwest side of Spring Creek (elevation 1900 feet). The entrance is through breakdown at the face of a cliff. A passage 400 to 500 feet long turns east just beyond the entrance and a small room is to the left of the passage at the entrance. The passage is developed in breakdown throughout its length and varies from a squeezeway to rooms up to 30 feet square and 20 feet high. The south wall is bedrock while the north wall is breakdown. Near the end the passage turns abruptly to the south. A stream flows east along the passage disappearing in a mud fill at the turn near the end. The cave is in the Union Limestone, Greenbrier Group.

(Hermine Zotter: Netherworld News, v. 10, no. 7, July, 1962, p. 121; v. 10, no. 8, Aug., 1962, p. 143.)

McFERRIN WATER CAVE 37°58'07" N.; 80°22'45" W. White Sulphur Springs Quadrangle.

This cave (elevation 1900 feet) is a part of the Spring Creek subterranean course. The entrance is an opening 35 feet wide and 7 feet high in a cliff on the east side of the valley. Spring Creek pools at the cave entrance forming a lake 10 feet beneath the entrance room. The water enters through a deep fissure and flows for 100 feet along the east side of the dry entrance passage, which is 30 feet wide and 6 feet high. At 100 feet the dry passage ends abruptly at a vertical wall while the stream passage widens out to form the main channel, 15 feet wide and 6 feet high for 400 feet. Near the end this passage turns east ending in a debris choked siphon. Near the siphon, on the south side of the passage, are two muddy crawlways connecting with a room 50 feet long. This room is blocked by mud and breakdown at both ends. Long stalactites are in the center of the room.

At the end of the dry entrance passage, a wet crawlway trends southwest. Driftwood and other debris indicate the cave is flooded at high water. The cave is in the Union Limestone, Greenbrier Group.

(Hermine Zotter: Netherworld News, v. 10, no. 7, July, 1962, p. 119-121; v. 10, no. 8, Aug., 1962, p. 143.)

McMILLAN PIT 38°03′30″ N.; 80°21′12″ W. Lobelia Quadrangle.

At the southwest end of Parker Mountain, about 100 feet above Robbins Run (elevation 2250 feet), is a rectangular opening 3 feet long and 1½ feet wide that enlarges to a pit about 15 by 30 feet in size. Four small pits open in the base of this pit and the overall vertical depth of the pits is about 90 feet. A clay bridge spans the first pit about 20 feet below the entrance. The entrance area is dangerous as part of it is formed of clay and leaves forming a thin roof over the pit.

(Hermine Zotter: Netherworld News, v. 9, no. 1, Jan. 1961, p. 17.)

ORGAN-HEDRICKS CAVE SYSTEM (p. 92, 113).

The north-south upper level passage formerly indicated as a crawl over flowstone (5,000 feet north of the Big Room with 40 foot waterfall) continues as a crawlway 50 feet long opening to a stream passage 500 feet long. At this point another flowstone reduces the passage to a crawlway. To the west this crawlway is 300 feet long, enlarging to a walkway and stoopway connecting with a room 40 feet below. Breakdown fills much of this room and stream flows across it. Beyond this room is muddy breakdown and an adjacent high vaulted room.

The Humphrey entrance (Erwins Cave) to the Organ-Hedricks system is in a sinkhole about 1 mile SW of the entrance to Organ Cave. A 50-foot crawlway leads to a 20-foot drop. Beyond the drop is a low stream walkway several hundred feet long trending northeast to a 35-foot drop. At the base of this drop is a breakdown-filled passage trending southwest-northeast. This passage is a major passage of the Organ-Hedricks system extending south towards Second Creek and north to the junction of Hedricks and Organ Caves. A small cave entrance 100 feet north of Humphreys

(Erwins) Cave opens into a crawlway with a stream draining to Humphreys Cave.

(Roger Stafford: Cavalier Caver, v. 1, no. 1, May, 1959, p. 6; John F. Fisher.)

RAPPS CAVE (p. 124).

On the left side of the entrance room a small passage slopes steeply upwards to a crawlway. The crawlway enlarges in a short distance and has 2 small drops and a 25-foot pit. Beyond the pit the passage continues to the top of a room filled with breakdown and speleothems. A lead to the left at the entrance to the room goes to a long sloping area and a 40-foot pit with a waterfall. A mud slope in the left side of the breakdown room connects with a canyon-like section ending in a choke-off. The far end of the breakdown room drops 3 to 4 feet and connects with another room where prismatic jointing is prominent in the ceiling and in fallen rock. Beyond this room is a wide, long, 3 to 4 feet high room with a slippery mud floor.

Beneath the breakdown extending from the entrance room of the cave are several short passages on a lower level. Beyond the breakdown the main cave extends northeast as a canyon-like passage to a huge breakdown. A small room is to the left of the breakdown. North of this breakdown the cave drops sharply and ends in a series of low passages.

At the canyon-like passage northeast of the entrance room, access to an upper level is by a small opening in back of a flowstone speleothem on the left wall. This connects with a speleothem-covered ledge 30 feet above the canyon. The upper level passage angles off to the west and is 15 feet high and wide for 1,375 feet, ending in a tight crawlway. There are several areas of breakdown along this passage, and adjacent to the passage near the beginning is a domepit 35 feet in diameter and 100 feet high with water pouring down it. The passage intersects the domepit 30 feet above the base. The floor in the front part of the passage is thin, with holes opening to the lower main passage.

(John E. Cooper: Baltimore Grotto News, v. 5, no. 3, March, 1962, p. 71-77.)

RENICK RIVER CAVES 37°59′ N.; 80° 21′ W. White Sulphur Springs Quadrangle.

Along the Chesapeake and Ohio Railroad a mile south of Renick are seven caves. Six of the caves are walkways or crawlways

80 feet or less in length. One cave, about 200 feet south of Milepost 24, opens 20 feet above the tracks. The passages are 600 feet long and consist of a sinuous fissure connecting with offset walkways and stoopways and an intersecting T passage at the rear. The rear passage is about 250 feet long. These caves are in the lower Greenbrier.

(Victor Schmidt: Netherworld News, v. 9, no. 8, Aug., 1961, p. 153.)

SSS CAVE 37°45′00″ N.; 80°25′44″ W. White Sulphur Springs Quadrangle.

This cave is 1,500 feet south of the south part of Fuller Cave. The entrance (elevation 2200 feet) is about 15 feet wide and a foot high at the northwest end of a karst valley. The cave passage trends northwest and is 10 to 15 feet wide and 2 feet high increasing to 9 feet high. Two hundred feet from the entrance the passage reduces to a fissure 3 feet high. One hundred feet farther the fissure opens into a canyon 30 feet deep with a waterfall. Beyond 400 feet the canyon trends west for 400 feet and then north for 350 feet. Most of this part of the passage is 25 to 35 feet high except for a section 100 feet long, 750 feet from the entrance where the height is 5 to 6 feet. A second waterfall occurs just south of the area of low ceiling. At the end of the fissure-canyon passage the cave trends west as a wide crawlway grading to a straight narrow fissure passage connective with the south part of Fuller Cave, which is about 1,300 feet to the northwest. A stream flows along the canyon and disappears at its north end. SSS Cave is in the Alderson Limestone, Greenbrier Group.

(Mason Sproul: Cavalier Caver, v. 6, no. 2, June, 1964, p. 38.)

SNEDEGAR-CROOKSHANK SYSTEM (SNEDEGARS STAIR-CASE ENTRANCE) 38°04′33″ N.; 80°18′42″ W. Lobelia Quadrangle.

The entrance is an inconspicuous, narrow 30-foot pit in a sinkhole in Friars Hole just southwest of the Pocahontas-Greenbrier County line (elevation 2500 feet). To the northeast the passage from the pit is a narrow fissure 100 feet long to a series of interconnected domepits. Southwest from the pit is a narrow, sinuous fissure stream channel. One hundred feet and 200 feet from the entrance are drops of 15 feet. Forty feet from the second drop is a 60-foot pit with a shallow pool at the base. Beyond the pit the stream passage is a canyon 330 feet long to a junction with another passage to the northeast. At this point the stream exits to the south in a siphon. A waterfalls from the northeast passage plunges into the siphon pool. At the top of the falls is a passage extending northeast 200 feet to six dome rooms, 70 feet high. In one dome water cascades from a crack 15 feet above the base of the dome and the passage continues northeast for 100 feet to breakdown. From the junction of the two main passages a small crawlway extends west for 50 feet and connects with the large stream passage of the Snedegars-Crookshank Cave System. The connection is just west of the siphon at the end of Snedegars Cave. Snedegars Staircase Cave is in the Alderson-Union Limestone, Greenbrier Group.

(Lew Bicking: Baltimore Grotto News, v. 7, no. 8, Aug., 1964, p. 234-239.)

SPENCER CAVE (p. 128).

At the level of Spring Creek is a cave opening with a passage extending 30 feet to breakdown. Fifty feet beyond the breakdown is a large pool of water choked with logs and other debris. Methane gas is present in this pool.

(Tom Tucker: D. C. Speleograph, v. 20, no. 10, Oct., 1964, p. 74.)

TAYLOR CAVE NO. 2 (p. 130).

A narrow canyon forms the last 100 feet of the cave and is blocked at the end by speleothems.

(John F. Fisher, personal communication.)

TOOTHPICK CAVE 38°04'08" N.; 80°18'35" W. Lobelia Quadrangle.

This cave is in a valley draining west to Friars Hole, 1 mile southwest of Droop School. The entrance passage is a sewer 5 feet high. The cave trends west for 550 feet with the passage varying from 3 feet to 10 feet high. Most of the passage is a tortuous, narrow fissure. At 550 feet is a drop of 35 feet below which the passage trends south for 250 feet. This passage is 2 to 16 feet high and up to 10 feet wide with a wedge-shaped cross section. It ends in a domepit 40 feet high. Fifty feet from the end is a passage to the east. This extends for 150 feet and is up to 30 feet high terminating

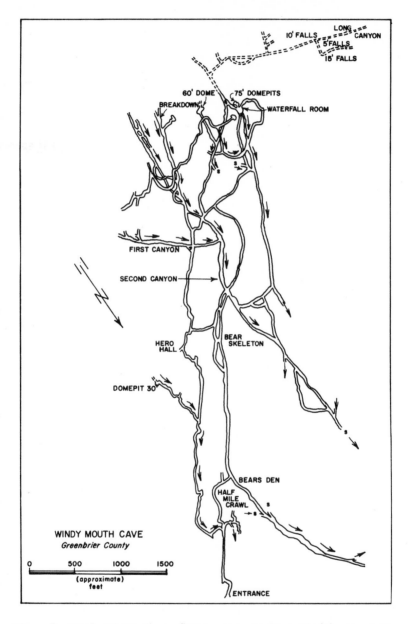

Figure 7.—Windy Mouth Cave. Sketch survey by West Virginia Association for Cave Studies. Arrows indicate direction of flow of cave streams; S indicates siphons.

in a domepit 50 feet high and 50 feet in diameter with a waterfall. A stream flows north along the lower passage. The cave is in the Greenbrier Limestone.

(Dick Cope: Netherworld News, v. 13, no. 2, Feb., 1965, p. 39-41.)

U. S. 219 CAVE (p. 131).

The crawlway is a few hundred feet long and emerges on the north side of U. S. 219. The stream flowing south from Cave Farm Cave enters the north end of U. S. 219 Cave.

(John F. Fisher, personal communication.)

WIND (WINDY MOUTH) CAVE (p. 132).

Wind Cave consists of a complex of intersecting passages totaling over 30,000 feet in length. The first 890 feet is a wide crawlway beyond which the cave consists of narrow walkways and crawlways. Most of the major passages contain streams.

Longanacre Water Cave is believed by local residents to connect with Wind Cave.

Two small caves, one a crawlway, the other a room 100 feet long, 50 feet wide and 20 feet high, open in the river bluff near Wind Cave.

(West Virginia Association for Cave Studies.)

A number of pits and small caves have been reported in Greenbrier County:

Brushy Mountain Cave—One mile east of Friars Hole Cave (Lobelia Quadrangle), a waterfall drops into a large cave entrance containing a small stream passage 150 feet long, and an unexplored crawlway near the entrance. (38°03'57" N.; 80°19'11" W., elevation 2450 feet).

Dead Bottom Pits Nos. 1 to 5—Near Clyde Cochrane Sinks, 5 pits from 20 to 50 feet deep.

Sollins and Adamsons Cave—Small cave on Court Street in Lewisburg, ¾ of a mile south of the Court Street Cave.

Robbins Run Cave—On Robbins Run, 0.4 miles northwest of Beulah Church (Lobelia Quadrangle), 2 small rooms.

Tucks Hole—South end of the karst valley, ¾ mile southeast of Organ Cave, fissure passage 50 feet long.

The following caves have been reported in Greenbrier County in the vicinity of Muddy Creek, but nothing concerning their exploration has been published:

  a. Five caves in the vicinity of Frog Hollow.
  b. Small cave ¼ mile NW Asbury.
  c. Two hundred-foot pit 1 mile NNE of Asbury.
  d. Pit on side of Muddy Creek Mountain, opposite Brushy Ridge School.
  e. Three caves 1 mile east of Asbury.
  f. Two small caves north of Feamster Cave, ½ mile SE of Asbury.
  g. Two caves 2 miles ENE of Alta. One of these may be Tuckwiller Cave (p. 131).

(Clifford Forman: Boston Grotto Newsletter, v. 3, no. 3, March, 1960, p. 2.)

JEFFERSON COUNTY

MOLERS CAVE (p. 153).

The lower level of the cave enlarges beyond the terminus of the upper level and is a long water passage with a waterfall along it.

(Lois Grime: Potomac Caver, v. 5, no. 7, July, 1962, p. 42.)

McDOWELL COUNTY

A large cave entrance, visible from the road, is reported to exist just north of the town of War.

(John Cooper: Baltimore Grotto News, v. 3, no. 9, Sept., 1960, p. 140.)

MERCER COUNTY

ABBS VALLEY CAVE (p. 156).
The cave is not in West Virginia.

BEACON CAVE 37°14′36″ N.; 81°13′27″ W. Bland Quadrangle.

This cave is on the north side of East River Mountain about 1½ miles south of Bluefield, West Virginia (elevation 2600 feet). The entrance is in a sinkhole 1,000 feet off the Cumberland Road. A crawl passage through breakdown for 150 feet connects with the

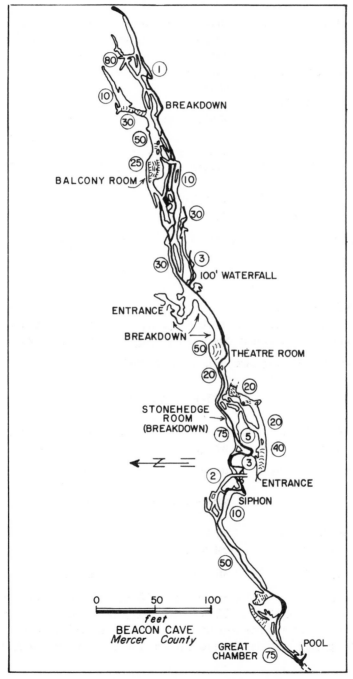

Figure 8.—Beacon Cave. Surveyed by T. Bunker, R. Janke and R. Eaton, 1958. (NSS News, v. 18, no. 1, Jan., 1960).

main passage. The main passage contains a stream and extends ENE for about 1,400 feet. Two or 3 dry passages and rooms are developed on a higher level parallel to the stream passage in this part of the cave. The main passage is large with ceilings up to 30 feet, for 700 feet beyond which it is mainly a crawlway. West of the entrance passage, the main passage trends west and southwest for 1,000 feet to a deep pool 30 feet long. The cave continues beyond the pool for considerable distance ending with the ceiling lower to water level. Several large rooms are along the main passage in this section. Most of the main passage is 20 to 50 feet high. Three hundred and fifty feet west of the entrance passage, two leads connect with a parallel passage 300 feet long, 20 feet high and wide, at the west end of which is a narrow fissure opening to the surface. The east end of this passage is a slippery mud slope leading to a shear drop of unknown depth. A pit, 60 feet deep, on the north side of this passage near the west end may connect with passages on a lower level. Beacon Cave is in Middle Ordovician limestone.

(Thomas Bunker: NSS News, v. 18, no. 1, Jan., 1960, p. 6-8.)

CALDWELL CAVE 37°18'48" N.; 80°55'56" W. Narrows Quadrangle.

A large opening in a shallow sink, ½ mile from the north base of East River Mountain (elevation 2300 feet) gives access to a walkway passage with a stream. At 200 feet the passage divides. The right fork is a short passage ending in a small room; the left fork is a crawlway 50 feet long beyond which it is too small for access.

(John R. Holsinger: D. C. Speleograph, v. 18, no. 10, Oct. 1962, p. 70-72.)

CAVE RAT CAVE 37°18'50" N.; 80°55'25" W. Narrows Quadrangle.

This cave is east of Caldwell Cave (elevation 2300 feet). A few feet inside the entrance a stream flows into the main passage, which is a crawlway enlarging to a walkway. A short distance from the entrance a small passage on the left connects by a 6-foot drop to a low ceiling room. Several crawlways lead from the room. The main passage is short and divides in an area of breakdown. The right passage from the breakdown is blocked by logs and debris.

The left passage divides after short distance, with a small crawlway to the left and a short passage to the right to a rimstone pool. The ceiling in the right passage is up to 40 feet high. Cave Rat Cave is in Beekmantown limestone.

(Gary McCutcheon: Cavalier Caver, v. 3, no. 1, Fall, 1964, p. 22.)

DEAD HORSE CAVE Narrows Quadrangle.

A 40-foot quarry face 2½ miles southeast of Oakvale contains a cave opening 8 feet by 10 feet in size. A 5-foot drop to a ledge and a debris slope opens into a room 80 feet long, and 40 feet high increasing to 90 feet high at the southeast end. From the north end of the room a passage extends 50 feet to breakdown. A passage on the southeast side of the room is 25 feet long to a vaulted chamber, 35 feet in diameter and 80 feet high. A passage 4 feet wide and 5 feet high continues for 150 feet beyond the room. To the right and above the passage connecting the entrance room and the vaulted chamber is a walkway reducing to a squeezeway which trends southwest for 30 feet, turning abruptly for 15 feet to a pit 4 feet square and 100 to 125 feet deep.

(Robert G. Tucker: Netherworld News, v. 11, no. 11, Nov., 1963, p. 197.)

HONACKER CAVE (p. 157). 37°18'54" N.; 80°56'06" W. Narrows Quadrangle.

The entrance is a walkway in a quarry face (elevation 2300 feet) connecting with a short narrow passage and a very small squeeze leading to a lower level. The lower level contains rimstone pools and is blocked by two speleothems that restrict the width to a very small squeeze. The passage inside the entrance is covered with manganese dioxide. Beyond is a 12-foot pit and a larger passage. Another cave with a 100-foot pit entrance and a larger lake and stream passage is reported near Honacker Cave. The cave is in Beekmantown limestone.

(John E. Cooper: Baltimore Grotto News, v. 3, no. 9, Sept., 1960, p. 139-140.)

MONONGALIA COUNTY

PETERSON CAVE Morgantown Quadrangle.

This cave is reported to be about a half mile north of the Reedsville-Morgantown Road, 5 miles west of Reedsville. The en-

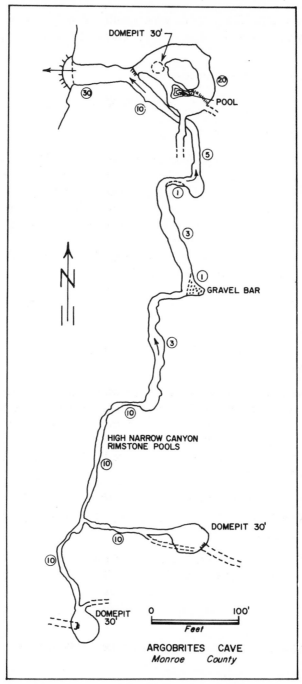

Figure 9.—Argobrites Cave. Sketch map by J. M. Berry, J. B. Copley, and John Fisher, 1963.

trance is a cleft about 3 feet wide slanting steeply downwards. A walkway passage is at the base of the entrance and is over 200 feet long.

(Felix Robinson, personal communication.)

MONROE COUNTY

ARGOBRITES CAVE (p. 164).

The stream passage beyond the low ceiling, 200 feet from the junction, can be traversed for over 1,000 feet. It is 1 to 3 feet high with a very low crawlway over a gravel bar 400 feet from the junction. Beyond this the passage is 3 feet high with a hard floor and a small shallow stream. Two hundred feet from the gravel bar the passage is a narrow canyon, 10 feet high, with a floor formed of rimstone dams with pools 3 feet deep. Several hundred feet beyond the canyon the passage divides into two narrow passages, each 10 feet high and about 150 feet long, leading to domepits 30 feet high. Small passages lead off from the top of the domepits.

(John Fisher, personal communication.)

BILLY GOAT CAVE 37°33'07" N.; 80°40'25" W. Alderson Quadrangle.

This cave is 300 feet north of the water entrance of Greenville Saltpeter Cave (elevation 1700 feet). The cave is primarily a stream passage extending a few hundred feet to the south. To the north the passage is a crawlway 60 feet long to a 20 foot drop. At the base of the drop is a large pool. The cave is in the Union Limestone, Greenbrier Group.

(Tom Tucker: D. C. Speleograph, v. 15, no. 12, Dec., 1959, p. 87-88.)

BLACKBERRY CAVE 37°33'12" N.; 80°39'58" W. Alderson Quadrangle.

This cave is 300 feet southeast of Cross Road Cave in a sinkhole on the hillside (elevation 1700 feet). The entrance is 4 feet wide and a foot high with 20 feet of crawlway connecting with 2 small rooms. Blackberry Cave is in the Union Limestone, Greenbrier Group.

(Tom Tucker: D. C. Speleograph, v. 15, no. 12, Dec., 1959, p. 87-88.)

CHAMBERS (LUSKS) CAVE (p. 167).

An upper level with numerous speleothems exists above the first large room. Several domepits are near the rear of the cave.

(R. E. Whittemore: Tech Troglodyte, v. 3, no. 2, Winter, 1965, p. 51-55.)

CROSIER CAVE (p. 170). 37°30'17" N.; 80°29'20" W. Ronceverte Quadrangle.

Crosier Cave is on the south side of the road, ¼ mile east of Zenith School (elevation 2550 feet). The entrance is in a shallow sinkhole with small fissures and crawlways leading down a 20° slope to a maze of zigzag sewer passages and a room. A hole in the floor of the room drains the cave. Crosier Cave is in Middle Ordovician limestone.

(R. E. Whittemore: Tech Troglodyte, v. 3, no. 2, Winter, 1965, p. 51-55.)

EVELYN MILLERS CAVE 37°30'13" N.; 80°29'39" W. Ronceverte Quadrangle.

A cleft in the side of a sinkhole ⅛ mile southwest of Zenith School (elevation 2550 feet) leads 20 feet down to the south to an abrupt turn to a passage trending west. This passage is a narrow, zigzag fissure 100 feet long to a domepit and breakdown. At the base of the entrance slope is a hole in the floor opening into a pit 30 feet deep ending in a room full of breakdown. At the lower end of the room is a passage to a large room beyond which is a canyon passage with an intermittent stream. Beyond the canyon are crawlways with side rooms and an upper level formed by a maze of sewer passages. The cave is in Middle Ordovician limestone.

(R. E. Whittemore: Tech Troglodyte, v. 3, no. 2, Winter, 1965, p. 51-55.)

GREENBRIER CAVERN SYSTEM

Organ-Hedricks Cave and Lipps Cave No. 2, along with other major passages, form an integrated cavern system extending towards Second Creek. Over 15 miles of the cavern system has been reported mapped and an estimated 15 more miles explored. Including Lipps and Organ-Hedricks the cave system has seven entrances.

HUNT CAVE   Alderson Quadrangle.

Hunt Cave is near Sinks Grove. The entrance is a 10-foot pit in the bottom of a sinkhole. At the base is a small chamber with two crawlways. One is 15 feet long and enlarges to a walkway 2,700 feet long. A stream flows along the passage and, in places, canyons with cascades occur. An upper level with larger passages is also present. Forty-four hundred feet of the cave has been explored.

(John Charlton: Tech Troglodyte, v. 3, no. 1, Fall, 1964, p. 7.)

LAUREL CREEK CAVE (p. 183).

About 100 feet beyond the Theater Room a small passage opens on the side of the upper level near a point inscribed on the wall as "Bears Tooth." The side passage is a walkway extending 1,000 feet to breakdown.

The south-trending passage that opens from the lower level, 100 feet from the Theater Room, normally ends in a siphon at 900 feet. During very ʻlow water this siphon can be passed and the passage beyond is high and narrow with pools and a stream. A large amount of decaying vegetable remains are in this part of the passage. The passage reaches the surface in a sinkhole 240 feet northeast of Cross Road Cave and the lower part is known as Saddle Cave.

(Janet S. Eyler: D. C. Speleograph, v. 18, no. 12, Dec., 1962, p. 82-83.)

MADDYS CAVE (p. 201).

This cave is the same as the Head of Mill Pond entrance of Greenville Saltpeter Cave.

RIMSTONE CAVE 37°33'08" N.; 80°40'24" W. Alderson Quadrangle.

Rimstone Cave is 400 feet north-northeast of the water entrance of Greenville Saltpeter Cave (elevation 1700 feet). A large stream flows out of the entrance and the main stream passage is over 500 feet long. Near the entrance a side passage at the top of a 20-foot mud bank contains large rimstone pools up to 5 feet wide. At 50 feet the side passage divides, the right lead goes 50 feet to a pool 4 feet deep, and the left lead is 100 feet long to a small room, beyond which is a crawlway with a stream. Rimstone Cave is in the Union Limestone, Greenbrier Group.

(Tom Tucker: D. C. Speleograph, v. 15, no. 12, Dec., 1959, p. 87-88.)

SADDLE CAVE 37°33'16" N.; 80°39'58" W. Alderson Quadrangle.

This cave is 240 feet north-northeast of Cross Road Cave and connects with Laurel Creek Cave (elevation 1700 feet). The entrance is in the bottom of a shallow sink with a passage extending 20 feet to a 15-foot drop and a stream passage. Fifty feet downstream this passage ends at a siphon. Upstream it extends 500 feet to an area where methane gas concentration makes further traverse dangerous. At this point the water is up to 5 feet deep on stream bed of mud and decaying vegetable matter. The cave is in the Union Limestone, Greenbrier Group.

(Tom Tucker: D. C. Speleograph, v. 15, no. 12, Dec., 1959, p. 87-88.)

TURKEY CREEK CAVE 37°31'25" N.; 80°28'20" W. Ronceverte Quadrangle.

A 30-foot sloping pit in a sinkhole 500 yards south of the road along Turkey Creek, 1 mile east of McGlone (elevation 2400 feet), opens into a trash-filled room. The main passage of the cave trends south for about 400 feet and consists of a series of small rooms and pockets with mud floors. Near the end of the cave are several dome-pits. Turkey Creek Cave is in Beekmantown Limestone.

(R. E. Whittemore: Tech Troglodyte, v. 3, no. 2, Winter, 1965, p. 51-55.)

WOODLAND SCHOOL CAVE 37°34'37" N.; 80°27'30" W. Ronceverte Quadrangle.

There are seven entrances to this cave, the main entrance of which is 1,000 feet southwest of Woodland School, near the head of Burnside Branch (elevation 2250 feet). The cave consists of three parallel sewer passages trending northwest for several hundred feet, interconnected by another set of sewer passages trending southwest. The cave ends in a small lake and siphon at the northwest end of the main passage. In addition to subterranean streams, storm drainage from Little Mountain flows into all the entrances. The cave is in the Sinks Grove Limestone, Greenbrier Group.

(Howard S. Decker, personal communication.)

PENDLETON COUNTY

BLOWHOLE (p. 206).

Beyond the breakdown in the main passage the cave continues as a crawlway with a stream several hundred feet long. At the end is a very small opening to the surface on the east side of Timber Ridge.

(Wes McGrew: Baltimore Grotto News, v. 6, no. 7, July, 1963, p. 156-157.)

CAVE MOUNTAIN CAVE (p. 207).

At the end of the second level is a pit connecting with a lower third level. The third level extends parallel to the upper levels, and a pit on the left of the level gives access to a fourth level.

(Bob Keiper: Met Grotto News, v. 14, no. 5, Sept.-Oct., 1964, p. 42-44.)

COON CAVE 38°45'10" N.; 79°23'45" W. Onego Quadrangle.

Coon Cave is in Germany Valley about a mile southeast of Seneca Caverns (elevation 2350 feet) . The entrance is a pit 20 feet deep. From the entrance a sinuous passage trends south for about 350 feet. The ceiling of the passage ranges to 20 feet in height and the passage increases from a few feet wide near the entrance to about 25 ft wide at the south end. Two complexes of pits are in the floor at 100 and 200 feet from the entrance. At the end of the passage is a flowstone mound broken by two deep pits. Short side passages lead east and west just north of this pit. The passage to the east is cut by a deep pit near the main passage. Coon Cave is in Middle Ordovician limestone.

(Jay Edwards: Netherworld News, v. 7, no. 9, Sept., 1959, p. 171-172.)

HELLHOLE (p. 213).

A small hole near the floor on the left wall of left-hand passage near the base of the guano slope opens into a narrow pit about 100 feet deep.

(William Plummer: Baltimore Grotto News, v. 2, no. 7, July, 1959, p. 9.)

KLEINFELDS CAVERN 38°47'05" N.; 79°22'36" W. (approximate) Onego Quadrangle.

This cave was opened by excavating the base of a sinkhole west of Schoolhouse Cave (elevation 2225 feet). A 20-foot shaft was sunk and opened into the side of a large dome room. The opening beneath the entrance is 100 feet deep and the entrance room is formed by three connected domepits, the eastern one of which is 130 feet high. The cave trends east as an inclined, wedge-shaped passage, 3 to 5 feet high, with several offsets. Fifty feet from the entrance room is a crawlway connecting with a drop of 50 feet on the side of an intersecting passage. Beyond this point the cave is formed of a series of narrow connected domepits and fissures along the main passage and another intersecting passage at the end of the cave. The fissures and domepits are up to 70 feet high. The cave is in Middle Ordovician limestone.

(Gene Reynolds: Baltimore Grotto News, v. 4, no. 12, Dec., 1961, p. 200-208.)

LAWRENCE DOMEPIT CAVE (p. 257).

Four hundred feet east of the junction of the Judy Springs and Seneca Caverns roads is a pit 3 feet in diameter and 17 feet deep. This opens into a room 12 feet high, with a fissure passage on the south end. A small hole on the left wall of the fissure opens into the main passage of the cave. To the north the main passage trends N20°E to N45°E for about 350 feet and is 4 to 11 feet high and 10 feet wide, narrowing to 4 or 5 feet in the last 100 feet. Seven small domepits and pits are along or adjacent to the passage. A small tube is parallel and 6 feet below the main passage from a point 100 feet north of the entrance. South of the entrance the main passage is 300 feet long, 5 to 27 feet high, and 2 to 10 feet wide. Four domepits and numerous speleothems are along this section of the cave.

(J. Haas: Nittany Grotto Newsletter, v. 7, no. 5, Jan., 1959, p. 76-80.)

LITTLE SENECA CAVERN   Onego Quadrangle.

This cave is south of Ruddle Cave and consists of a single, sinuous passage trending 300 feet at N25°E. The passage, 3 to 10 feet wide and 2 to 25 feet high, ends in breakdown. The cave is in Middle Ordovician limestone.

(George Hixson: Netherworld News, v. 7, no. 3, March, 1959, p. 72.)

NAMELESS CAVE 38°45'48" N.; 79°23'27" W. Onego Quadrangle.

A collapse sink is 300 feet northwest of Seneca Caverns (elevation 2150 feet). A small fissure at the bottom of the sink connects with a passage sloping 35° downward for 50 feet. The main passage of the cave is 15 feet wide and 170 feet long trending northwest and curving to the west and southwest. The ceiling is level with a height of 6 feet near the entrance increasing to 25 feet near the end because of the slope of the floor. Thirty feet from the end of the passage is a side passage trending south and west for 90 feet. It is 2 to 3 feet high with a floor of clay and flowstone. The cave is in Middle Ordovician limestone.

(J. Haas: Nittany Grotto Newsletter, v. 7, no. 5, Jan., 1959, p. 75.)

RIVER GAP CAVE 38°40′16″ N.; 79°19′26″ W. Circleville Quadrangle.

1.2 miles north of Franklin on the northwest side of the gorge of South Branch is a large cave entrance (elevation 1650 feet). After 30 feet the passage reduces to a crawlway and ends in 50 feet. The cave is in limestones of the Helderberg Group.

(W. McGrew: Netherworld News, v. 6, no. 10, Oct., 1958, p. 214-215.)

ROARING CREEK MILL CAVE (p. 232).

The passage trending northwest beyond the waterfall extends 250 feet to a large room. A deep stream flows along the floor of the passage leaving a ceiling clearance of 8 inches to 3 feet. The room is 35 feet long, 25 feet wide, and 15 feet high. Breakdown blocks the end of the room. Beyond the breakdown is a passage a little larger than the one leading to the room and about 200 feet long. Another room, 25 feet long, 15 feet wide, and 10 feet high, interrupts the passage beyond which the stream passage extends for 50 feet to breakdown. A side passage opens about 3 feet above the floor in the second room and extends to the breakdown at the end of the first room.

(Jerry Frederick: Netherworld News, v. 8, no. 11, Nov., 1960, p. 193.)

SINNIT (SINNETT) CAVE (p. 241).

Along the north wall in the central part of the Big Room is a small opening that leads southwest to a small room 15 to 20 feet above the floor of the Big Room. Recent breakdown fills much of this room. A crawlway passage extends west to a room with a clay slope 70 feet long sloping at 45° to 70°. On the high side of the room at the end of a ledge is a narrow fissure leading to a small room with very unstable, dangerous breakdown. The highest point in this room is 130 feet above the Big Room. A crawlway through the breakdown extends to a small room with the passage continuing as a crawlway connecting with the northeast end of the main passage of Thorn Mountain Cave, at a point at the opposite end from the deep pit.

The lower level keyhole passage continues beyond the base of the Silo to a waterfall. Beyond the waterfall are short crawlways connecting with a small maze of passages with a stream. A wedge-shaped canyon, 5 feet wide at the base and 50 feet wide at the top, 60 feet high, continues for 400 feet from the maze, terminating in a high earth fill.

(Bill Nelson: Cavalier Caver, v. 2, no. 2-3, Dec., 1959, Feb., 1960, p. 16-18. Lynn Ferguson: Cavalier Caver, v. 6, no. 1, March, 1964, p. 25. Lew Bicking: Baltimore Grotto News, v. 5, no. 7, July, 1962, p. 165-167.)

VANGUARD CAVE 38°40′13″N.; 79°19′15″ W. Circleville Quadrangle.

At the south end of a cliff 100 feet high on the west bank of the South Branch in the gorge north of Franklin (elevation 1675 feet) is a cave entrance 10 feet high. The cave is a solution fissure about 75 feet in length. The cave is in the limestones of the Helderberg Group.

(W. McGrew: Netherworld News, v. 6, no. 10, Oct., 1958, p. 214.)

VANDEVANDER CAVE 38°34′15″ N.; 79°22′16″ W. Circleville Quadrangle.

One hundred yards above the Thorn Creek road, ¾ mile south of the site of Hoffman School, is a shallow sinkhole with a cave entrance (elevation 2300 feet). A short drop connects with a room 50 feet wide, 5 to 15 feet high, and 60 feet long. The floor of talus slopes to the southeast where a drop of 6 feet connects with another room about 35 feet long, 25 feet wide, and 8 feet high. A passage 3 to 5 feet high and up to 10 feet wide trends northeast for 75 feet to a mud fill. On the southwest side of the room is a crawlway over 100 feet long. Vandevander Cave is in the limestones of the Helderberg Group.

(Denny Dingley: Neog Log, v. 1, no. 1, May-June, 1964, p. 8.)

Other caves reported in Pendleton County are:

Chucks Cave—One mile northeast of Seneca Caverns (Onego Quadrangle); 20-foot pit opening to a room 40 feet in diameter, 10 feet deep.

Fieldhouse Cave—¼ mile southwest of Seneca Caverns (Onego Quadrangle); two short passages and interconnected domepits 40 to 65 feet high.

Flute Cave No. 2—Germany Valley (Onego Quadrangle); 15-foot fissure with crawlway to pit and fissure 60 feet deep; ends in high room.

Folly Dome Pit—North end of Neds Mountain, 1 mile east of Mouth of Dry River (Circleville Quadrangle); 55-foot pit; small fissure at base.

Mullenax Cave—Head of middle fork of Moyers Run, 2 miles northwest of Cave P.O. (Circleville Quadrangle); crawlway entrance sloping down to a room 50 feet long, 10 feet wide, and 3 to 6 feet high; three crawlways to left near entrance; 18-foot pit midway along main passage.

Mullenax Water Cave—Two hundred yards south of Mullenax Cave (Circleville Quadrangle); low, water passage; stream flows out of cave.

Rebs Cave—One mile northeast of Seneca Caverns (Onego Quadrangle); 15-foot fissure entrance connecting to a room 15 feet in diameter, 4 feet high.

Thompsons Pit—South of Ruddle Cave (Circleville Quadrangle); 110-foot pit connecting at base with 2 domes; base of main pit has subordinate pit extending 40 feet below floor level. Entrance pit sealed off by filling with stone and other debris in 1960.

POCAHONTAS COUNTY

BABER ROOM CAVE 38°07′12″ N.; 80°15′43″ W. Lobelia Quadrangle.

This cave is along the valley draining Droop Mountain between Martha Clarks Cave and Hughes Creek Cave (elevation 2500 feet). It consists of a large waterfall pit connecting with a room 25 feet long and 20 feet high and wide. This leads to another room 70 feet long, 50 feet high, and 25 feet wide with a floor covered by breakdown. The cave is in the middle part of the Greenbrier Group.

(Hermine Zotter: Netherworld News, v. 11, no. 9, Sept. 1963, p. 167.)

BARNES PIT (p. 259).

The main passage is 2 feet high leading to a waterfall drop of 8 feet and continuing as crawlways and walkways to a 25-foot overhang drop in an area of very dangerous, unstable breakdown. At the base of the drop is a stoopway passage with a stream trending southwest for 1,500 feet in the direction of Cave Creek Cave. A low, wet, side passage leaves the main passage near the breakdown drop and trends towards Carpenters Pit. The stream entering this pit comes from Carpenters-Swago Pits and resurges at Cave Creek Cave.

(Vic Schmidt: Netherworld News, v. 7, no. 10, Oct. 1959, p. 195-196.)

BEARDS (BLUE HOLE) CAVE (p. 260).

From the large, deep pool in the bottom of the sink a stream passage several hundred feet long leads to another sink southwest of Blue Hole. Exit is gained here by climbing up through breakdown and loose earth. A small passage just inside the main entrance leads to the surface and opens in the shallower of the two sinks which form Blue Hole. The upper part of this passage is a dry, circular tube 100 feet long.

(Vic Schmidt: Netherworld News, v. 10, no. 10, Oct. 1962, p. 197-198.)

BEVERIDGE PITS AND CAVES (p. 279, 297, 298).

The preferred spelling of the name is **Beverage.** Because of the widespread use of the former spelling the caves and pits should be cited as **Beveridge (Beverage).**

BLUE LICK HOLE 38°11′30″ N.; 80°13′06″ W. Marlinton Quadrangle.

A small cave consisting of a room 15 by 6 feet in size with two small domes open at the base of a 6-foot drop. The floor of the cave is water covered. The entrance is in a sinkhole midway along Blue Lick Run (elevation 2875 feet). The cave is in the top of the Greenbrier Group.

(Hermine Zotter: Netherworld News, v. 8, no. 8, Aug., 1960, p. 134.)

BLUE SPRINGS (p. 260).

The main stream passage is 5 to 8 feet high, 10 to 15 feet wide, extending 2,000 feet to a breakdown room. Eight feet above the floor of the room is a small hole with a stream falling from it. To the left from the room is a 4-foot high dry passage that pinches out at 200 feet. To the right is a large walkway that extends 2,000 feet to a siphon. A stream crosses this passage several times. The Blue Springs resurgence is partly derived from Steam Cave.

(Wes McGrew: Netherworld News, v. 8, no. 9, Sept., 1960, p. 161.)

BRUFFEY CREEK CAVE (p. 261).

The water-filled passage east of the junction with Hills Creek is 30 feet wide with water 4 to 6 feet deep, and only a few inches of air space to the ceiling. It extends east several hundred feet to a gravel bank, followed by 1,000 feet of walkway passage, ending in breakdown.

The stream entering Bruffey Creek Cave flows ENE through Hughes Creek Cave, probably through Lower Hughes Creek Cave and Marthas Cave, then flows south and finally resurges at Locust Creek Cave.

(Vic Schmidt: Netherworld News, v. 11, no. 12, Dec. 1963, p. 216.)

BUCK MOUNTAIN PIT (DRY CREEK INDIAN CAVE) (p. 298).
38°14'08" N.; 80°07'46" W. Marlinton Quadrangle.

On the northwestern slope of Buck Mountain, ¼ mile northeast of Beveridge Pit, is a large open pit (elevation 2950 feet). The vertical entrance is 38 feet deep with a steep debris slope extending 50 feet into the hill and 20 feet down. To the right of the room is a semicircular wall which is peeling off as breakdown. To the left is a small domepit approximately 40 feet deep. The total length of the cave is 50 feet; total depth is 80 feet.

(Hermine Zotter: Netherworld News, v. 11, no. 10, Oct. 1963, p. 178.)

CACKLEY CAVE 38°11'23" N.; 80°11'54" W. Marlinton Quadrangle.

Cackley Cave is 1⅜ miles NNW of Trinity School (elevation 2800 feet). It is 300 feet long, primarily a crawlway with several side passages and a series of domepits, 40 to 90 feet deep. Cackley Cave is in the top of the Greenbrier Group.

(Charles Plantz: Netherworld News, v. 7, no. 12, Dec., 1959, p. 221. G. Wallace: Netherworld News, v. 8, no. 5, May, 1960, p. 81.)

CARPENTERS-SWAGO PIT (p. 261).

West of Carpenters Pit entrance and southwest of Crumbling Gallery is a complex of domepits and multilevel passages connecting with a stream passage 250 feet long trending southwest to a long, narrow domepit, 20 feet high.

Crumbling Gallery leads to Arrowhead Avenue which is a shallow water walkway passage about 3,200 feet long, terminated in series of domepits. Along the ceiling of this avenue is a prominent meander channel. Beyond the domepits at the end of Arrowhead Avenue is a narrow winding canyon passage to other domepits and a room with a large balcony. A stream flows over the balcony to a passage leading to a keyhole-shaped room 30 feet high and 40 feet long. To the left of this room is a passage extending 50 feet to a waterfall over breakdown. To the right is a similar passage 100 feet long ending in breakdown with a waterfall. A small passage continues from the breakdown.

A side passage leading from the stream passage near the entrance is a dry walkway 500 feet long ending at two large domepits, one with a large opening in the top.

A crawl passage leading from the breakdown at the end of Crumbling Gallery bypasses the breakdown and develops into a narrow fissure 500 feet long to a stream passage in Arrowhead Avenue.

A stream flowing through this cave system resurges near the mouth of Barnes Pit, flows through it, and resurges again at Cave Creek Cave.

(Dave Thompson: Netherworld News, v. 8, no. 7, July, 1960, p. 118-119. William Plummer: Baltimore Grotto News, v. 2, no. 3, p. 6; v. 2, no. 4, p. 6.)

CASSELL CAVE SYSTEM 38°27'24" N.; 79°53'48" W. 38°27'22" N.; 79°53'45" W. Cass Quadrangle.

This system consists of Cassell and Cassell Windy Caves. They are on the South Fork of Trout Run on the east flank of Back Allegheny Mountain and contain over 17,000 feet of passages. The entrance pit of Cassell Cave is 775 feet west of Back Mountain Road and 725 feet west of the Cassell Windy section (elevation 3060 feet). At the base of the 96-foot entrance pit is a large entrance room. To the southwest a fissure extends for a short distance and is blocked. The former parallel passages extending southwest are blocked by collapse and filling. To the north the passages are a series of crawls to breakdown and a series of large rooms. On the east side of the last room is a series of flowstone steps leading 10 feet down to a crawlway 50 feet long, trending southwest to a T-intersection. The right passage at the intersection extends 100 yards to a crawlway 200 yards long ending in a steeply sloping tube leading up to a room

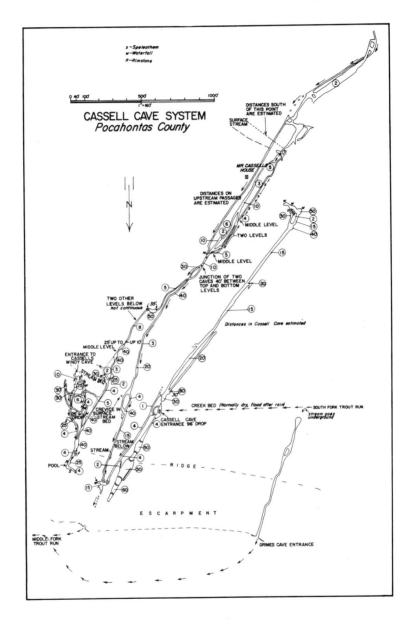

Figure 10.—Cassell Cave System. Surveyed by Eddy, Errington, Hager, Williamson, Barton, Cameron, Heller, Long and Medville, 1964-65. (Philadelphia Grotto Digest, v. 4, no. 2, March-April, 1965).

150 feet long and 100 feet high. From this room several passages lead off. One of the passages continues southwest for over 5,000 feet. It ends in a series of large rooms 60 to 80 feet high with waterfalls entering from above. Scaling poles are required to ascend these waterfalls. The passages leading from them are wet and very decorated.

To the left of the T-intersection is a passage to the northnortheast paralleling the older section of the cave. Two hundred feet down this passage is a room in which all of the cave streams join. From this room the main Cassell stream passage trends SSW for 1½ miles. Two thousand feet from this room the section formerly known as Cassell's Windy Cave joins it 40 feet above. The surface entrance to the Cassell Windy section is a small tortuous opening at the base of an abandoned quarry on the south fork of Trout Run, 50 feet west of the road along the east flank of Back Allegheny Mountain (elevation 2950 feet). A stoopway runs 50 feet to the northwest to a small room. From it the main passage 2 to 5 feet wide and 5 to 10 feet high trends north-northeast for 210 feet over clay and breakdown. Several small dome rooms and one large room, 3 feet long, 20 feet wide, and 40 feet high, are along the passage. Passages lead out of this room at several levels. The upper passage to the north-northeast terminates in a 30-foot drop from which the cave continues to the west-northwest for 125 feet as a narrow passage with several drops up to 17 feet deep. A small dome is to the south midway along this passage. At the end this passage connects with a large passage extending 150 feet northeast to a pool and crawlway. To the southwest it has been explored for 1,000 feet. In this area the passage is in three or four levels formed by small passages connected in places by small vertical openings. Four hundred feet along this multilevel passage is a 35 foot canyon interconnecting all four levels.

Beyond the canyon the passage is on the highest level and is a low, wide bedding plane opening with a slot in the center. At 1,500 feet the passage intersects a passage with a stream by way of a 40-foot drop. This is the main stream passage of Cassell Cave and is the point at which the two caves intersect to form one large system with a total length of over 3½ miles.

Upstream the passage extends as a walkway 200 feet to a siphon. The siphon can be bypassed by dry, parallel, upper level crawlways 1,000 feet long. The passage continues to the southwest through breakdown. Beyond the breakdown there is about 2,000 feet of stream walkway to more breakdown. Small water crawlways can be traversed in the breakdown for 500 feet to where the cave is completely blocked. Scattered speleothems include rimstone, flowstone, stalactites, stalagmites and cave coral. An intermittently strong draft is encountered at the Cassell Windy entrance. The Cassell Cave System is in the lower part of the Greenbrier Group.

(Douglas Medville: Philly Grotto Digest, v. 4, no. 2, March-April, 1965, p. 12-15. Steve Emery: Potomac Cave, v. 7, no. 11-12, Nov.-Dec., 1964, p. 63-64. D. B. Williamson, P. R. Errington, personal communications.)

CUTLIP CAVE 38°06'48" N.; 80°17'06" W. Lobelia Quadrangle.

The entrance to Cutlip Cave (elevation 2450 feet) is in a limestone ledge at the end of the valley of Hills Creek, 1½ miles southeast of Lobelia. Several tight openings, partially clogged with debris, connect with a passage 5 to 10 feet wide and 20 feet high leading to a T-intersection. The right passage leads to a room filled with breakdown and a stream at the bottom. The left passage from the T-intersection leads to a balcony overlooking a stream. A traverse above the stream passage leads to several rooms. A traverse in the downstream direction eventually descends to the stream level. The stream continues through several breakdown-filled rooms to a deep lake. Swimming the lake leads to the last sizeable room of the cave. The stream sinks into breakdown. Several crawlways lead from this room. One of these exhibits an odd breathing pattern also seen at Joe Hollow Cave. Cutlip Cave is in the middle of the Greenbrier Group.

(Jim Wolf: Netherworld News, v. 12, no. 5, May, 1964, p. 69; v. 12, no. 6, June, 1964, p. 80-81.)

DROOP MOUNTAIN CAVE 38°04'28" N.; 80°16'06" W. Lobelia Quadrangle.

A large sinkhole on the east side of Droop Mountain, about 1¼ miles east of Droop Mountain School (elevation 2600 feet), contains a 15-foot pit. At the base of the pit is a room 100 feet long, 75 feet wide, and 50 feet high containing a large amount of unstable breakdown. To the right of the room is a large domepit 40 feet deep with a passage leading off 20 feet from the base. A small stream falls into the pit from this passage. Another passage in the right wall opens 30 feet above the floor and connects with a small room. The stream passage from the domepit continues for a hundred feet where it divides. The left fork contains a stream and reduces to a very narrow fissure in a short distance. The right passage leads 200 feet to several small rooms. The cave is in the upper part of the Greenbrier Group.

(Wes McGrew and Hermine Zotter: Netherworld News, v. 8, no. 10, Oct., 1960, p. 176; v. 10, no. 2, Feb., 1962, p. 23. William Plummer, Baltimore Grotto News, v. 4, no. 7, July, 1961, p. 111.)

FRIELS CAVE (p. 268).

The passages near the entrance of this cave interconnect to form a partial maze, then change into a multilevel complex, which finally becomes a stream canyon. At the bottom of a 35-foot waterfall the stream enters a low crawlway which is negotiable for an unknown distance. The stream continues towards Cave Creek Cave where it resurges.

Also in the Waterfall Room is a small passage, 25 feet long, partway up one wall. Still higher up the wall, across the top of the waterfall, the main stream passage appears to continue amid loose and muddy rocks.

(Wes McGrew: Netherworld News, v. 7, no. 10, Oct., 1959, p. 194, p. 194a-b, maps by George Simon.)

GENERAL AVERELL PIT 38°07'09" N.; 80°14'51" W. Marlinton Quadrangle.

One-quarter mile northwest of the junction of U.S. Route 219 and Locust Creek Road (elevation 2375 feet) is a huge collapsed pit 35 feet long, 30 feet wide, and 50 feet deep. Entry without rigging can be gained at one end. Small coral and flowstone-covered fissures exist at the base throughout massive breakdown. At the deepest end of the pit a labyrinth of passages extends down into the breakdown for a vertical depth of 90 feet or more and several hundred feet horizontally. The cave consists of large pieces of breakdown lying against the west wall of the pit. The rooms and passages become progressively larger with depth. Legend has it that the cave continued through the mountain. It is located midway between Martha Clarks and Locust Creek Caves.

(H. Zotter & F. Donofrio: Netherworld News, v. 12, no. 8, Aug., 1964, p. 109. Chuck Plantz: Netherworld News, v. 12, no. 7, July, 1964, p. 98.)

GRAND VIEW PIT 38°07′54″ N.; 80°13′45″ W. Marlinton Quadrangle.

One-half mile northwest of Sherman Beard's house and ½ mile northeast of Beards Blue Hole (elevation 2375 feet) is a pit entrance in a sink on top of the hill. It is 53 feet deep and at the bottom is a room 26 feet high, and 35 feet wide and long. A stream enters this room down a cascade of rimstone dams, some forming large pools. About 50 feet up this cascade the stream enters as a waterfall from a dome. Downstream from the entrance room the stream continues a couple hundred feet in a high, narrow, meandering, multilevel passage which increases in height from 15 to 50 feet downstream. A second ladder climb to the lower stream level revealed a flowstone obstruction beyond which the stream passage continues. This stream is believed to resurge at Beards Blue Hole.

(Hermine Zotter: Netherworld News, v. 12, no. 6, June, 1964, p. 82; v. 12 no. 9, Sept., 1964, p. 125. Chuck Plantz: Netherworld News, v. 12, no. 7, July, 1964, p. 98.)

HAUSE WATERFALL CAVE (p. 271).

The passage extending southwest is 500 feet long and ends in a mud fill. The stream entering this cave resurges at Cave Creek Cave.

(J. Fisher, Jack Wehman: Netherworld News, v. 7, no. 8, Aug., 1959, p. 161.)

HOOKS CAVE 38°35′52″ N.; 79°50′19″ W. (approx.) Durbin Quadrangle.

Hooks Cave is 3½ miles NNW of Durbin, ½ mile north of U. S. Highway 250 (elevation 3050 feet). The entrance is a small hole connecting with a mud slope 50 feet long on the side of a dome. At the base is a stream passage 15 feet wide trending north to a complex breakdown. The stream is on a lower passage 5 to 10 feet down, and a series of pits connects the two levels. Beyond the breakdown the upper passage forks forming two parallel passages each about 200 feet long.

The stream passage drops 50 feet over a series of overhanging ledges in two rooms to a waterfall and pool beyond which the cave continues as a very low water passage. The length of explored passages is about 1,500 feet. Nearby is a low, wide entrance to a water crawlway 300 feet long (Cherry Run Cave). Hooks Cave is in the lower part of the Greenbrier Group.

(Bert Blosser: D. C. Speleograph, v. 20, no. 7, July, 1964, p. 51-52.)

HUGHES CREEK LOWER CAVE (p. 273).

Part of the cave is a maze of wet, muddy crawlways and low stream passages. During flood stage the water from Upper Hughes Creek Cave overflows and completely inundates the Lower Cave.

(Al Haarr: Netherworld News, v. 12, no. 8, Aug., 1964, p. 114.)

LOCUST CREEK CAVE (p. 275).

The cave trends southwest, curving to the west. It is a stream passage for 1,000 feet. The first 200 feet is a 6 to 10 foot deep water passage. At 200 feet the stream flows beneath a series of ledges and breakdown. A small waterfall is along the north wall at this point. The remainder of the cave is a walkway along the stream ending in a rounded chamber in which the stream enters the cave by a siphon. The water emerging from this cave is derived from Hills Creek, Bruffey Creek and Marthas Caves, and possibly other sources.

(Bruce Godwin: Netherworld News, v. 11, no. 8, Aug., 1963, p. 144-145.)

MARTENS CAVE NO. 2 38°08'05" N.; 80°16'28" W. Lobelia Quadrangle.

The entrance is 1,000 feet west of Martens Cave and is 20 feet above the valley floor in a low ledge of rock (elevation 2625 feet). The cave is a single passage 40 feet wide, 200 feet long, 5 to 15 feet high on breakdown. A small passage extends 150 feet to the north at ceiling level at the end of the cave. This cave is in the top of the Greenbrier Group.

(William E. Davies.)

MARTHAS CAVE (p. 275).

The pool area on the lower level passage is 300 feet long, beyond which the passage is up to 80 feet wide and 40 feet high with a stream 3 to 6 feet deep bordered by high, steep mud banks. This passage (Alices Gallery) extends about 1,500 feet. On the right side, near the end, is a side passage at the top of the mud bank that opens into a large room of breakdown (Rubble Room). A small passage leads from the breakdown room but ends in a breakdown choke. The stream in this cave resurges at Locust Creek Cave.

(Bill Plummer: Baltimore Grotto News, v. 5, no. 1, Jan. 1962, p. 19-20. Vic Schmidt: Netherworld News, v. 10, no. 1, Jan., 1962, p. 14-15.)

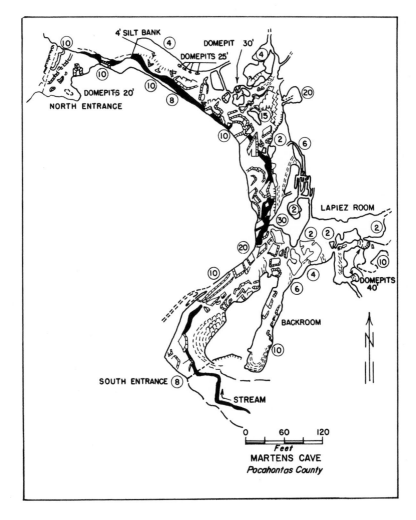

Figure 11.—Martens Cave. Surveyed by William E. Davies, 1948, revised 1959.

McCLOUD CAVE 38°18′22″ N.; 80°02′46″ W. Mingo Quadrangle.

This cave is near the top of a ridge 3½ miles east of Edray along Cloverlick (elevation 3650 feet). The cave consists of a crawl passage about 300 feet long with a second passage on the right near the entrance. This passage is 75 feet long and contains rimstone pools and several small domepits. During wet weather a stream enters the cave and flows along the main passage. Several shallow pits (Smith Pits Nos. 1, 2, 3, 4) up to 20 feet deep are in the vicinity of McCloud Cave. McCloud Cave is in the top of the Greenbrier Group.

(Wes McGrew: Netherworld News, v. 7, no. 10, Oct., 1959, p. 190. Hermine Zotter: Netherworld News, v. 11, no. 5, May, 1963, p. 78.)

McNEEL CAVE 38°09′42″ N.; 80°10′52″ W. Marlinton Quadrangle.

One-half mile north of Mill Point on the east side of a tributary to Stamping Creek, named McNeel Run, is a limestone bluff 20 feet high in which a crawlway entrance opens (elevation 2300 feet). This crawlway slopes 15 feet to a water passage which continues 20 feet to a point where the water is within 6 to 10 inches of the ceiling; during dry weather it is 6 feet deep and siphons during wet weather. This low spot is 15 feet long beyond which is a wide muddy crawlway leading 200 feet to the left, apparently back to the entrance room. At this point a stream passage intersects the crawlway. To the right the passage is 4 feet high, 6 feet wide, and continues 20 feet to a mud and debris choke. This cave is in the lower part of the Greenbrier Group.

Two **McNEEL PITS** are nearby: one is 30 feet deep consisting of a large crevice entrance belling out at the bottom, located 50 feet north of McNeel Cave; another is 50 feet uphill from the first pit and is 25 feet deep.

(Hermine Zotter: Netherworld News, v. 8, no. 8, Aug., 1960, p. 133-134; v. 10, no. 8, Aug., 1962, p. 143-144. Wes McGrew: Netherworld News, v. 8, no. 9, Sept., 1960, p. 161.)

McNEELS MILL RUN CAVE 38°06′54″ N.; 80°13′53″ W. Marlinton Quadrangle.

Three miles southwest of Hillsboro, at the head of a small valley, is a cave entrance 15 feet wide and 2½ feet high in a limestone bluff (elevation 2200 feet). The main cave is a stream passage more than

2,300 feet long, averaging 15 feet wide and 2 feet high with a water depth of 6 inches. Minimum headroom above water is 6 inches and maximum water depth is 2½ feet. The passage is subjected to flooding. The floor and ceiling contain large rounded flint nodules. Near the entrance a dry passage is on the left opposite a long, low flowstone with rimstone pools on it. The cave is in the base of the Greenbrier Group. Poor Farm Water Cave is the source of Mill Run, which resurges from McNeels Mill Run Cave.

(Hermine Zotter: Netherworld News, v. 8, no. 8, Aug., 1960, p. 133.)

NANCY SHARP PIT 38°14′30″ N.; 80°07′02″ W. Marlinton Quad-rangle.

A sinkhole with a narrow fissure 10 feet deep gives access to a small cave on the east side of Stony Creek Mountain about a mile and a half west of Campbelltown (elevation 3025 feet). At the base of the fissure the floor slopes down to a depth of 20 feet. A passage from the base of the slope ends in breakdown at 20 feet and a small domepit is alongside the passage. Nancy Sharp Pit is in the top of the Greenbrier Group.

(Hermine Zotter: Netherworld News, v. 9, no. 9, Aug., 1961, p. 148.)

NEWMAN CAVE 38°10′11″ N.; 80°09′22″ W. Marlinton Quad-rangle.

Midway between Buckeye and Mill Point, about 1,700 feet north of U. S. Highway 219 (elevation 2350), is a large sinkhole. At the end of the sink is a cave entrance 2 feet high and 4 feet wide. A horizontal water passage extends for 700 feet beyond the entrance, after which it continues as a water and mud crawlway. Newman Cave is in the base of the Greenbrier Group.

(Hermine Zotter: Netherworld News, v. 8, no. 8, Aug., 1960, p. 134.)

OVERHOLTS BLOWING CAVE (p. 278).

At the end of the Mountain Room is a short drop to the stream passage, which is a 1,000-foot crawlway and fissure with some breakdown, opening near the end to a large passage with a broad shelf at waist height. This continues to the Cathedral Room which is a high fissure, narrow at the base and widening out to a high roomy dome. A 60-foot waterfall enters the room from a hole in the ceiling and a small subordinate falls issues from a hole in the wall. A pile of breakdown, 30 feet high, leads above the small falls. The cave continues from the top of the high falls as a narrow, twisting stream passage leading back, somewhat parallel to the Mountain-Cathedral Room section, and then along a narrow ceiling crack above a room. A third waterfall is in a dome adjacent to the ceiling crack. Beyond this is a long stream passage leading to a walkway (The Turnpike) with a dry, gypsum sand floor 300 feet long. From here the cave extends 2,000 feet to Disappointment Dome by low stream crawls and some narrow walkways. A waterfall, 30 feet high, drops into this 50-foot dome. From this waterfall the passage extends for 600 feet as a large canyon with breakdown, passing a fifth waterfall, and ending in a small room. Several short crawls lead from the room and a 500-foot crawl connects with the Rat Room, a small room marking the end of the cave.

Just beyond the Mountain Room is a small hole that gives access to the Empire Room, lying above the Mountain Room. This room is cylindrical in shape and 100 feet high. South of the Cathedral Room, a side stream passage, Alcoa Avenue, leads off to the right for about 2,000 feet, ending in a low crawl.

Beyond the breakdown room in Annes Avenue a passage leads to a higher room (Attic Room) beyond which is an area of clear pools and a lower-level, coral-lined canyon connecting with 2 other rooms and a maze of small side passages.

A side passage to the left of the main cave, about 3,200 feet from the entrance, is a fissure and crawlway, 300 feet long, connecting with several domepits up to 80 feet high. The water emerging from this cave is derived from caves and pits that drain the western slopes of Dry Creek valley.

(Wes McGrew and Jerry Frederick: Netherworld News, v. 7, no. 6, June, 1959, p. 123-125; Jim Fisher and Bob Dunn: Netherworld News, v. 7, no. 9, Sept, 1959, p. 174-175. Vic Schmidt: Baltimore Grotto News, v. 3, no. 3, March, 1960, p. 42-48. W. B. White: Netherworld News, v. 8, no. 12, Dec., 1960, p. 198-206. Allen McCrady, Jerry Frederick, Fred Kissell: Netherworld News, v. 11, no. 1, Jan., 1963, p. 2-5. Fred Kissell: Netherworld News, v. 8, no. 11, Nov., 1960, p. 191.)

RASPBERRY CAVE 38°12′02″ N.; 80°09′34″ W. Marlinton Quadrangle.

This cave is ⅜ of a mile above the mouth of Blacklick, a tributary of McClintock Run (elevation 2750 feet). The entrance is a pit 10 feet deep connecting with a slope 15 feet long. The slope opens into a passage 10 feet high, 5 feet wide, and 40 feet long with a smooth mud floor. This cave is in the upper part of the Greenbrier Group.

(George Simon: Netherworld News, v. 7, no. 10, Oct., 1959, p. 191-193.)

RED LICK PIT 38°17'02" N.; 80°07'07" W. Mingo Quadrangle.

Red Lick Pit is 1 mile due north of Pine Grove School (elevation 2900 feet). The entrance is a small opening at the top of a domepit 85 feet high. The cave consists of seven interconnecting domepits with comparatively level floors of rimstone. The domepits range in height from 80 to about 130 feet and are about 15 feet in diameter, except õne which is 20 feet long and 10 feet wide. The pits are in the middle part of the Greenbrier Group.

(Bob Anderson: Netherworld News, v. 8, no. 10, Oct., 1960, p. 176. Bruce Goodwin: Netherworld News, v. 8, no. 5, May, 1960, p. 82.)

ROCKHOUSE NO. 2 38°17'35" N.; 80°06'46" W. Mingo Quadrangle.

On the west fork of Dry Creek near its head (elevation 2900 feet) is a cave with an entrance 12 feet wide and about 5 feet high, opening to a room 20 feet wide, 5 feet high, and 35 feet long, beyond which extends a narrow dry passage for 150 feet to a small room. Rockhouse No. 2 is in the middle part of the Greenbrier Group.

(Guy Wallace: Netherworld News, v. 7, no. 6, June, 1959, p. 123. Earl Thierry: Netherworld News, v. 9, no. 1, Jan., 1963, p. 12.)

SALMON (HATCHERY SPRING) CAVE 38°16'20" N.; 80°06'17" W. Mingo Quadrangle.

This cave is near the fish hatchery on Dry Creek at Onoto (elevation 2500 feet). The cave has two entrances; the east one is a narrow stream channel 8 feet high and 1½ feet wide, usually flooded. The west entrance, through recent breakdown, opens into a room 10 feet high and wide and 40 feet long. Near the ceiling, 10 feet from the floor, a stream passage opens. The water in this stream passage flows out through a side channel to the east entrance rather than into the west entrance room. Beyond the entrance area the stream passage is about 4 feet high, 2 feet wide with 2 feet of water, and is covered by a salmon-colored deposit. About 500 feet from the entrance is a room covered with white flowstone (Candy Room). The cave continues as a crawlway over rimstone for 50 feet to a domepit 60 feet high containing flowstone, draperies, and deep potholes. Beyond the domepit are several hundred feet of walkway passages leading to a series of pools. The first is 400 feet long with an average depth of 3 feet; Lake II is 100 feet long and 6 feet deep; Lake III, 50 feet long, 10 feet wide, with an average depth of 4 feet. The ceiling drops to within a foot of the water surface over the lake. This lake is 1,600 feet from the entrance. A sewer-type passage, 3 feet high, 6 feet wide, continues for 100 feet beyond the lakes and near the end several holes in the ceiling lead to a room 300 feet long, 50 to 75 feet wide, and 30 feet high. The floor of the room is covered with damp silt and clay. North of the room is a large stream passage about 1,000 feet long to the Pearl Room, 120 feet wide and 200 feet long. Beyond this room the passage is 75 feet wide and 30 feet high extending 300 feet to the Lake Siphon. The lake is 20 feet in diameter and 8 feet deep where the water enters. On the left side of the lake a small crawlway extends 300 feet to a walkway 200 feet long which joins the stream passage beyond the siphon. The stream passage is 15 feet high and 20 feet wide for 100 feet to a second siphon. On the right of the siphon is a small fall of water over stalagmites. This cave is in the lower part of the Greenbrier Group.

(Guy Wallace: Netherworld News, v. 7, no. 6, June, 1959, p. 122; v. 7, no. 9, Sept., 1959, p. 172-173. Jim Fisher, Hermine Zotter: Netherworld News, v. 7, no. 8, Aug., 1959, p. 16.)

SALTPETER (LOBELIA) CAVE (p. 287).

A stream passage as well as large, long, open passages are reported to form an extensive network extending from the lower part of the cave.

(Douglas S. Hall, personal communication.)

SHARPS CAVE (p. 289).

At the base of the entrance are two small passages trending north for 25 feet where they open into a northwest passage up to 25 feet wide and 5 to 8 feet high. Breakdown covers much of the floor. This passage is 125 feet long, and at its northwest end is a side passage on the southwest opening into a room 75 feet long, 50 feet wide, and 9 feet high. A narrow passage to the southwest from his room for 25 feet connects with a room 20 feet wide and over 100 feet long. The main cave continues northwest from the junction of the side passage as a room 30 to 60 feet wide,

14·to 20 feet high, and over 400 feet long. A lower, narrow passage parallels the main cave and is connected by a slope on the north wall 200 feet from the entrance. Near the end of the main cave is a waterfall and stream passage connecting with the lower level.

(French E. Johnson, personal communication.)

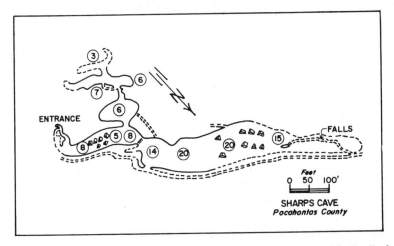

Figure 12.—Sharps Cave. Surveyed by French E. Johnson, A. M. Fredlock and J. L. Miles, 1962.

SHINABERRY CAVE NO. 2 38°20'30" N.; 80°01' 30" W. Mingo Quadrangle.

This cave is on the east side of Cloverlick Mountain 2¼ miles NNW of Poages Chapel (elevation 2850 feet). The entrance is on the north side of the valley and is an arch 10 feet wide with a stream flowing in. Twenty feet inside the passage reduces to a crawlway between ceiling pendants. Gravel and surface debris, mainly drift-wood, blocks the passage after about 100 feet. This cave is in the upper part of the Greenbrier Group.

SNEDEGAR-CROOKSHANK SYSTEM (SNEDEGARS ENTRANCE) (p. 290).

The main passage continues beyond the pool (siphon) for over 3,000 feet as a large walking passage 30 feet wide and 8 to 10 feet high to breakdown. Two hundred feet along this passage is a side passage to the north which connects with Snedegars Staircase Cave.

Beyond the breakdown is a small waterfall and a canyon passage 10 feet wide, 20 to 25 feet deep, and 100 feet long. At the end of the canyon is a side walkway and crawlway passage on the left which is semicircular in plan for 300 feet, connecting with a small passage several hundred feet long to two domepits 40 feet high. Another small passage from the semicircular one connects with passages of Crookshanks (Lewis) Hole. This connecting passage is about 100 feet long, over half of which is a very small crawlway. Downstream from the canyon, the main stream passage of Snedegars Cave is a 200-foot crawlway to a siphon, beyond which is a large passage up to 40 feet high. Between the Snedegars Staircase and Crookshank connections a side passage 1,500 feet long leads to breakdown. This passage is a crawlway opening into a large walkway.

(Tom Tucker: D. C. Speleograph, v. 20, no. 10, Oct., 1964, p. 74-75; v. 19, no. 12, Dec., 1963, p. 77-78.)

STEAM CAVE 38°09′37″ N.; 80°11′50″ W. Marlinton Quadrangle.

Steam Cave is a mile northwest of Mill Point (elevation 2325 feet). The entrance is a pit 4 feet in diameter and 10 feet deep connecting with the main cave by a narrow passage 30 feet long. At the junction is a large room with east-west passage, 10 feet wide, extending about 150 feet. Near the midpoint of the passage is a T-intersection with the main cave. East of this junction the passage is 10 to 20 feet wide and 2 to 10 feet high, for 300 feet. A stream flows west along this passage. Many speleothems are developed along this passage. The main passage trending south (downstream) is a low water crawl with intervening walkways merging into a narrow high stream passage about 5,000 feet long. Rimstone dams are common along this passage. Near the end of the passage are deep pools, waterfalls, and narrow, high, muddy passages. Beyond this the passage enlarges for a short distance and then ends in a siphon. Beyond the siphon there is 200 feet of passage in a T-pattern ending in breakdown and another siphon. Steam Cave and Blue Springs Cave are apparently connected by a siphon. The stream in Steam Cave resurges at Blue Springs Cave. Steam Cave is in the lower part of the Greenbrier Group.

(Hermine Zotter: Netherworld News, v. 10, no. 9, Sept., 1963, p. 172; v. 8, no. 8, Aug., 1960, p. 134-135.)

STONY CREEK CAVE 38°16'10" N.; 80°08'06" W. Mingo Quadrangle.

Stony Creek Cave is a mile west of Pine Grove School (elevation 2550 feet). The entrance is a 25-foot shaft at the base of which is a dirt slope 30 feet long to a room 20 feet wide, 15 feet high, and 40 feet long. A passage 30 to 40 feet wide with a ceiling up to 20 feet high trends east for 100 feet beyond the room, ending in a pit in breakdown. A few small passages, each less than 25 feet long, extend beyond the breakdown pit. This cave is in the lower part of the Greenbrier Group.

(William J. Stephenson: D. C. Speleograph, v. 16, no. 10, Oct., 1960, p. 103.)

TUB CAVE (p. 295).

The stream channel in the northwest corner of the room is negotiable upstream for an unknown distance. It is a stoopway enlarging to a fissure trending N 45°E and containing two rooms. The west wall is solid rock; the east side is breakdown. At 600 feet along the passage the stream pools and the ceiling drops low over the water leaving minimum head room. The stream in this cave resurges at Cave Creek Cave.

(Al Haarr: Netherworld News, v. 12, no. 8, Aug., 1964, p. 110.)

TURKEY ROOST CAVE 38°15'06" N.; 80°08'40" W. Mingo Quadrangle.

One mile south of West Union School at the road junction (elevation 3050 feet) is a large sink 15 feet deep and 35 feet wide. A small opening at the base of the sink leads to a low entrance room 25 feet long. To the left and forward is a duck-under (which sometimes fills with gravel) leading to a second room 10 feet high and 60 feet long. To the right of this room is a complex of small rooms with an active stream. At the left end of this room a traverse near the ceiling leads to a pit which is circular, 12 feet in circumference and 120 feet deep. At the bottom and to the left, another domepit extends upwards, the two being named Twin Silos. In front of the entry pit is another 10 foot pit. To the right is a crawlway leading to a third pit, but a removable obstruction did not permit entry.

(George Beck and Fred Donofrio, personal communication.)

A number of pits and small caves have been reported in Pocahontas County:

Apple Cellar Pit—On McNeill Run, unnamed western fork of Swago Creek (Marlinton Quadrangle), 20 foot domepit; fissure at base connects with stream passage.

Baber Pit—A large 50-foot pit extending into cliff face located ½ mile north of Baber Room Cave. **Cricket Hole,** a 25-foot-long sewer passage, is 50 feet uphill from Baber Pit.

Barlow Pit—North of Pine Grove School (Mingo Quadrangle), 80 foot pit.

Barlow Pit No. 2—One-half mile west of Onoto (Mingo Quadrangle), narrow pit 21 feet deep.

Black Lick Pit—One mile from mouth of Blacklick, a branch of McClintock Run (Marlinton Quadrangle), steeply sloping, shallow cave, 50 feet long and deep.

Blue Lick Hole—One mile upstream on Blue Lick Run (Marlinton Quadrangle), 6-foot drop into small room, former spring house. **Kellison Hole** is ½ mile south of Blue Lick Hole.

Burdette Pit—Spur of Rodgers Mountain 2 miles NNE of Mill Point (Marlinton Quadrangle), pit, 80 to 90 feet deep.

Chute Cave—100 feet upstream from Rockhouse No. 2 (Mingo Quadrangle), narrow muddy passage about 100 feet long.

Clutter Cave—One mile NNW of Edray (Mingo Quadrangle), 2 small rooms connected by a narrow high passage, all covered with flowstone.

Dry Creek Fissure—75 feet NW of Beveridge Hole in the Dry Creek Valley (Marlinton Quadrangle). Hole beside road with narrow fissure sloping down to small pit, 25 feet deep, skylight.

Duncan Cave—Several hundred yards west of West Union Church (Mingo Quadrangle), crawlway south for 40 feet turning west for 15 feet.

Edgar's Crawlway—One-and-a-half miles north of Hillsboro and 1½ miles west of Mill Point (Marlinton Quadrangle), at base of sink is a stream crawlway.

Forgotten Pit—1,000 feet south of Buck Mountain Pit in the Dry Creek Valley (Marlinton Quadrangle), 80 foot narrow pit.

Fox Den Pits—One-and-a-half miles north of Mill Point (Marlinton Quadrangle, 38°10'19" N.; 80°11'02" W., elevation 2750 feet), three multiple pits, up to 125 feet deep.

Garbage Pit—One mile SW of Onoto (Mingo Quadrangle), small passage near surface, collapsed dome dropping into crawlway, leading into small room, continuing passage.

Gillilan Mountain Pit—One mile due north of Mill Point (Marlinton Quadrangle, 38°10'15" N.; 80°10'53" W., elevation 2850 feet), 95 foot pit with crawlway at base to second domepit.

Hanna Pit—One-and-a-third miles north of mouth of Buck Run (Marlinton Quadrangle), pit, 20 feet deep, small interconnected side pit.

Hills Chapel Cave—One-half mile NE of Jacox (Lobelia Quadrangle, 38°05'39" N.; 80°18'10" W.) Crawlway about 100 feet long, 2 to 3 feet in diameter, with a small stream.

Hollow Meadow Pit—Spur of Rodger Mountain, 1 mile NNW of Ruckman School (Marlinton Quadrangle, 38°10'22" N.; 80°10'30" W., elevation 2750 feet). Pit, 84 feet deep, traverse and continuation.

Horse Heaven Pit—Three-quarter mile east of Mt. Zion Church (Lobelia Quadrangle), 50 foot pit, 12 feet in diameter near bottom.

Jacks Cave—200 feet downhill from Hause Waterfall Cave (Marlinton Quadrangle), low, narrow twisting passage, 75 feet long, small side crawlway near end. Fifty feet downhill, in the streambed, is **Fringe Falls Cavelet** consisting of one small room.

Joe Hollow Cave—One-quarter mile SSW of Cutlip Cave (Lobelia Quadrangle), low crawl entrance in streambed to sewer passage 20 feet long, 15 foot drop to room, mud slope to upper room, choked lower passage believed to connect with Cutlip Cave. **Milk House Fissure,** a 25 foot long fissure passage, is ½ mile east of Joe Hollow Cave.

John's Cavelet—One-and-a-half miles north of Mill Point, Marlinton Quadrangle), 20 foot walkway.

McClintocks Corkscrew Pit—One-half mile up Blacklick, a branch of McClintock Run (Marlinton Quadrangle), 30 foot pit, offset 5 feet down, low passage 15 feet long at base.

McClure Hole—One-half mile NW of Ruckman School (Marlinton Quadrangle), 25 foot pit.

McClure Pit—One-and-a-half miles north of Mill Point (Marlinton Quadrangle), breached pit, 10 foot slope and 25 foot drop on breached side, 80 foot wall and waterfall on opposite side.

McKeevers Waterfall Cave (p. 298). This cave is on Camp Secret Hollow (western fork, head of Swago Creek) (28°13′10″ N.; 80°09′30″ W., Marlinton Quadrangle, elevation 2800 feet), and not on Bear Pen Hollow (northern fork of Swago Creek) as shown on Figure 71 (p. 279); small pit in breakdown with waterfall entering. **Camp Secret Shelter Cave** and Camp Secret Waterfall are 1,000 feet upstream to the west.

McLaughlin Pit—Eastern slope of Stony Creek Mountain, 100 yards west of Jericho Road (Mingo Quadrangle), fissure opening 37 feet deep, belling out to room 10 by 20 feet in size. **Waugh Pit,** of similar depth, 50 feet downhill, consists of a series of narrow walls.

McNeill Pit—50 feet from Apple Cellar Pit, undoubtedly connecting with the same stream passage. Four small domepits are interconnected with a narrow stream passage 100 feet long, ending in a 10-foot waterfall and pool.

Osborn's Pit—Five-eighths mile up Blacklick, a branch of McClintock Run (Marlinton Quadrangle), pit of unknown size.

Poor Farm Water Cave—One-quarter mile SE of Poor Farm entrance. The stream entering the Water Cave resurges at McNeels Mill Run Cave.

Railroad Pit—One-half mile SSW of Hefner School (Marlinton Quadrangle), 70 foot pit.

Ralph Sheets Pit—West side of Asbury Knob (Cass Quadrangle), 30-foot pit interconnected with a 40-foot pit.

Ray Horners Cave—One mile north of Gum Springs School (Cass Quadrangle), pit of unknown size.

Ruckman Hole—One-half mile NW of Ruckman School (Marlinton Quadrangle), small pit.

Shanahans Drop Cave—One-and-a-half miles NW of Edray (Mingo Quadrangle), 3-foot high fissure, 16 feet long.

Sheets Pit—Three-quarters of a mile NW of Hillsboro (Marlinton Quadrangle), double domepit, 20 feet deep.

Sheriff Pit—0.3 mile southwest of West Union Church (Mingo Quadrangle), narrow fissure 30 feet deep and 30-foot talus slope to room 10 by 25 feet.

Sherman Beards Cave—One-quarter mile NW of Poor Farm Cave (Marlinton Quadrangle, 38°07'35" N.; 80°13'32" W., elevation 2300 feet). Crawlway and stoopway 800 feet long with stream, blocked by driftwood and debris.

Spring House Cave—One-half mile southeast of Caesar Mountain School (Lobelia Quadrangle, 38°08'15" N.; 80°15'05" W., elevation 2300 feet). Entrance room 10 feet high, 6 feet wide, 15 feet long, two crawlways, right one 25 feet long, dry; other with stream 170 feet long.

Stony Mountain Sink—75 feet uphill from Nancy Sharp Pit (Marlinton Quadrangle) is a large sheer-walled sink with a wet crawl passage extending 50 feet and several fissures. The stream entering this sink resurges to form both Price Run and Sharp Run.

Tree Stump Pit—One-quarter mile NE of Blue Springs Cave (Marlinton Quadrangle), narrow fissure connecting with a 15-foot domepit.

Wolfes Swallow Hole—Crawlway located on Big Run, a branch of Dry Creek (38°13'50" N., 80°08'15" W., Marlinton Quadrangle, elevation 2800 feet). 200 feet upstream is one-room **Ripped Coveralls Cavelet** on the right, and solution tube, **Big Run Cave,** on the left. Still further upstream is one-room **Dad's Cavelet** on the left. Downstream is a solution tube, **Bob's Crawl.**

PRESTON COUNTY

KELLY QUARRY CAVE   Bruceton Quadrangle.

The entrance to Kelly Quarry Cave is reported to be in an abandoned quarry west of Cranesville and 8 miles north of Terra Alta. The cave consists of a walkway passage 150 feet long and a low, side passage. Beyond 150 feet the main passage continues as a crawlway less than 3 feet high. The cave is dangerous because of loose, fractured rock. The cave is in the Greenbrier Limestone.

(F. R. Corliss, Jr.: NSS News, v. 17, no. 10. Oct., 1959, p. 147.)

RANDOLPH COUNTY

ALPENA CAVE NO. 1 (p. 305).

Recent exploration indicates the cave is 2,200 feet long and is mainly wet crawlways with short sections of dry, high passages interconnecting with the crawlways.

(Lew Bicking: Baltimore Grotto News, v. 6, no. 9, Sept., 1963, p. 183.)

BEALES CAVE   Mingo Quadrangle.

A cave is reported near the Pocahontas-Randolph County line, 1 mile from Mace and U.S. Highway 219. The entrance is in a sinkhole on a steep slope south of the road. The entrance is a 35-foot pit connecting with 25, 10 and 30 pits and a short passage to a small chamber blocked by massive breakdown. The cave is in sandy limestone of the Greenbrier Group.

(Warren Brown: Cavalier Caver, v. 7, no. 1, March, 1965, p. 5.)

KISAMORE CAVE NO. 2   Onego Quadrangle.

This cave is on Spruce Run, 75 feet east of the spring that forms the head of the run. The entrance is a 13-foot drop connecting with a passage 4 feet high and 6 feet wide which leads to the spring. A small squeezeway extends 50 feet northwest from the spring. The main passage trends southeast for 150 feet to breakdown and is 6 feet wide and 4 feet high. Beyond the breakdown is a room 12 feet wide, 30 feet long and 10 feet high. 200 feet beyond is a low room 30 feet in diameter and 2 feet high. The passage continues as a fissure 4 feet high and 18 inches wide. A small stream flows through the cave and the second room has a lake about a foot deep. The cave is in the lower part of the Greenbrier Limestone.

(Paul Clifford: Baltimore Grotto News, v. 6, no. 9, Sept., 1963, p. 178-179.)

SIMMONS-MINGO CAVE (p. 312).

The lower level and total depth of the cave are about 250 feet below the entrance.

SINKS OF GANDY CREEK (p. 312).

A water passage, 200 to 300 feet long, extends west near the upstream entrance. The passage ends in a siphon.

(W. McGrew: Netherworld News, v. 7, no. 8, Sept., 1959, p. 177.)

TUCKER COUNTY

ARBOGAST-CAVE HOLLOW SYSTEM (p. 318, 319).

This cave system consists of two interlacing parallel passages extending south from the Cave Hollow entrance for 1,900 feet. Beyond this point the cave consists of three major passages trending south and southwest. Another large passage trends south for 1,400 feet from the Arbogast entrance. In 1964 a rock fall blocked this passage at the Arbogast entrance. In the section 300 feet northwest of the Arbogast entrance are several large domepits up to 70 feet high. Streams flow along the main passages between the Arbogast and Cave Hollow entrances and along the westernmost passage in the inner part of the cave. The main passages vary from crawlways to galleries over 50 feet high. The Arbogast entrance is a steep slope for 30 feet connecting with three passages at the base.

(Ted Will: Baltimore Grotto News, v. 2, no. 8, Aug., 1959, p. 2.)

BIG SPRINGS CAVE (p. 318).

The entrance passage trends south for 400 feet and a stream follows part of it. At 200 feet a side passage extends 400 feet to the west. This passage is interconnected with two other passages that also trend west. At the west end of the cave a north-south stream passage at a lower level than the other passages is over 300 feet long. At the south end of the entrance passage is a passage extending to the west for 400 feet. At the end this passage intersects the stream passage. There are two domepits along the north-south stream passage and three others at or near the end of the interconnecting north-south passages.

(Lew Bicking: Baltimore Grotto News, v. 6, no. 9, Sept., 1963, p. 180-182.)

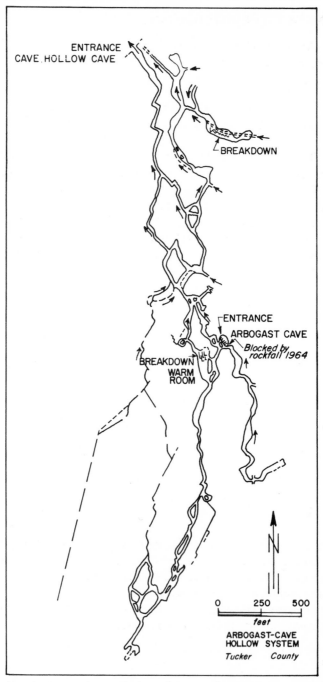

Figure 13.—Arbogast—Cave Hollow System. Surveyed by Conner and Eichenmuller, 1964, additional data from W. T. Plummer and S. Plummer.

BONNER PIT Parsons Quadrangle.

At pit 100 feet deep with a passage 80 feet to the northeast at the base is on the flank of Mozark Mountain on State Highway 72 about a mile east of Moore.

(Ted Kayes: Baltimore Grotto News, v. 6, no. 6, June, 1963, p. 122.)

HARPER CAVE 39°01'37" N.; 79°33'15" W. Parsons Quadrangle.

This cave is about 1 mile west of Mill Run Cave (elevation 2500 feet). The entrance is in a sinkhole 300 feet north of the Dry Fork Road. A 12-foot shaft at the entrance connects with a passage trending N 80° E, the first 200 feet of which is a crawlway. Beyond 200 feet the passage is 6 to 12 feet high and 20 feet wide. Four hundred feet from the entrance the passage is a low, wide crawlway for 200 feet, beyond which it is a walkway. A pool, 30 feet long, is 600 feet from the entrance and a small waterfall is near it. Four hundred feet from the pool stalactites block the passage. A short passage trends S 80° W from the entrance for 100 feet. The cave is in the Greenbrier Limestone.

(F. R. Corliss, Jr.: NSS News, v. 17, no. 10, Oct., 1959, p. 148.)

LAWRENCE PIT.

This pit is 2 miles northwest of Laneville (Onego Quadrangle) (elevation 3050 feet). It is 35 feet deep with an offset 20 feet below the top. The pit is in the Greenbrier Limestone.

(Denny Dingley: Neog Log, v. 1, no. 1, May-June, 1964, p. 10.)

SMITHS CAVE 38°59'40" N.; 79°27'10" W. Onego Quadrangle.

Smiths Cave is 2.4 miles northwest of Laneville (elevation 2800 feet). The entrance is a 45° slope down 12 feet over logs. At the base is a narrow, wet passage 7 to 8 feet high and 100 feet long, the last 20 feet of which is a crawlway. A smaller cave is about 100 yards from the entrance to Smiths Cave and consists of a steeply sloping entrance, 10 feet long, with a passage 15 feet long to a pit and waterfall. The cave continues beyond the pit but is unexplored. The cave is in the Greenbrier Limestone.

(Denny Dingley: Neog Log, v. 1, no. 1, May-June, 1964, p. 9.)

WAYBRIGHT (WADEBRIGHT) CAVE (CAVE OF BABEL)
39°13'36" N.; 79°41'35" W. Parsons Quadrangle.

Three miles north of St. George and ½ mile north of Limestone Mountain Cave is an opening with a small stream flowing in (elevation 2500 feet). The opening gives access to a wedge-shaped fissure passage, a foot wide at the base and up to 8 feet wide at the top. This passage grades into a walkway farther in the cave. The ceiling is 10 to 60 feet high. The main passage is 2,200 feet long with a stream throughout. At 100, 750, and 1,000 feet from the entrance, side passages branch from the main passage. The side passages are walkways with streams. Fifteen-hundred feet from the entrance the main passage is narrow except for short stretches 20 to 40 feet long where it widens out. At the end of the cave is a room with a waterfall beyond which is another room. The end of the second room is blocked by breakdown. In portions of the cave a second level is developed parallel to the main passage. The cave is in the Greenbrier Limestone.

(Norman Ingold, Bob Mahood: Potomac Caver, v. 4, no. 5, May, 1961, p. 1; v. 4, no. 6, June, 1961, p. 1-4; v. 4, no. 7, July, 1961, p. 3-4.)

CORRECTIONS

The following corrections should be made in the text of the 1958 edition:

Page

81 **Carlisle Cave:** correct longitude to 80°32'15" W.

92 **Hanna Cave:** the north arrow is inverted.

97 **Higginbothams Cave No. 2:** change position to 37°55'56" N.; 80°24'28" W.

98 **Higginbothams Cave No. 3:** change position to 37°55'47" N.; 80°24'30" W.

99 **Higginbothams Cave No. 4:** change position to 37°55'53" N.; 80°24'28" W.

99 **Higginbothams Cave No. 4:** the waterfall is 15 feet high.

101 **Jewel Cave:** change longitude to 80°33'43" W.

104 **Johnson Cave:** change position to 37°52'54" N.; 80°30' 30" W.

148 **Charles Town Cave:** change position to 39°17'27" N.; 77°51' 33" W.

148 **Chapman Cave:** change longitude to 77°55'46" W.

158 **Thompson School Cave:** change elevation to 2560 feet.

191 **McClung Zenith Cave:** change position to 37°30'08" N.; 80° 31'17" W.

192 **Mott Hole:** change longitude to 80°34'45" W.

209 **Ferris Cave:** The proper spelling is Pharis.

222 **Mill Run Cave:** change elevation to 2050 feet.

225 **Moyers Caves:** change longitude to 79°22'45" W.

254 **Warners Cave:** change longitude to 79°23' 12" W.

264 **Cass Cave:** last line change 200 to 2,000.

275 **Martens Cave:** change second longitude to 80°16'35" W.

294 **Swago Roadside Pit:** change name to Roadside Pit; change latitude to 38°12'57" N.

299 **Aurora Cave:** change latitude to 39°19'42" N.

299 **Beaver Hole:** change position to 39°36'36" N.; 79°46'53" W.

312 **Schmidlen Shafts:** change longitude to 79°37' 18" W.

318 **Arbegast Cave:** change spelling to Arbogast; change position to 39°00'31" W. Change elevation to 2,600 feet.

319 **Cave Hollow Cave:** change position to 39°00'50" N.; 79°34' 45" W. Change elevation to 2,500 feet.

INDEX OF CAVERNS

72   CAVERNS OF WEST VIRGINIA (SUPPLEMENT)